# For All
# CHILDREN
## Everywhere

**Children's Mercy**
KANSAS CITY

**1897-2017**

Thomas McCormally

First edition
ISBN: 978-1-943338-12-2
   Library of Congress Control
Number:  2017939793

Published by
Chandler Lake Books

Editor: Monroe Dodd
Book designer: Jean D. Dodd

Printed in the U.S.A.
by Walsworth Publishing,
Marceline, Missouri

*Photos: Right, Daniel Loental,
RN, and patient. Facing page,
sunroom at 414 Highland, circa
1910.*

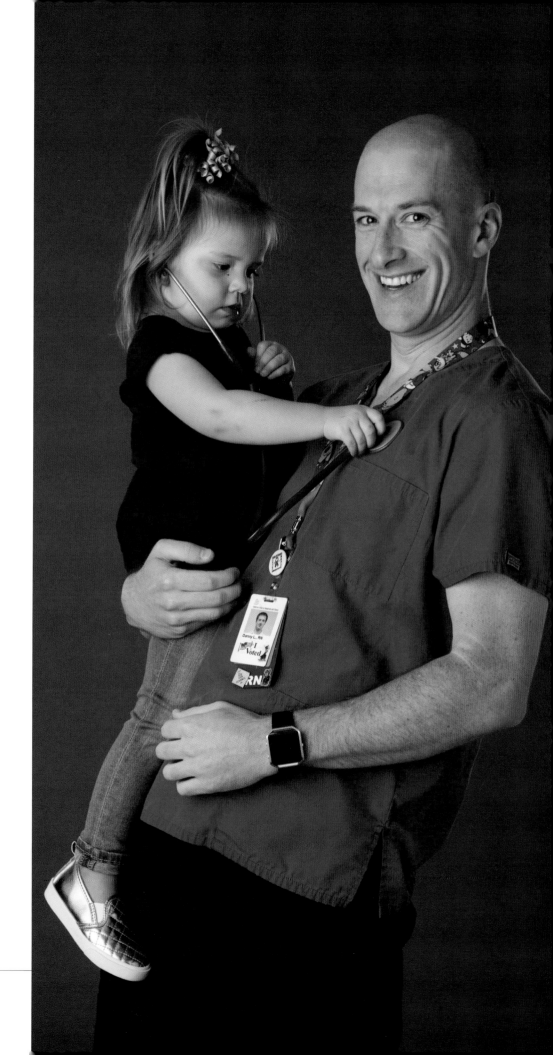

# Contents

# Introduction

*"There are only a few things that are fundamental. If I have been an influence for good, that good will live and … will be my monument."*

— Katharine Berry Richardson

This is a love story.

This is also a story about a little children's hospital that grew, over a century, into a complex academic medical center. But mainly it's a story about love.

It's about love given to children and parents. And love given by doctors and nurses and all kinds of people who make this children's hospital go. It's about an institution that survived and expanded for a century and more, yet managed to keep a big, loving heart.

The story begins far away, in time and space, from 21st-century Kansas City. It begins with a man and a woman who taught their daughters in the antebellum South about the Golden Rule, about loving their neighbors and helping others. It's about love between sisters, each of whom sacrificed her time and talent so the other could get an education, and each of whom encouraged the other in a quest to care for the less fortunate.

It is about how love of others – especially children – led one of the sisters, Alice Berry Graham, to rescue a crippled little girl from the dirty streets of 1890s Kansas City. Love drove her to declare to her sibling, Katharine Berry Richardson: "It's time someone took a greater interest in helping children like this. And Katharine, I think you and I are the ones to do it."

In these pages, you will find the love of a community, which, despite changing times and hard times, embraced this ideal and did not let the sisters' dream die. Community leaders and doctors gave tirelessly of themselves, many over and over again and some for decades, out of a pure love of doing what was right.

This is a story of how, early in the 20th Century, Children's Mercy worked its way into the hearts of many in Kansas City and this part of the Midwest. There in their hearts it has remained for generations as the pre-eminent worthy cause, socially acceptable and morally desirable.

The founding sisters sometimes were spurned by the male-dominated business and medical communities, and

*A Children's Mercy nurse and her charges: Through the years, care and compassion characterized the hospital.*

sometimes were mocked by newspapers. But they persevered. We can all learn something from them about life, passion, love and commitment.

For 120 years, Children's Mercy has benefited from a multitude of generous souls: from the richest families to those who barely had enough for themselves and, remarkably, from children. Donors and volunteers speak of love as they give

*Children and families in the waiting room, 1940s. Among the millions who have passed through the doors of Children's Mercy.*

their time, talent and treasure to make better lives for children and families. They pass that love and dedication to their own children and grandchildren.

"The sources of Mercy Hospital power are great," one of the hospital's earliest and most dedicated physicians proclaimed on its Golden Anniversary in 1947. "The first is the spirit of the founders. How high their ideas, how great their love … Mercy hospital does things to people."

When I first walked into Children's Mercy in 1994, I sensed something different. Employees spoke more often of "family" rather than "co-workers" or even "team members." Patients weren't cases or conditions; they were "our kiddos." Marvin Kolb, MD, who served as medical director at Children's Mercy in the early 1990s, has said people who work at a children's hospital are "cut from a different cloth."

On top of the dedication of the medical staff, there are nurses and administrators, chaplains and groundskeepers and many more who are equally in love with the mission and vision of Children's Mercy. In an era when the average American stays at a job less than five years, the average length of service of the nearly 8,000 Children's Mercy employees was 7.6 years as of December 2016. More than 25 percent of employees had more

than 10 years of service; about 600 had more than 20 years. One had more than 50.

Taking care of children and families is everyone's job. The family of Children's Mercy goes above and beyond the call of duty. For some, it's a spiritual duty – a love of children and of justice.

This book has been an amazing odyssey. When research began, no one knew all the stories that would become a part of it. The last official history of the hospital was published in 1961 and a lot happened in the next 56 years. Some stories are told here for the first time and some facts corrected from earlier reports. In all, there are 120 years of characters, every one with a story.

Millions of children have come through the doors – not a single one turned away – in search of hope and cure. Most found healing. All found love. Not all of the stories are included here; it would be impossible. But the common thread is.

"I love Children's Mercy for so many reasons."

That came from a note sent to me by a mom in the summer of 2016. "I love them because I felt I finally had someone fighting just as hard as I was to help my medically fragile child. I found a sense of belonging."

Melanie Traynham, the mom, has five children, a job and is going to nursing school. Her son Aamir has a rare genetic condition that comes with a long list of complications. He and his mom spend lots of time with doctors and nurses. She admits life is a little crazy. And yet Melanie finds time to help other parents at Children's Mercy and to serve on one of the parent advisory boards. Love makes you do crazy things.

Another mom sent an email because her daughter wanted to share her story.

*I was born sick. I needed to go to Children's Mercy. I … spent 84 days in the NICU. I am healthy now because of Children's Mercy. My brother, Kolton, goes to Children's Mercy now because he has cancer. Thank you Children's Mercy for helping me and my brother.*

*Kinley Melcher, age 8*

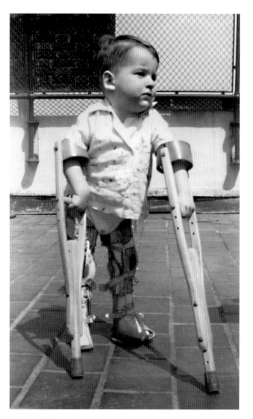

*A mid-20th-century patient on the sun roof at the hospital's Independence Avenue location.*

These are the stories that keep Children's Mercy going. Sometimes, even those who work here aren't aware just how special it is. Brooke Poindexter, a nurse in the Home Care division, has witnessed Children's Mercy both as an employee and as a mom.

"I am astounded by the level of care and compassion for kids," she wrote after experiencing firsthand care for one of her sons in spring 2016.

At Children's Mercy, extraordinary things happen so often that they begin to seem ordinary. Maybe by recounting those stories in this book, and making sure we share them with future generations, the remarkable nature of this place will remain etched in the heart of our community.

One hundred twenty years have passed since Alice Berry Graham lovingly took in that abandoned, crippled girl on a summer's night in 1897 and convinced her sister that this was their lives' calling. They couldn't have known where their love and devotion would lead. But they knew that it was the right thing to do and that children deserved nothing less than the best efforts.

Children's Mercy today – its sprawling Adele Hall Campus on Hospital Hill and locations circling metropolitan Kansas City like a caring embrace – is much different from 1903, when the first hospital that was entirely "Mercy" opened its doors on Highland Avenue in the remodeled home of a socialite. But its DNA is the same, as is its mission and its commitment to building better lives and a better world, one child at a time. Its love remains steadfast.

As I talked with scores of people about the hospital then and now and into the future, children remained at the forefront of their work and dreams. The stories selected for this book demonstrate variety, challenge and motivation. They show the love of Children's Mercy.

Children's Mercy was founded to be nonsectarian always, which meant it wouldn't subscribe to any single religion. That hasn't changed. But neither does it mean there is no place for spirituality within the walls. In fact, you would be hard-pressed to find anyone who has spent much time at Children's Mercy who does not believe in miracles – and not just the miracle of modern medicine.

One of the more well-known and oft-repeated verses from the Christian Bible comes from the second letter written by the Apostle Paul to the church at Corinth. When we think about all that Children's Mercy has endured, against seemingly insurmountable odds throughout its history, I am reminded of that letter. And how it applies to this story.

"Love … always protects, always trusts, always hopes, always perseveres. Love never fails."

*Thomas McCormally*
*June 2017*

*Facing page: A 1910s photograph retouched to leave no doubt about Mercy's commitment to build a better world, one child at a time.*

# BIRTH OF A HOSPITAL

*"The journey of a thousand miles begins with a single step."*

– Chinese proverb, Lao Tzu

One warm summer night in 1897, Alice Graham picked up a sick little girl from the dingy streets of Kansas City. Little did she know that this single act of kindness and compassion would change not only her life and the life of that young child, but also the lives of hundreds of thousands of people and the face of the city.

As the story goes, a saloon owner in the old meatpacking and warehouse district of the West Bottoms knew of a woman who was trying to give away her 6-year-old daughter because she could not care for her. The barkeeper knew Alice Berry Graham, a dentist, and knew she had a kind heart. He told her about the poor girl.

Alice Graham found the weeping child that June night, swaddled her and carried her to the downtown apartment and office that she shared with her sister, Katharine Berry Richardson, and Katharine's husband. The sisters cleaned up the girl and took care of her.

*Alice Berry Graham*

Eventually, they took the child to the Hospital for Women and Children, which operated in an old house east of downtown near 15th Street and Cleveland Avenue. There, the sisters rented a single bed and the little girl stayed. Katharine, a surgeon, operated on her hip. She and Alice provided physical therapy, medicine and proper nutrition. Eventually, the girl walked again and they found an orphanage to take her in.

Neither Alice nor Katharine had children of her own. One night, in the room with the little girl as she was being nursed back to health, Alice came to believe in destiny. She looked at her sister, smiled and said:

"It's time someone took a greater interest in helping children like this. And Katharine, I think you and I are the ones to do it."

With that, Children's Mercy was born.

## A moral compass

In fact, the story of this amazing institution really began long before that night and far away from the smoky air of a booming cowtown at the end of the 1800s. It began about 600 or so miles east of Kansas City, in Bourbon County in eastern

*Left: Disease, abuse, genetic defects and accidents plagued the children of Kansas City's poor at the turn of the 20th century. Two sisters, one a dentist and the other a physician, brought them hope and healing.*

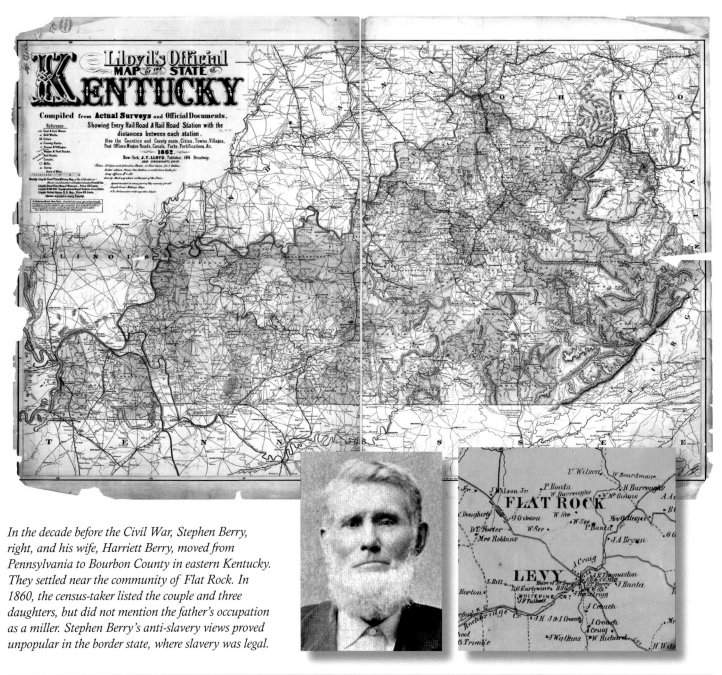

In the decade before the Civil War, Stephen Berry,
right, and his wife, Harriett Berry, moved from
Pennsylvania to Bourbon County in eastern Kentucky.
They settled near the community of Flat Rock. In
1860, the census-taker listed the couple and three
daughters, but did not mention the father's occupation
as a miller. Stephen Berry's anti-slavery views proved
unpopular in the border state, where slavery was legal.

| | | | | | | | | |
|---|---|---|---|---|---|---|---|---|
| 33 | 299 | 303 | S. B. Berry | 65 | M | | 400 | 500 | Ky |
| 34 | | | Harriet do | 37 | F | | | | Penn |
| 35 | | | Alice do | 11 | F | | | | do |
| 36 | | | Clara J. do | 6 | F | | | | Ky |
| 37 | | | Kate B. do | 2 | F | | | | do |

Kentucky near a tiny farming community known as Flat Rock.

There, in an unremarkable but thoroughly American 19th-century countryside, two girls learned the roots of hard work and service above self, and found their life's calling of helping others.

In the 1850s, the decade before the Civil War, Kentucky was a slave state. Because it bordered Northern free states, Kentucky contained patches of Union sympathizers. One of them was Stephen Paine Berry, who had migrated to Kentucky from Pennsylvania, where the census listed him as a farmer. Berry and his wife, Harriett Benson Berry, brought with them the first of their three daughters, Alice, born March 3, 1850.

It's not known why they left Pennsylvania, and Kentucky seems an unusual destination given Stephen Berry's anti-slavery leanings. Nevertheless, the Berrys made a home near Flat Rock, where he worked as a merchant and miller. They had two more daughters – Clara, born January 27, 1854, and, Katharine, born September 28, 1857.

Decades later, Stephen Berry's obituary would describe him as a man of "peculiar characteristics, decided in his thoughts and often aggressive."

"He might have had more friends," it continued, "but they would not have made him as conspicuous as he was with less. Still, he was a genial, companionable man, full of ideas, sometimes wrong and sometimes right, but all the time he was Stephen P. Berry, nor did he try to be anyone else."

Many of those same things could have been said in later years about his third daughter, Katharine. But that's getting ahead of the story.

One idea Berry championed was that slavery was immoral. When the Civil War began in 1861, he refused to sign an oath of allegiance to the Confederacy and tacked a notice on his door that proclaimed his allegiance to the Union. In his little section of Kentucky, that defiance made him a wanted man, so he fled to Ohio and joined the Union Army.

With only Harriett and the three girls left in Flat Rock to defend the Berry property, Southern soldiers seized their mill to grind grain to help feed hungry Rebels. But they underestimated Harriett Berry. Under the cloak of darkness one evening she dismantled parts of the mill and buried them in the woods. They were never discovered. The mill wheel

*Katharine Berry in her youth, wearing a ribbon resembling one bestowed as an award.*

turned no more to benefit the Confederacy.

Her daughters would one day demonstrate the same grit and mettle in the face of adversity

Harriett Berry died on December 30, 1863, and no record has been found of who helped care for the girls immediately after their mother's death. The job may have fallen mostly on the oldest sister, Alice, who was 13 at the time and to whom Katharine would later give credit for much of her eventual success. There may have been family friends. At some point, Stephen Berry returned to the family property; one story says he led a band of Northern soldiers to Flat Rock and drove out Southerner sympathizers.

Regardless, he did not want the responsibility of raising

three girls on his own. So he packed his belongings and his daughters and returned to the home of his youth, Warren County in northwestern Pennsylvania. He married again, to Emily Lincoln, who had three young children of her own. He worked in the oil business. His family owned considerable property in the vicinity, including some sold to railroads.

Berry had other strong values besides opposition to slavery, and he and his wives worked to instill them in the girls. One of the lessons, as quoted long after his death: "Wherever you go, whatever you do, wherever you live, you owe something to your community – and to the people that live there. It is your duty to always do something to help others and to help make good citizens of your neighbors."

Being a good neighbor, he insisted, involved taking care of each other and taking care of those who could not care for themselves. That included children.

"The mother who looks after her own children derives no special consideration," he was quoted as saying, "nothing more than a cow or a horse or even a wild beast. The truly charitable woman is big enough to help children other than her own."

Stephen Berry set his daughters on a course that transformed a myriad of lives through their devotion to others, all of them children other than their own.

Lena Dagley, who would serve for years as secretary to Katharine Berry Richardson and who collected her stories, wrote about the importance of those early years to Alice and Katharine:

"We all know that the time to mold the habits and character of a child is during the early and formative years. And no doubt, that little thought/seed of unselfish service to other people implanted in the minds of those two little girls during the plastic period of their lives was the real beginning of Mercy Hospital."

> "Wherever you go, whatever you do, wherever you live, you owe something to your community – and to the people that live there. It is your duty to always do something to help others and to help make good citizens of your neighbors."
> — Stephen Berry

## One helping the other

The Berrys insisted the girls get an education, a progressive and uncommon practice in the days after the Civil War, when women were expected to be primarily good wives and mothers. Clara, the middle daughter of Stephen and Harriett, chose the latter path and, by one account, eloped. She and her husband would have four children.

Alice and Katharine, meanwhile, began their lives' service by helping one another. Because the Berry family had little money to pay for college or advanced degrees, Alice and Katharine made a pact: One would work and the other would go to school. Upon graduation, the roles would be reversed.

Katharine, the younger, went first. In 1876, at age 18, she enrolled at Mount Union College in the northeastern Ohio town of Alliance. Alice took her licensing exam and got a teaching job to pay the bills. Katharine also did a bit of tutoring on the side to help make ends meet.

At least in hindsight, Mount Union College seems a perfect choice for Katharine and the values instilled by her family. According to the college's official history, Mount Union was founded in 1846 as a place "where men and

*Chapman Hall at Mount Union College in Alliance, Ohio, where Katharine Berry earned two degrees.*

women could be educated with equal opportunity, where science would parallel the humanities, where laboratory and experimental subjects would receive proper emphasis, and where there would be no distinction due to race, color, sex or position." The college was affiliated with the Methodist Episcopal Church and was supported, at least in part, by the Pittsburgh Conference of the church.

Katharine graduated from Mount Union as a member of the class of 1882, receiving a bachelor's degree in philosophy. In 1887 she earned a master's in psychology. Through college, her nickname was "Kitty."

She was popular among her classmates and showed signs of both leadership and scholarship, serving as class vice president and presenting the valedictory address as the top of her class. Even then, she looked to the future with a bow to the joy of college days:

"With time and hope ahead, the future makes such glowing promises that, were it not for what we are leaving, we could take up our new responsibilities with glad hearts and feel no fear of what is waiting for us."

After that, Katharine seems to have disappeared from the Mount Union scene. The next year, in a retrospective document produced by her classmates at Mount Union, there appeared only this information about the valedictorian of '82:

Though "gone," it said, she was "not forgotten."

"Miss Berry taught in Newton Falls [35 miles north of Alliance] nine months of the past year; nothing more is known of her history, all inquiries have failed to elicit an answer. She has probably been absorbed by some enterprising young man."

Little did they know. Katharine was working to have enough money to attend medical school and to help Alice get her education. No man required.

After a while, Alice and Katharine moved to Philadelphia. Alice continued to teach school so that, in 1884, Katharine could begin her studies at the Women's Medical College of Pennsylvania. The college was a Quaker institution and the first medical school in the country for women. It had opened in 1850 and had struggled not only financially but also with "an intensely hostile male medical profession." The medical school took three years, including two as an "apprentice" to a practitioner, almost always a woman.

Katharine studied the complications of pregnancy

*As valedictorian, Katharine Berry gave the final address of the program at Mount Union College Class Day in July 1882, above. Below: In 1887, she appeared in the roll of graduates at the Women's Medical College of Pennsylvania.*

and childbirth, and her thesis submitted to the faculty for the degree of doctor of medicine was on the hygiene and pathology of pregnancy. Displaying colorful and straightforward prose, Katharine referred to Mother Nature: "Her gifts of health and endurance, while amply sufficient to meet any reasonable strain, are yet not so lavishly displayed as to permit of prodigality in their use. She is a loving mother, but an exacting mistress."

She seemed to be drawing attention to the extraordinary

burden women faced in the world. She also showed herself to be a woman of strong opinion. In her thesis, Katharine rejected the practice of some doctors who ordered months of bed rest during pregnancy. Although rest might be nice, she wrote, exercise was vital for the woman and child, improving circulation and avoiding "puerperal eclampsia," or life-threatening convulsions associated with childbirth.

## Just getting by

Living in Philadelphia on Alice's teacher's salary gave the sisters little discretionary income. There were times when Katharine reportedly put newspapers in the soles of her worn-out shoes because she could not afford new ones. What money they made, they stretched. One newspaper

account said Alice gave what little money was "left over" to help care for poor children.

So it is no surprise that at the time of her graduation from medical school, Katharine had no money for a graduation dress or a big celebration.

On graduation day, as the story goes, Katharine cleaned her black dress as best she could and then went out to run errands. When she returned, someone had placed on her bed, quite by surprise, a new, sparkling white dress. She wore it with gratitude.

She never learned where the dress came from, but she told friends many years later that as she cared for poor, sick children she felt as if she was paying back the benefactor. The sisters viewed it as further confirmation of something their father had taught them: Helpfulness makes the world go around.

Instead of an optional fourth year at the medical school, Katharine spent three months at a maternal and infant clinic in

*La Crosse, Wisconsin, in the late 1880s, when Katharine Berry opened her first practice. The map was produced in the bird's-eye-view format popular at the time. Above: A downtown apartment building where she and later her sister Alice lived.*

## Stephen P. Berry's obituary

This week we are enabled to give a more full history of Stephen P. Berry, than we were able to do last week, whose death occurred on the 8th inst. He was the youngest of nine children of John M. and Eunice P. Berry, all of whom preceded him to the better land. He was born in Saratoga Co., N.Y., Feb. 3, 1814; came with his parents to Warren county in 1823, and was married to Harriet Benson, Jan 18, 1847. In 1851 they moved to Kentucky, where his wife died Dec. 30, 1863. From that union there were three daughters, of whom Alice A., and Kate D., survive him. Clara J., wife of Victor Gretter, died Feb. 20, 1890. The deceased returned from Kentucky to Petroleum Center, Venango Co., Pa., in 1866. In November 22, 1863, he married Mrs. E.J. Lincoln and came to North Warren, March 12, 1870, where he resided until his death, aged seventy-seven years, four months and five days. His early life was active, and he was engaged extensively in lumbering and the oil business at different periods of his life, and the last twenty years were quietly passed in North Warren, at the old homestead. He had peculiar characteristics, decided in his thought, and often aggressive. He might have had more friends but they would not have made him as conspicuous as he was with less. Still he was a genial, companionable man, full of ideas, sometimes wrong and sometimes right, but all the time was Stephen P. Berry, nor did he try to be anyone else. As a member of the Farmers Club, when able to attend, he kept the members busy combating what was termed absurdities or agreeing with his better judgment. Often he took absurd positons in order to wake up the sessions, and to find out whether the members had any ideas, which he sometimes did, to his own inconvenience. For many years he was the LEDGER's North Warren scribe, over the nom de plume of "Stub Pen." All the LEDGER's readers know his peculiarities in this capacity. He was never sleepy when putting his pen to paper, and he kept up his correspondence long after disease racked his frame and age had done its work. He did this for recreation – to pass away the hours which hung heavy. Writing made him forget for the moment his severe sufferings. The LEDGER knows Stephen P. Berry better, perhaps, than many who thought they knew him best. While he laughed at the follies of the world, he deplored them, and did what he could for the betterment of mankind. He was a man of more ideas than are given to the majority, but lacking diplomacy, sometimes made enemies by his writings, when he believed he was doing his best work. The LEDGER liked Stephen P. Berry, and will miss his kindly face and genial presence, as will many others. He was a character distinguished from the thousands one meets.

*– As printed in the* Warren Ledger
*(Warren County, Pennsylvania), June 19, 1891*

---

New York operated by Dr. Elizabeth Blackwell. Dr. Blackwell was the first woman in the United States to receive a medical degree, in 1849.

As the sisters had agreed, Katharine then began working to support her older sister. Alice had decided to attend dental college in Philadelphia.

Eventually, the sisters decided that Katharine should move to another city to begin her medical practice and Alice would stay behind at school. Katharine would send money to Philadelphia. The question was, Where should Katharine go? West, they agreed, for the opportunities of the expanding country, but where?

The sisters put a map on the floor of their living room and tossed a coin into the air. They agreed that wherever it landed, that's where the next chapter of Katharine's life would commence. Her destination, determined by the coin: La Crosse, Wisconsin, a Mississippi River town of 25,000.

Katharine packed her bags and headed west to begin her medical practice. The sisters parted for the first and only extended separation of their lives.

## Concern for the poor

Alice, meanwhile, began sharing what little extra she had with those less fortunate. According to a newspaper article written after her death, as a dental student Alice "stinted herself while studying for her profession that she might give part of her small means to help the unfortunate children." This may have been the genesis for her work with poor, crippled children in Kansas City.

While she lived in Philadelphia, Alice married a man named Graham. Little is known about her husband, not even his first name, and he died not many years later. Alice graduated in

*Notice of Alice's graduating class in an 1890 Philadelphia newspaper.*

*By the 1890s, when Alice Graham, Katharine Richardson and James Ira Richardson moved to Kansas City, the West Bottoms bustled as the city's economic engine. Railroad lines, stockyards, grain mills, packing plants and warehouses ruled the landscape. Below, James Ira Richardson.*

1890 – the only woman among 57 students in her class – from the Philadelphia Dental College and Hospital of Oral Surgery. Her thesis was on the extraction of teeth.

In the sisters' time apart, they lost their father and their middle sister. Stephen Berry was 77 when he died July 8, 1891, in Pennsylvania. According to Berry's obituary in *The Warren Ledger,* his daughter and Alice's and Katharine's sister Clara had died the preceding year at 36.

Heartbroken and alone, Alice traveled as a young widow to La Crosse to join her sister. By 1893, Alice was operating a dental practice there.

Katharine, meanwhile, had met James Ira Richardson, a widower with no children who operated the family mercantile store in La Crosse. Katharine had lived on the second floor above the store. They were married August 9, 1893.

Alice, along with Richardson's parents and a few close friends, attended the Episcopalian ceremony.

After the wedding, the couple left by train for the World's Fair in Chicago and then other points west.

Katharine, her husband and her sister did not remain long in Wisconsin. In late 1893 they gathered their belongings and moved to Kansas City. No evidence has been found for why they made the move. Possibly Katharine and James had visited Kansas City on their honeymoon. Perhaps they saw more opportunity for their practices in the larger city.

## Booming but unruly

Their new hometown had blossomed quickly in the years since the Civil War. In 1865, Kansas City and its 4,000 or so inhabitants stood in the shadow of two cities farther up the Missouri River – St. Joseph, Missouri, and Leavenworth, Kansas – each of which boasted about 15,000 people. That relationship changed dramatically when the railroad bridged the Missouri River in 1869, not at either of the larger towns but at Kansas City. Passengers and freight-shippers now had connections to Chicago and the major cities and ports of the East. Almost instantly, Kansas City turned into a booming crossroads.

By 1870, Kansas City's population had exploded to around 32,000. St. Joseph and Leavenworth, still without a rail bridge, numbered about 20,000 and 18,000, respectively. Twenty years later, according to the census of 1890, Kansas City's population hit 132,000.

Amid the rapid growth, Kansas City in those days was not pretty, nor was it clean or safe. Its unpaved streets turned from dust in sunshine into bogs of mud after rains. Water in the Missouri and Kansas rivers turned putrid from open sewage. Scores of saloons operated among the stockyards, grain elevators and warehouses of the West Bottoms, along with houses of prostitution.

This was hardly a healthy place for children, but children there were. And for many, there was no one to take care of them. Part of the blame can be placed on the way society looked upon children – they were considered property and a source of cheap labor.

This was the era of the "orphan trains," which symbolized a growing problem for poor children in the big cities of America. The so-called Orphan Train Movement was established by the New York Children's Aid Society to solve two problems: an abundance of destitute children in the cities of the east and a shortage of workers in the rural areas of the expanding United States. Over the years, more than 200,000 children were shipped west.

New York City at the time was awash in poor, abandoned children. With families unable or unwilling to support them, thousands roamed the streets, stealing to stay alive or begging for food or a few coins. Orphan asylums sprang up but did not meet the need. The Orphan Train Movement justified sending them west on the premise that the children might be spiritually and physically saved if they were removed from the "moral decay" of the cities. The

railroads made it easy to ship the "problems" far across the country. Trains filled with orphans carried the children into the unknown.

As early as 1867, orphans began arriving in Kansas City, which, along with the railroad hubs of St. Louis and Chicago, served as staging grounds for the children's final destinations in the country. In all, more than 4,000 were placed in Missouri and Kansas before 1910. Some were adopted by families and their lives were greatly improved. Others, however, experienced a form of indentured servitude and other abuse.

Although the Kansas City of the 1890s might not have seemed a thoroughly desirable place, its cruder aspects might have been exactly why Alice and Katharine were drawn to it. The sisters grew up believing it was their responsibility to care for those less fortunate and to make good citizens of their neighbors. Where was there a greater opportunity than a place teeming with destitute children, poor laborers, poor sanitation and few hopes for escaping it?

This was the dawn of the Progressive Era in the United States. Born out of the economic and social problems brought by the rapid growth and changing economy of the Industrial Revolution, the movement held that the problems facing society – poverty, violence and class warfare among them –

## The need was clear

Dr. Jane Knapp, who took a special interest in the history of the hospital, doesn't want it forgotten that Children's Mercy was created for children who had nowhere else to turn.

"It was founded for all the right reasons," says Dr. Knapp, an emergency medicine physician at the hospital in the latter part of the 20th century. "It wasn't founded for personal gain for Alice Berry Graham and Katharine Berry Richardson. They knew and recognized that poor children needed medical care and weren't getting it."

Their determination, Dr. Knapp says, was remarkable. Alice and Katharine showed "grit in the face of sometimes amazing odds."

could best be addressed by providing a good environment, education and a safe workplace. In addition, Progressives targeted the exploitation of children.

The fight for women's rights also was gaining traction. Katharine and Alice already had overcome some of the barriers that made it difficult for women to become educated. As doctors and businesswomen in their new city, they would continue to struggle for respect from their peers and the public. Yet a growing number of women were raising their voices.

It was against this backdrop that James and Katharine Richardson and Alice Graham moved to Kansas City in 1893. It was in Kansas City that they chose to make their home – and to leave their mark.

## Women doctors in a man's world

The sisters began their medical and dental practices in their living quarters, Suite 617 of the New Ridge Building at Ninth and Main streets. The site overlooked the bustling intersection popularly known as the Junction in downtown Kansas City, where Delaware, Ninth and Main met, along with multiple cable-car lines.

Despite the busy location, the sisters' practices did not flourish. The novelty of women doctors may have kept many patients away. Few if any male doctors would have referred patients to them. Alice handled her dental practice in the living room. Katharine may have seen a few patients there, but mostly made house calls. She charged $2, but only if families could afford to pay.

The sisters took a lot of charity cases. Katharine told her future confidante and secretary, Lena Dagley, that the doctors made sure to get up early and eat breakfast before dawn so dishes were clean and the aroma of ham and eggs had escaped their combined home and office before the arrival of patients, many of whom were hungry and could not afford to eat.

All this happened long before it became common for women to work outside the home, particularly in a profession such as medicine. Women doctors were an oddity and not welcomed in the men's clubs. Bankers ignored them and wanted to talk only to their husbands. Widows were allowed to own property, but that was one of a woman's few property rights. Women had to petition a judge to buy a house, start a business, or open a hospital. They wouldn't be allowed to vote until the 19th amendment to the Constitution was ratified in 1920.

In the late 1800s, men had secret societies where they connected with other men, conducting business, making friends. Women trying to start a business had no such network to turn to. The patriarchal walls were high.

*Their first neighborhood in Kansas City: The sisters and James Richardson set up shop on the east side of Main Street, right, not far from the Junction, where Main was joined by Delaware and Ninth.*

*According to hospital lore, Alice found her first young patient in Kansas City's lively but smoky and dirty river bottoms. Processing plants, cattle pens and innumerable trains shared space with the tiny homes of poor families, which supplied those industries a cheap workforce.*

The Berry sisters managed to get by through careful planning. Records of their businesses before the founding of Children's Mercy evidently have not survived, but the frugal practices they learned while in school undoubtedly helped.

Income from James Richardson's work was important, too. The 1894 business directory of Kansas City listed him as a broker in the flourishing livestock trade. But he would soon change professions. Perhaps encouraged by his sister-in-law, he decided to go to dental school. He is listed as a member of the graduating class of 1897 from Western Dental College in Kansas City. There are no records that he ever went into practice, and a year after graduation James joined another local dentist, W. H. Pfahler, to open a dental supply company. Richardson and Pfahler operated out of the New Ridge Building from a suite adjacent to the unit where James Richardson lived with Katharine and Alice.

By 1900, Alice, Katharine and James established separate business and home addresses. Alice moved her dental practice to the Shukert Building on Grand Avenue between 11th and 12th streets, and her residence to the Pepper Building at Ninth and Locust Streets. Katharine continued her practice from the old residence in the New Ridge building, but she and James moved to a boarding house at 16th and Central streets.

By 1904, James Richardson had designed and built a new and somewhat spacious home on Clinton Place in northeast Kansas City. This stone-and-wood home was to serve as his and Katharine's residence – and later Alice's, too – for the rest of their lives. It was still standing in the 21st century. Eventually it also became the office and a center of fundraising, public relations and other activities for Children's Mercy.

No information remains about James Richardson's involvement with the sisters' effort to create a hospital. Sometime in the early 1900s he fell ill, and one source suggested he became an invalid. He died January 15, 1908, only a few years after moving to the Clinton Place residence. He was buried in Eau Claire, Wisconsin, where he was born.

## That first patient

It is impossible to know for sure the story of that first Children's Mercy patient back in summer 1897.

In 1924, a *Kansas City Star* reporter wrote that Alice

Graham found that first child in a trash bin. Another source said the crying child was found on the street. Still another said Alice Graham came upon the 5-year-old girl – or maybe she was 6 – and her mother in the backroom of a dance hall.

"Confronted by the indignant doctor about her lack of care for the girl," this account maintained, "the mother complained that she was tired of the child's bawling. Borrowing a shawl to wrap up the dirty, ragged little girl, she took the child from her mother and brought her back to the office building where Alice and her sister worked – and lived."

Regardless of the exact origin, several sources agree that the time was definitely June 1897. We know that what today is Children's Mercy began with that single child whose name has been lost to history. Was she taken directly from her mother? Was she found alone? Either way, she was abandoned. And she needed care.

As the 20th century neared, children's needs were great. Aside from the sisters, apparently no other doctors in town cared for poor waifs. Much later, Katharine would write that one of the values of her work – and the reason the residents of Kansas City should support it – was that with help those poor, devastated children could grow up to become contributing members of society, not drains on it. She was recalling her upbringing and urging of their parents to "make good citizens."

In large part, children of that era were treated simply like little adults. Poor children were considered nothing more than labor. Katharine and Alice knew better.

Pediatrics was a relatively recent specialty; the first children's hospital opened in 1855 in Philadelphia.

"The specialty of pediatrics was just emerging as a science, but not much had been accomplished along that line," recalled Dr. Charles C. Dennie, who trained at Children's Mercy as part of the Class of 1912 at the University of Kansas School of Medicine. In the 1960s, he would write a series of articles about the history of the hospital for the *Greater Kansas City Medical Bulletin*.

"When children were hospitalized in the 19th century," Dennie said, "they were placed in the same ward with adults where they were subject to cross infections. Feeding was primitive … year-old infants were fed corn and other rough food with the consequences that cholera morbis [a

## Not a new idea … but different

Hospitals for children were not a new idea when Alice Graham and Katharine Richardson started their endeavor in 1897. In fact, Children's Mercy was the 23rd children's hospital established in the United States, according to the Children's Hospital Association.

There are distinctions, however, that help Children's Mercy stand out from that pack.

For one, Children's Mercy is a stand-alone children's hospital, not a pediatric service inside an adult hospital, known in some instances as a hospital-within-a-hospital. The children's hospital in Columbia, Missouri, falls in the latter category. Children's Mercy is also independent, meaning it is not owned by a university or a chain of hospitals.

For another, Children's Mercy is a comprehensive medical center, treating all kinds of illnesses and injuries. Some members of the Children's Hospital Association are specialty hospitals. Shriners Hospitals, for instance, specialize at different locations: orthopedics in St. Louis, burns in Galveston. Some Shriner locations have more than one specialty. St. Jude's in Memphis treats only select cancer patients.

Most of the hospitals founded in the 1880s took both paying and non-paying, or charity, patients. Children's Mercy took only patients who could not pay, a policy unaltered until the 1950s.

Two other facts set Children's Mercy apart: First, it took patients from anywhere, not just its hometown. That explains why patients came from as far away as New Mexico or North Dakota, often passing other children's hospitals on the way. Second, it was nonsectarian, meaning it did not subscribe to any particular religion or denomination, in contrast with children's hospitals that were opened by or closely affiliated with churches or religious orders.

*(In the appendix: a list of other American children's hospitals.)*

gastrointestinal illness], which is almost unknown today, was widespread and the mortality was great ….

"If children developed various infections, they had to depend on their own defense mechanism and good nursing care to see them through. Typhoid fever … had a high mortality. Tetanus serum was used only as a preventive because if lockjaw had appeared the result was fatal.

"These were a few of the hazards that Dr. Richardson and Dr. Graham had to overcome. But like strong swimmers, they dived into this maelstrom of diseases, Dr. Katharine being the surgeon and Dr. Alice taking care of the dental work."

But where to do the work?

## A noisy, smoky neighborhood

That first "home" of Children's Mercy was a bed within the Hospital for Women and Children at 3713 E. 15th Street, near Cleveland Avenue. The property, once a residence, lay in an industrial area near the Belt Line Railway, which carried trains around the southern edge of downtown.

Although the building was old, the hospital inside was new, having opened earlier in 1897. It grew out of an earlier effort by the East Side Women's Temperance Union that ended in bankruptcy. The Women's Refuge and Maternity Hospital, as that earlier facility was named, was designed for "sisters" who failed to safeguard their chastity. It was run solely by women and served as a reminder of the "pitfalls of city life into which the weak spirited tumble," according to a history by the Jackson County Medical Society. The hospital was open only to women who repented their sexual improprieties and desired moral rehabilitation. It went broke in 1896.

A year later, the owners donated the furniture and equipment to the Hospital for Women and Children, which had been organized by a group of women doctors headed by Avis E. Smith. According to one account, Dr. Smith was the first qualified female physician to practice medicine in Jackson County, Missouri. Alice and Katharine worked with Dr. Smith and the board of the hospital to provide beds for poor children, a sort-of hospital within a hospital.

There, the first little girl found a place for her care, a place of hope and healing.

The building itself was not much, particularly by modern standards. It was a rather dilapidated old house along a dirt road crossed by railroad tracks with frequent traffic by smoke-belching steam locomotives. South across an alley lay a brickyard. The neighborhood was loud and dirty. Dust and smoke blew directly into the patients' rooms. Access to the hospital was up a long flight of stairs.

But it was a start.

To support the occupants of their one free bed, Alice and Katharine in 1897 began the Free Bed Fund Association for Crippled, Deformed and Ruptured Children. It was incorporated in 1901 with the State of Missouri. In 1919, the hospital took the name The Children's Mercy Hospital.

The Free Bed Fund was a charitable organization to provide care for children who could not pay. That would remain a guiding principle for decades to come: No child who could afford care would be admitted. Alice and Katharine were not only the founders, they were also on the boards of directors and trustees and they were the only two charter members.

Alice was clearly the driving force. She served as the business manager of the Free Bed Fund, the principal fundraiser and the primary public advocate. Katharine provided medical care and continued to see patients in her private practice to supplement their income.

The Hospital for Women and Children agreed to set aside one bed – and more later – exclusively for a child

*The sisters moved their first charity patient to a rented bed at the Hospital for Women and Children in 1897. The hospital occupied a house at 3713 E. 15th St. In this 1896 map north is to the left.*

supported by the Free Bed Fund. In return, the Free Bed Fund agreed to provide the basic necessities and supplies for the bed plus a fee of $7 a week when the bed was occupied.

*When the Hospital for Women and Children moved to the corner of 11th Street and Troost Avenue in 1898, the sisters' charity operation moved with it.*

One of the first examples of public support for this work came not from the well-heeled members of the Kansas City community, but from children. Alice, writing in the *Messenger* newsletter in 1912, told the story:

"In 1897, some little girls in Kinsley, Kans., sent to a little bed at an old house at 15th and Cleveland, sheets and blankets and pillows and everything nice that the bed needed, and then the little girl, with her legs all drawn up in a wad came from Greeley, Kansas, to lie and grow straight in this bed."

## A name for itself

The story of how the Free Bed Fund became known as "Mercy" is interesting. Despite popular assumptions, the name does not have a religious basis. At the end of the 19th century, groups calling themselves Bands of Mercy were formed in many communities across the country to promote the idea of kindness toward others, the protection of children and proper care of animals. Humane societies were an outgrowth of this movement.

Alice introduced the head of the local Band of Mercy, Edwin R. Weeks, to one of the patients and asked whether her hospital could carry that name. Weeks loved the idea and he wanted to do more to help. He called upon all his members – young and old – to help.

Alice, writing later in the *Messenger*, continued:

"The Bands of Mercy, in Kansas City, saw the little girl (Stella Samuels from Kinsley, Kansas) and said, 'We are sorry for her too; we will give her clothes and crutches and braces

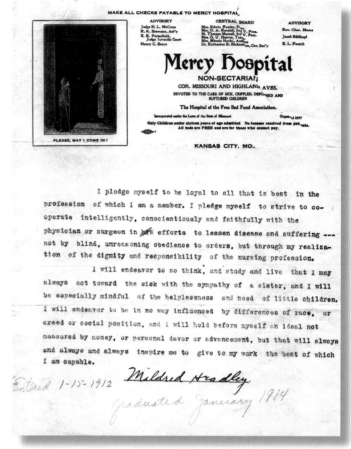

*The hospital began a nursing education program in 1901. Each graduate was expected to sign this pledge.*

and food and laundry and everything else she needs.' So they opened their banks and gave her their pennies. They divided their candy and gum money with her. They danced for her, sang for her, gave little vaudevilles and Spelling Bees. They sewed for her and soon they had more money than one bed needed."

In its first years, the Free Bed Fund grew enough to support five hospital beds. That was good news for the children who needed care, but it further taxed the facilities of the hospital at 15th and Cleveland.

In August 1898, the hospital moved to 11th Street and Troost Avenue, where it remained in the hands of women as administrators and physicians. Renovations to the building were done by hospital staff.

Although the fund was beginning to receive community support, some people in town didn't think highly of the operation. One of Kansas City's newspapers published a cartoon mocking Dr. Richardson. It depicted her working outside the hospital, and the caption had her shouting: "For

Women Only. No Men Allowed."

Despite the difficulties and the occasional scorn, it was hard to deny that, for children, the hospital was working.

As the result of its success, the Free Bed Fund on June 18, 1901, filed formal Articles of Incorporation with the state of Missouri. Article 2 set forth the goals:

"The object of this association and corporation shall be, by all lawful means, to aid in preventing neglect of and cruelty to crippled, deformed, ruptured and otherwise afflicted children; to assist children by surgical or medical means, or by nursing, also to promote the intellectual and temporal welfare of children under its care."

Officers of the association included Alice Graham as president and Katharine Richardson as corresponding secretary.

## No small plans

Of particular note was Article 7, which provided for the Association to raise funds, receive endowments, purchase land and buildings, create and maintain a hospital, and maintain a training school for nurses, including their graduation and issuance of diplomas. Clearly, the Free Bed Fund founders had big plans for the future.

And for good reason: There were few hospital beds for children at all, and beds for parents who couldn't afford care were non-existent except for the one, then two, at the

"Why do people say that Mercy Hospital is so popular and has more friends than any other one institution in Kansas City? Oh, that's easy to answer: children. It is because so many heartstrings are tied to The Mercy's."

— *Alice Berry Graham*

### BLACK ART FOR CHARITY.

**Entertainment in Magic by a Celebrated Japanese in Aid of a Deformed Children's Ward.**

Soto Sunetaro, a Japanese magician, has been engaged by a number of Kansas City ladies interested in charitable work to give one of his exhibitions of the black art for the benefit of the free bed fund of the deformed children's ward of the Women's and Children's hospital, at Fifteenth street and Cleveland avenue. The entertainment will take place this evening at the old hall of the Y. M. C. A., Ninth and Locust streets. Children wearing Band of Mercy badges will be admitted to the entertainment to-night at reduced prices.

### An Entertainment for Charity.

An audience that comfortably filled the old Y. M. C. A. hall at Ninth and Locust streets assembled last night to witness the entertainment given by a Japanese magician for the benefit of the Hospital for Women and Children, located at 3713 East Fifteenth street. The money realized by the entertainment will be applied to the fund for supplying free beds for the deformed children's ward of the hospital. The officers of the hospital are Dr. Catherine B. Richardson, president; Dr. Emily S. Colt, first vice president; Dr. Avis E. Smith, second vice president; Dr. Dora Green Wilson, secretary; Mrs. Emily Hornbrook, treasurer; Dr. Eliza Mitchell, auditor; Dr. Alice Graham and Mrs. Noble Prentis, trustees.

*The sisters' never-ending efforts to raise money included exhibitions such as this, noted in the pages of the* Kansas City Journal *in spring 1898.*

Free Bed Fund. The sisters appealed to women's groups and churches for help. Although some male physicians referred patients to the sisters, little support arose at first from most in the profession, except those few women doctors at the Hospital for Women and Children. Mostly, the work of Alice and Katharine was ignored, as was the need to care for the poor children.

The sisters started a School of Nursing in 1901. At the time, nurses were rated simply as trained or untrained; the word "graduate" was rarely used. Katharine fully appreciated and valued the contributions of nurses, long before it was popular among others in the medical profession. Katharine knew that it was the nurses who spent more time with the children than the doctors and even suggested the nurses were an equal partner in the care team – daring thoughts in the early 1900s. Nurses were also a source of cheap labor; the student nurses worked at the hospital as part of their education.

To minimize expenses, Alice and Katharine and the other women on the staff at the hospital did all the housekeeping chores and other maintenance tasks. For living expenses and the cost of providing the care, the sisters managed to squeeze in a couple of hours of work each day to take care of patients who could pay for their help. The sisters never accepted a salary from the work of Children's Mercy.

The Free Bed Fund and the Hospital for Women and Children existed side by side until 1902, when the agreement began to break apart. As the hospital struggled financially, it sought more money from the Free Bed Fund, which was filling more and more beds, eventually as many as 12. At one point, after Alice, as business manager for the Fund, refused to make the additional payments, the hospital confiscated its equipment and supplies and, somehow, even its bank account. After Alice sued, a settlement was reached awarding all the disputed

*A Thanksgiving plea to Kansas Citians by Alice Graham to remember the young patients of the Free Bed Fund. It appeared in the* Kansas City Journal *in November 1899. Below: That same year, the Bands of Mercy, from which the hospital took its name, met at Convention Hall.*

property back to the Free Bed Fund. Alice served as litigator for the Free Bed Fund to save on attorney's fees.

By then, the sisters had no choice but to remove their patients from the hospital, but there was no other hospital to take them. For the next year or so, patients were cared for in private residences in the suburbs and countryside.

Money was running out. There was barely enough time in the day to make house calls. The sisters continued to speak to any groups that would listen, broadening their call for donations beyond Kansas City as much as possible. As Katharine said when they were preparing for their first public appeal for funds: "We run this hospital for the sick children of this community. And the community ought to help pay."

## Adept at raising funds

Alice worked the women's civic organizations; Katharine leaned on prominent men in the city. Both were successful. The first endowment for the hospital came from a Sunday school class at the First Congregational Church.

Referring to the seven children from Kinsley, Kansas, who had supported that early patient, Alice wrote that then came "… more help and more love and more friends until the seven little friends had grown into thousands – not all little friends, because the big folks saw what the little folks were doing and they became friends, too.

"The nurses were kind and the doctors were wise and faithful and everybody knows that everything is done as it should be as nearly as possible and that good use is made of all the children

and big folks give."

The fund drive was so successful that the Free Bed Fund was able to purchase a building for itself, the Colonel R.H. Hunt home at 414 Highland Avenue in northeast Kansas City. Hunt, a wealthy businessman, was mayor of Kansas City in 1872 and 1873 and was instrumental in the early development of the city. Lena Dagley described the house as "standing on the crest of a hill that commanded a view of the Missouri River."

The structure, she wrote, was once "the scene of fashion and gaiety." Colonel Hunt had built the home for his niece. "The beaus and belles flitted through the spacious rooms and many a romance might be brought to light if those solid old walls could speak."

But now, it would become a children's hospital and have different tales of hope and love to tell.

After considerable renovation and expansion – and continued fundraising because Katharine and Alice insisted that debt be limited – the place was ready for patients. The contributions of materials by businessmen were essential and the free work of the union laborers vital. Men were beginning to contribute to the success of this endeavor to help children.

## A home on Highland

In November 1903, 27 patients moved into the new hospital building, a home entirely for poor, sick children. And for the first time, the name was engraved above the door: Mercy Hospital.

Barely half a dozen years old, Mercy already was finding a special place in the hearts and minds of Kansas Citians. Alice, in the *Messenger*, thought

*An annual spelling competition to benefit Mercy generated considerable attention at the turn of the century. The programs featured a performance by "our own drum major," Wesley Wilson.*

she knew why:

"Why do people say that Mercy Hospital is so popular and has more friends than any other one institution in Kansas City? Oh, that's easy to answer: children. It is because so many heartstrings are tied to The Mercy's. You see, in 1897, seven little hearts started the first little bed and they tied themselves tight to it, and that seven brought seven more and so on and so on.

"Next year, the Fifth, Sixth and Seventh grades of all the schools in Kansas City had a spelling bee for the little beds and tied their hearts to them, and their fathers and mothers and big sisters and brothers and aunts helped tie, too, and every year more and more hearts came, until there were thousands and they were all so tied and tangled together that you could not tell which from t' other.

"So now, when one of these strings is pulled at The Mercy, by even so weak a thing as the little skinny hand of a blue baby, the string that it touches sets a-jingling all the other strings all over Missouri, Kansas, Oklahoma and lots of other states and they all ring together and help the little hand of the blue baby."

With a new home for the sick children and newfound acknowledgement in the community of the value of their work, the Berry sisters settled into their lives' mission. There was a lot of work to do. There were many battles left to be fought. And there was no end in sight to the children who needed their help.

But at the new home atop of the bluffs of the muddy Missouri River, it was clear that the first child and that first act of charity by the sisters had started a journey that would change the lives of many.

## Chapter 2

# MERCY TAKES ROOT

*"Promise me you will always remember: You are braver than you believe,
stronger than you seem and smarter than you think."*

– A.A. Milne in *Winnie the Pooh*

Growing up is not easy. Not for children. Not for their parents. Not for those who care for them. And certainly not for a place that set out in the late 19th century to care for children who were sick, crippled and poor.

Yet despite the odds and the difficulties of the early days and beyond, the little hospital for poor children was on the right path by the early 1900s. With a new home at 414 Highland Avenue in northeast

*Nerve center of the Mercy operation: the Richardson home at 121 Clinton Place.*

Kansas City, the newly named Mercy Hospital was gaining momentum and support, thanks to the dedication of sisters and doctors Alice Berry Graham and Katharine Berry Richardson.

In a sense, business boomed. Parents from all over the Midwest brought or sent their children to Mercy. But there were growing pains, too. The hospital continued to treat only poor, non-paying patients, so Mercy's cupboard sometimes

was bare. It didn't take long for demand to outstrip supply – of doctors, beds, food, medicine and money. Like a toddler beginning to walk, the institution was unsteady on its feet.

The hospital on Highland opened in late 1903 with just five beds. As word spread of its successful treatments and its willingness to take patients regardless of religion or hometown and with no requirement to pay, demand grew. By 1906 more of the building, built as a residence, was remodeled and capacity increased to 27 beds.

Soon, even that would not be enough.

The long line of needy children stretched far beyond the walls of the hospital and far beyond Kansas City. Children came from as far away as the Dakotas and the desert Southwest. If local children couldn't come to them, nurses and doctors made house calls throughout Kansas City.

*At 414 Highland Avenue, Mercy's home from the mid-1900s into the late 1910s, nurses lined up for their portrait on a windy day.*

*Following pages: With natural light aplenty, Mercy's sun porch became crowded with patients, beds and caregivers.*

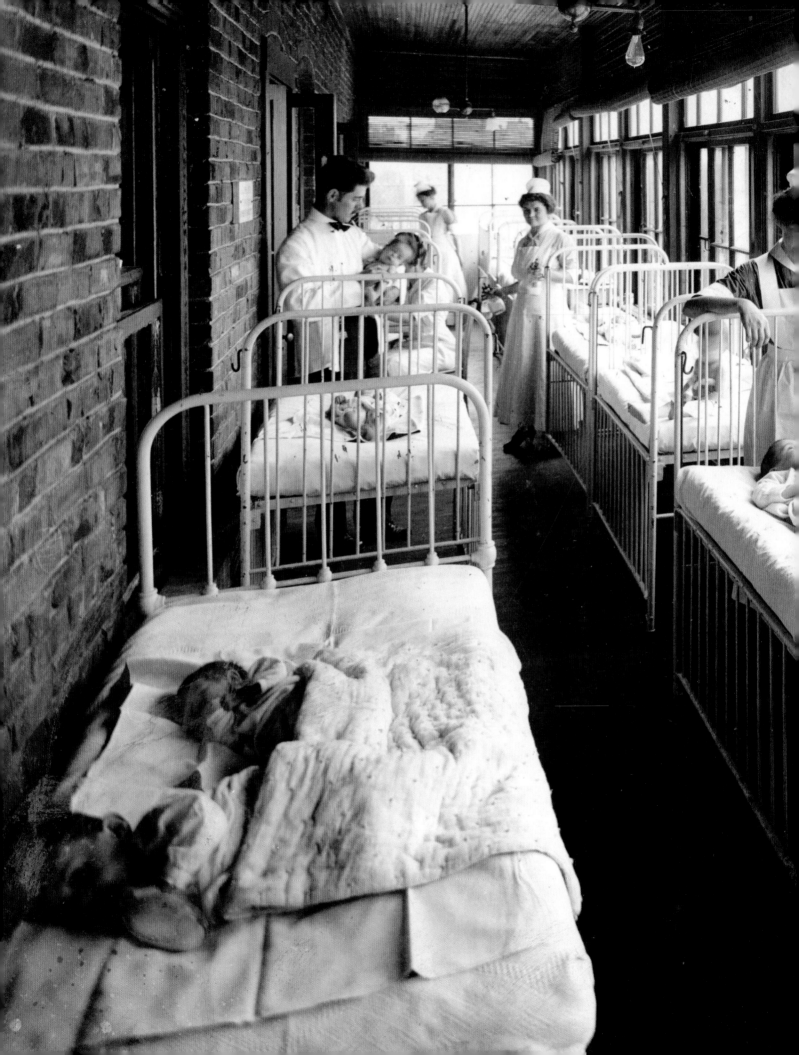

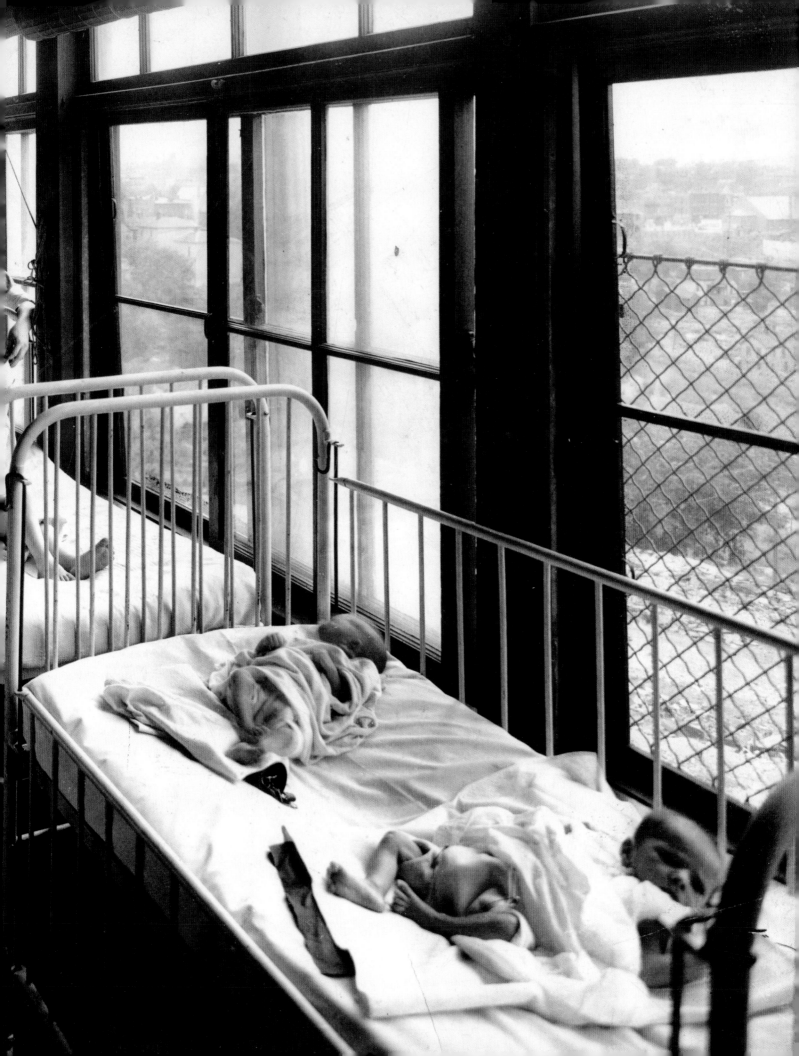

"We have much work to do," Katharine said. "There is no end to the sick children of this world."

The sisters, strong and smart and brave as they were, knew that they needed help.

## Young friends

First and foremost, Mercy Hospital needed financial support from its community. Making ends meet remained a challenge that required constant attention – even as the hospital enjoyed remarkable generosity from contributors big and small.

To remind people of the work of Mercy and also to solicit donations, Alice started a monthly newsletter, the *Messenger*, which was distributed to business leaders, other current and potential contributors and to newspapers that could spread the word to a wider audience. In it, she often reminded readers that the children led the way in philanthropy, too. Young people participated in spelling bees to raise funds. They put on carnivals and plays. They donated canned goods.

Sybil Silkwood was one of those young supporters. In the early 1900s, when Sybil was just 8 years old and living near 40th and Oak streets, she and her friends put on neighborhood plays. The audience at these outdoor affairs chipped in pennies, maybe nickels, to see the girls act, sing and dance. The girls, who called themselves the Mercy Hospital Club, donated the proceeds from those

*Neighorhood thespian Sybil Silkwood staged events to benefit Mercy Hospital. That spirit would live on through her family.*

performances to Mercy Hospital.

They also donated a stained-glass window for the hospital's chapel. It was dedicated November 8, 1905, and the window listed Sybil as vice president of the club. The window remained in the hospital chapel a century later, having been moved at least twice. Sybil's children and grandchildren, led by son James B. Nutter, would continue her spirit of giving into the 21st century, with gifts that funded the Sybil Silkwood Nutter Playground in front of the hospital and the Nancy Nutter Moore Garden near the Lisa Barth Chapel.

Another little girl who took up the cause was Mary Shaw. About 20 years after the Mercy Hospital Club donated the stained class, Mary, age 5, along with her mom, made a scrapbook for the children at Mercy to give them some pretty pictures to look at.

"The first time I heard of Children's Mercy was 1925," she recalled 90 years later, long after she had grown up to be Mary "Shawsie" Branton. "It was a beastly hot summer, and I was 5 years old. My mother said we would spend the summer making a notebook, a scrapbook, for Children's Mercy. I said, 'Great.' So, we sat on the floor and the fan was (blowing) on the ice cubes to keep us cool, and the draperies were all closed.

"And one day she said: 'Well, we're all done with the book. Now we'll take it to the hospital.'

"And I said: 'I don't think so. I like it. I want to keep it. I worked hard on it and now you're taking it away.'

"She didn't say anything. She went upstairs and changed her clothes and we both got in the car and took it to Children's Mercy and gave it to a little girl who was a patient [from Chillicothe, Missouri] … and she never saw her family. They wanted to come, but they couldn't make it. The nurse had told her that I was going to give her this notebook.

"And so I did and that was when I first learned that you really had a good day when you gave something you

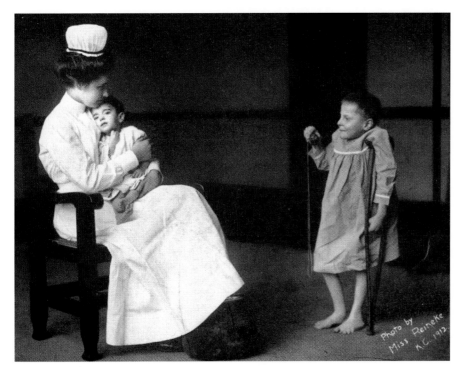

*Mercy nurse and patients, captured in 1912 by studio photographer Blanche Reineke. Her photos illustrated many a* Messenger *newsletter.*

really liked to somebody else, and that was Children's Mercy."

Although the scrapbook may not have had much financial value it did two important things: It brightened the day of at least one little girl, and it planted a seed of generosity in the heart of little Mary Shaw, who nine decades later still carried the torch of giving to others for Children's Mercy. She, too, would pass the spirit of giving to her children and grandchildren, including her daughter, Page Branton Reed,

*As a 5-year-old, Mary Shaw helped prepare a scrapbook for Mercy patients. As an adult, Mary "Shawsie" Branton carried on her support of the hospital and passed it along to her family.*

who served for many years on the hospital Board and two years as its chair.

Indeed, children did hold a special place in fundraising. Katharine kept a "Juniors List" of children who had donated anything in the last two or three years. In a 1916 solicitation letter to the children on the list, she called the recipients "the small boys and girls who at one time or another ... have in some way shown their interest in Mercy Hospital's little people."

"I want some help," she wrote. "We want it very much indeed, and I felt certain that I know how to get it. We are entirely out of fruit. Canned fruit.

"There haven't been any peaches or grapes anywhere near Kansas City and sugar has been so high that a great many people who usually help us to fill our fruit closets have this year not put up enough fruit, preserves, jellies ... and our shelves are empty for the first time in a good many years."

Fruit, according to a hospital newsletter of the era, was "one of the most valuable assistants in restoring health to our children."

The children responded and so continued what had become known as "The Passing" of fruits as an afternoon snack for patients. In 1928, The Passing was formalized with a gift from brothers and jewelry merchants Ernest and Walter Jaccard. They gave $5,000 in tribute to their mother, who for years had gone to market for fresh fruit to take to Children's Mercy. Katharine suggested that the money pay for a supplementary food tray, and also made sure nurses' daily baskets had varied treats, including cookies, juice and even candy.

## Old friends

Children, of course, weren't the only ones called upon to help Children's Mercy. Alice and Katharine spent a lot of time talking with civic clubs, church groups and just about anyone else who would listen. Thus began an extensive network of friends and supporters throughout the Midwest dedicated to helping children who could not help themselves.

*A daily ritual made possible by donor clubs and their members: "The Passing" of fruit to Mercy's children.*

As one story goes, businessmen knew that when they saw Katharine headed their way – sometimes with umbrella in hand to help make her point – they had better get out their checkbooks.

The first of what became known as the Mercy Clubs, later called Hospital Auxiliaries, was organized in 1904 as the Maywood Club, named for the neighborhood where its members lived. This group of devoted women met regularly to sew garments and to can fruits and vegetables. The motto of the Maywood Club was fitting: "Let Us All Work Together for Good and Do Unto Others as We Would Have Others Do Unto Us." The club changed its name officially to the Maywood Hospital Club in 1917. It also doubled its dues to 50 cents a month.

Other groups formed in Kansas City and outlying areas. The little girls from Kinsley, Kansas, whom Alice credited

FOR ALL CHILDREN EVERYWHERE

in the *Messenger* as the first group of young philanthropists, were just one example. A group of women from Maryville, Missouri, gave hundreds of jars of jelly.

The clubs that contributed to Mercy stretched from Kansas City through Missouri and Kansas, on into Oklahoma, Iowa, Nebraska and Arkansas and even beyond. At one point, as many as 800 clubs dedicated at least some of their work to Mercy, according to one of the early doctors who volunteered his time. These women's clubs became a lifeline for Mercy Hospital, helping keep the hospital open and providing hope when at times it seemed impossible to go on. If Katharine and Alice were the primary drivers of success, they were supported along the way by thousands of other strong women just as insistent on helping poor, sick children.

In the front lawn of the hospital on Highland Avenue the sisters installed a chalkboard sign listing the day's needs – eggs, sheets, fruit and so on. People walking or driving by saw the sign and, at least according to legend, by the end of each day those needs were filled.

As the needs of the hospital changed and grew, so did the focus of the Mercy clubs. They provided diapers and bed

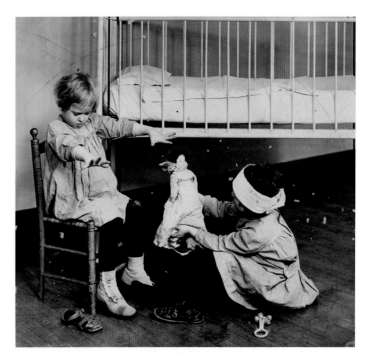

*Patients with impaired vision – often caused by gonorrhea, according to the hospital – received Mercy's help through the support of the Lucerne Club for the Blind.*

linens. They raised money wrapping gifts at department stores, holding bridge parties and hosting dances. The money helped provide for tile floors and a sunroom for tuberculosis patients.

The Charity Chest, formed in 1918 by the Kansas City Chamber of Commerce for various charities, helped raise money for Mercy's operating expenses, which amounted to about $2,000 a month.

The Century Club first set out to establish a "curative playground" at Mercy. This playground was designed not simply as a place for children to frolic, but as part of their medical treatment. Just as physical therapists of later decades used games and toys to help children stretch and to exercise muscles they might not ordinarily use, the curative playground was designed to help children heal – and maybe enjoy the treatment enough to continue it. The Century Club not only paid to build the playground but also maintained it, which was the usual practice for the Mercy Clubs.

Katharine's most important rule for the clubs – and for anyone donating to the hospital – was that the contributions come with no strings attached. She wanted to be able to spend the cash donations for what was needed most. She also wanted to make sure that the children came first, not the needs or wants of the various clubs or benefactors.

*Mercy's effort to form donor groups won support and publicity from* The Star *in April and June 1910, and from other Kansas City newspapers.*

*Time for arts and crafts in the basement of the hospital addition on Highland Avenue.*

## A different era

The clubs and fundraising were essential because in the early 1900s there was virtually no such thing as medical insurance. Some forms of disability insurance and so-called accident insurance existed, but nothing that helped pay for medical bills as later generations would know it. Even if medical insurance had been available, most poor families could not have afforded it.

There was no government support for health care, either. Social Security lay years away and Medicare and Medicaid even farther in the future. Add to that the general societal neglect of children in those days and it's easy to understand

why Alice and Katharine spent a lot of time soliciting contributions for money, bedding and food.

Fortunately for their cause, society's views on the treatment and welfare of children were changing. The Progressive movement, which by the turn of the century had become an important player in American political and social life, had as one of its targets the exploitation and neglect of children.

In early 1909, President Theodore Roosevelt convened a group of medical professionals and lay leaders for the first White House Conference on the Care of Dependent Children. This helped bring a national focus to the health and well-being

MERCY THE HOSPITAL OF THE LITTLE PEOPLE

Won't You Help Us?

*"The Hospital of the Little People" continually asked for money through its newsletter, local newspapers and personal appeals. In front of the Highland location stood a blackboard listing daily needs or otherwise seeking help. Passersby read it and responded.*

of children and provided an avenue for government leadership in childhood diseases, infant mortality and child-labor laws. The conference led to the development of the Children's Bureau under Roosevelt's successor, William Howard Taft, in 1912. The mission of the bureau was to "investigate and report upon matters pertaining to the welfare of children and child life among all classes of people."

Federal involvement was controversial, and cries of socialism came loud and clear. It also was controversial when Julia C. Lathrop was appointed to lead the new Children's Bureau. She was the first woman selected to lead a federal statutory agency. Clearly, however, national attention was being drawn to the kind of work being done in Kansas City at Mercy Hospital.

## Bursting at the seams

It also became increasingly clear that the number of beds at the hospital on Highland Avenue did not meet the need. Word continued to spread across the Midwest about Mercy, and stories were legion about families who tried to hand over even their healthy children for care. According to Beatrice Johns in her book about the founding sisters, *Women of Vision*, many healthy children had to be turned down, but only after the nurses and doctors – acting as the era's social workers – did all they could to help families find places to live or food to eat or train tickets to travel home.

In 1907, ground was broken for a three-story addition that would provide 58 more beds on Highland Avenue. In a letter to Mrs. Robert Gregory, an early supporter, Katharine explained the project:

"Mercy Hospital for Crippled, Deformed and Ruptured Children has outgrown its present quarters. $20,000 is needed for improvements, to be thus: $10,000 to build new addition, of wards, sunbath rooms, electrical rooms and out-of-door galleries; $3,000 for equipment; $2,000 for retaining walls and other stonework; $5,000 to clear present location of debt. The property is worth $13,000 on which is a debt of about $5,000."

The letter also described plans for a "kermiss," a term derived from the Dutch language and meaning a festival or presentation on behalf of a charity. The kermiss would include dancing and prizes to raise money.

The sisters were adamant that they not go further into debt. A 1913 account in the *Kansas City Star* noted that Katharine had initially bought the house at 414 Highland and leased it to the Free Bed Fund for $60 a month. As rent was paid, the mortgage was paid off.

As for the addition, construction proceeded as money came in; work stopped perhaps dozens of times when accounts ran dry. The Mercy Clubs, along with churches, labor unions and Kansas City individuals, came through. Merchants donated nails and other building supplies. Men and women donated their time to install flooring and do other work. A gift from Carrie Volker, sister of philanthropist William Volker, and a legacy gift from the estate of Lydia Gilbert were major contributions to the fundraising success.

On June 15, 1907, the property was deeded to the Free Bed Fund Association free and clear. In May 1909, construction of the addition was complete and Mercy Hospital had some breathing room. Added to the 27 existing beds, the addition brought the total count to 85.

*Fresh air and a chance to play figured strongly in Mercy's treatment plans for its patients.*

## Medical help

As news of the hospital's good work spread and Katharine used her powers of persuasion – and of creating guilt – a few male physicians volunteered to help.

The first was Robert McEwen Schauffler, a surgeon. Schauffler was a native of Kansas City, where his father was also a doctor. He was a graduate of Williams College and the College of Physicians and Surgeons of Columbia University in New York. During his internships, he worked in some of the toughest, dirtiest ghettos of New York City, according to his unpublished autobiography.

Schauffler returned to Kansas City in 1898 and began to get acquainted with his father's patients. Their office was in the Deardorff Building at 11th and Main streets. Schauffler also taught anatomy at the Kansas City Medical College, an independent medical school. Believing the days of independent medical schools were numbered, he worked with both the University of Missouri and the University of Kansas to provide medical training in the Kansas City area.

But his most notable accomplishment was his work with Mercy. In his autobiography, he wrote:

"Children's Mercy Hospital started in an old residence at Highland and Missouri Avenue, which Dr. Katharine Richardson bought with her own money. I was the first [male] doctor appointed on the staff. I was on active duty as an orthopedic surgeon for 44 years. I helped some in raising money for an addition and then for the fine new hospital.

"Dr. Richardson was a dictator and a wonderful money raiser. I had much influence on the professional ideals and the

## The early doctors

In the hospital's earliest years, most of the medical care and all of the surgery fell to Katharine Richardson. Caring for children was considered woman's work, and there were only a few dozen women doctors in Kansas City around the turn of the century.

In addition to Avis Smith, the doctor who headed the Hospital for Women and Children, where Alice and Katharine took their first little patient, other female doctors lent a hand from time to time. Four other women doctors appeared on a card for the hospital:

- **Emily S. Colt**, a gynecologist.
- **Elizabeth E. Enz**, whose specialty was a forerunner of today's pharmacologists.
- **Martha Cleveland Dibble**, who specialized in gynecology and nervous disorders of women.
- **Nannie Stephens**, who concentrated on children's diseases and served as vice president of the Jackson County Medical Society, the first woman to hold an officer's position.

All these women, along with Katharine and others, had served on the faculty of the Women's Medical College of Kansas City. The school was short-lived, opening in 1895 and closing in 1902, further limiting women's access to higher education.

After the turn of the century, male doctors began to volunteer at Mercy:

- **J.E. Hunt**, one of the pioneering pediatricians in Kansas City, with a special interest in nutrition. After Dr. Hunt died in 1915, **J.B. Cowherd**, his assistant, succeeded him.
- **William Trimble** and **Roger Brewster,** who tended to pathology and the laboratory.
- **Sam Roberts** and **Virgil McCarthy**. Together they developed an ear, nose and throat clinic.
- **R.J. Curdy**, an ophthalmologist.
- **Mont C. Carpenter,** the first dentist on staff. Alice Graham was a dentist, but she practiced very little for Mercy's children, concentrating her energies elsewhere. Dr. Carpenter happened to be the father of Harlean Carpenter, who became world famous in the 1930s as film star Jean Harlow.  He was followed at Mercy by **Frank E. Sheldon**.
- **Charles C. Dennie**, a member of the class of 1912 from the University of Kansas Medical School. He remained on the Mercy staff for years, operating the only free clinic in the United States to study and treat children suffering the effects of congenital syphilis.
- **Caldwell Summers** and **Harry M. Gilkey** joined as pediatric residents in the early 1920s.

selection of the staff. It was my greatest contribution to the public and the profession."

For several decades, Dr. Schauffler was involved in many of the major programs and accomplishments of Mercy Hospital. In 1950, the hospital's Central Governing Board presented Dr. Schauffler a plaque "in appreciation of his years of services as orthopedist, humanitarian, writer and man among men."

As the first male doctor on staff, Dr. Schauffler helped open the gate for others who had an interest in helping children. He persuaded several of his colleagues to volunteer their time and talent. One of those doctors was Clarence Benjamin Francisco. A graduate of the University of Kansas School of Medicine, Dr. Francisco did an internship in orthopedic surgery at the New York Hospital for the Ruptured and Crippled. In 1909, he became attending physician at Mercy. He remained on staff until 1914, when he joined the faculty at the KU School of Medicine. Two of his sons, W. David Francisco and Clarence B. Francisco, would later work on the staff of Children's Mercy.

Both these two early members of the medical staff were orthopedic surgeons. Dr. Schauffler was a general surgeon who said he developed a specialty in orthopedics by necessity. Far too many children suffered from broken bones, curvature of the spine, bow legs and other deformities. Those conditions were caused by a variety of factors, among them poor nutrition and pitiful working conditions in the days before child labor laws – not to mention physical abuse. Orthopedists were in great demand.

Dr. Schauffler, recalling the dominating, sometimes intimidating personality of Katharine Richardson, noted that the doctors were called "consultants without staff portfolio" in those early years. Yet Katharine knew she needed the help. The children, after all, came first.

The volunteer medical staff kept Mercy working for the multitude of children who needed care. It would take several decades, until the 1950s, for things to change and Mercy to have full-time paid physicians.

### Business matters

As the hospital grew physically and in staff size, it also grew in organizational complexity. Alice busied herself

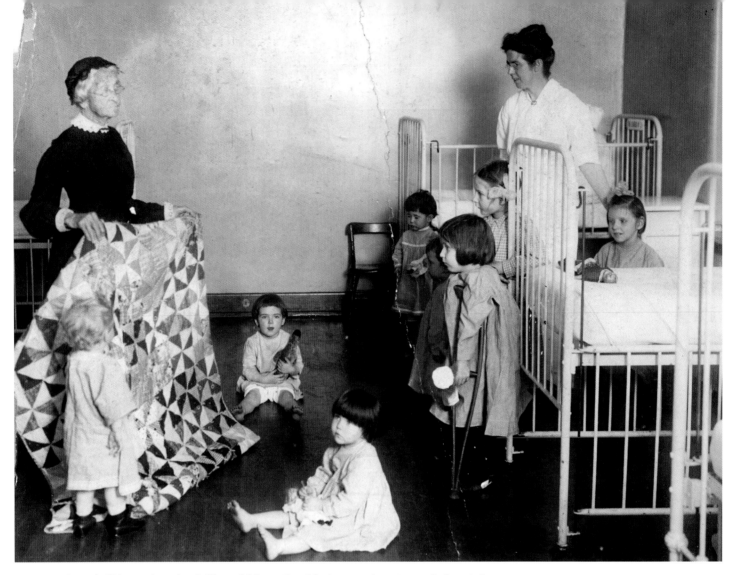

*A visitor showed off her quilt to the children of Mercy. Possibly, it was a donation to the hospital.*

with the business functions of the hospital while Katharine served as the primary physician and surgeon. Both worked tirelessly. Katharine recruited the medical staff, often scouted by Dr. Schauffler. But the business side of Mercy Hospital also needed outside help.

Since 1901, Mercy had been run by the Central Governing Board, composed of Alice as president, Katharine as secretary, and other women. In 1905, Mercy established an Advisory Board, which would later become the Board of Trustees. That board was made up entirely of men, two of whom were lawyers. At the time, men controlled most business and finance in Kansas City and elsewhere. Alice and Katharine, astute as they were, probably sought help from those most experienced at providing it.

One of the men who served in a variety of ways was R.R. Brewster, a former prosecuting attorney then in private practice, who had known Alice for several years. Once Brewster got on board, he was all in, and he served as chairman of the Trustees for many years.

Brewster had a reputation as one of the best lawyers in Kansas City. He had been a member of the defense team in the infamous local murder trial of Dr. Bennett Clarke Hyde, who was accused in early 1910 of killing Thomas Hunton Swope,

*R.R. Brewster*

one of Kansas City's wealthiest men. Hyde also was charged with killing a Swope nephew and poisoning other members of the millionaire's family. Hyde's trial featured all the necessary ingredients of a gripping murder mystery: money, greed, poison, dysfunctional families, mysterious deaths and mountains of evidence and expert testimony. In the end, Hyde was convicted, but the decision was overturned by the Missouri Supreme Court and three attempts at a retrial failed.

Brewster was as robust supporting Mercy as he was defending clients. He helped organize fellow businessmen.

Perhaps it was because of his work with Mercy, and seeing many children suffer because of their parents' abuse of alcohol, that Brewster became a staunch backer of Prohibition. He ran for the U.S. Senate in 1922, but lost to James A. Reed, who coincidentally had worked with the prosecution in the trial of Dr. Hyde for Swope's murder. Afterward, Brewster returned to his law practice and his work for Mercy.

Katharine's own feelings about the effects of alcohol were similar to Brewster's. In support of Prohibition, she would write in the *Messenger* in August 1931:

"When the saloons were here, abusive, drunken parents were everywhere in evidence. Injured and mistreated children, suffering because of drunken fathers and mothers, were always with us.

"From fear of drunken men, nurses were not allowed to go out alone at night, from the old Hospital to Independence Avenue and our Outworkers reported more than two thirds of the poverty and cruelty in the homes they visited were caused by drink. These things are not so now."

Nevertheless, Prohibition in the United States would end two years later.

## A sister slows

Alice, the older of the two sisters, was clearly the driving force behind Mercy, just as she had been with her siblings. She had helped Katharine grow up after their mother died, and she was the one who rescued that first abandoned child from the West Bottoms in 1897. It was Alice who suggested to Katharine that their mission should be to care for poor, sick children. So when Alice was diagnosed with cancer in 1904 not long after the move to Highland Avenue, a dark shadow hung over all those associated with Mercy Hospital.

At least initially, Alice refused to slow down. She continued to oversee the solicitation of money and other donations to keep the doors open, the medicine cabinets full

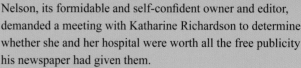

## A background check

So much attention was paid to Mercy by *The Kansas City Star* that William Rockhill Nelson, its formidable and self-confident owner and editor, demanded a meeting with Katharine Richardson to determine whether she and her hospital were worth all the free publicity his newspaper had given them.

Their conversation did not begin smoothly. From the outset, Katharine believed that "Colonel" Nelson acted condescending toward her. Nevertheless, she described to him the work of the hospital and her own background.

According to one account, Nelson made inquiries in the East about her credentials and liked what he found. Satisfied that the hospital and its matriarch were on the up-and-up, he continued to support Mercy within the pages of *The Star*. In recognition of her respect for Nelson, Katharine kept a portrait of him at Mercy. It stayed there at least until the 1950s.

and the children fed. Her one concession was to move in with her sister and brother-in-law at 121 Clinton Place, about two miles east and north of the hospital.

One of her primary tools continued to be the monthly *Messenger*. The newsletter was printed on heavy card stock so each copy would hold up to being shared among several readers. Typically, Alice included lists of the hospital's needs – from fruit to endowment dollars – and stories about children who were cared for. Most appeared in tiny print so lots of information would fit on the card.

Sometimes she included before-and-after photos of patients, showing remarkable improvement in malnourished children or those born with cleft lip or palate. Some staged photos and captions were intended to elicit feelings of sympathy or even guilt. In one, a poor waif asked a well-dressed woman with her bags all packed, "Hey lady, just what is a vacation?"

The constant need for money, food and materials made fundraising Alice's full-time job. Although the doctors donated their time, other staff – nurses primarily – needed to be paid. Meals were a large budget item, too. There were hundreds of mouths to feed, so demand for groceries, especially milk and fruit, was high. Sometimes farmers donated their produce directly to the hospital, but most other

*Squinting in the light of a sunny August afternoon in 1915, young patients and nurses along with friends of the hospital, gathered on the lawn at 414 Highland for a group photograph.*

FOR ALL CHILDREN EVERYWHERE

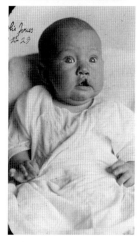 

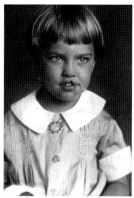 

*Katharine Richardson's surgical specialty was repairing cleft palates. In the 1920s she would commission these before-and-after photographs of patients for use in a lantern-slide program telling of the hospital's work.*

As John Oklahoma Entered The Mercy
July 3rd.

As John Oklahoma Left The Mercy in
April, Ten Months After.

**DEAR MOTHER FROM A FOREIGN LAND:—**
The Mercy wants to help you cure your sick child and to help you to keep your well child from getting sick. Let us be STRANGERS no longer. Let us be FRIENDS. Visit the Hospital. Ask questions, that you may understand all that you see there. If you cannot come and yet need us, send us your address and we will go to you.
All our beds are **free** and for those who **cannot pay.**

Visiting hours 2 to 5.—**ALL DAYS.** Out of town friends take notice.
We Urge a Visit.

Mercy Hospital is NON-SECTARIAN. Its employees are required to abstain from all expressions which might in any way be contrary to the religious belief of any patron of this institution. Visiting friends are earnestly requested to conform to this ruling.—CENTRAL BOARD

You have often said you wanted to help the Mercy. Do you, really? Then put this card into the hands of a poor Jewish mother who can read only Yiddish —or an Italian mother who only knows her own speech.
Rabbi Koplowitz and Mr. J. P. Deo have put our message in words that they can read.—Go take it to them.

*Mercy Hospital 414 Missouri & Highland*

## ITALIANI!!
**CARE MADRI!**
L'ospedale Mercy desidera di aiutare i vostri bambini di non cascare in malattie.
Venite al nostro Ospedale a farci visita onde tenerci in buona amicizia.
Venite qualsiasi giorno dalle 2 alle 5 P. M. domandateci qual sia questione che vi sia necessario.
Se avete bisogno di noi, e non potete venire, mandateci il vosto indirizzo che verremo noi da voi.
Tutti i letti del nostro Ospedale sono gratuiti, per quelli che non possono pagare.

**Please Do Not Destroy This Card. Read It and Pass It On.**

*Appealing to poor mothers "From a Foreign Land," the* Messenger *issued them an invitation to visit or contact the hospital. Readers of English were asked to pass this along, and the plea was translated into Yiddish and Italian.*

times the cooks needed money to buy it from the market.

Aside from the monthly newsletter, the sisters kept Mercy in the minds of the public by allowing visitors to see for themselves the work being done to help children. Visitors were allowed any time, and people in town for conventions often drove by or visited the hospital out of curiosity. The hospital also staged an official Visitors Day. The 1909 event attracted 200 to 300 people over three hours. Visitors were invited to "walk down the halls and past rooms filled with rows of white beds of small sufferers, exiles from the land of lullaby," according to the *Messenger*.

## Into the streets

One of the big fundraisers Alice helped organize was Silver Day. The first one was staged in 1908, during Kansas City's Carnival Week, an annual autumn festival with roots in agricultural fairs dating back to the 1880s. Each year, usually in September or October, thousands of people from around the region descended on Kansas City to see exhibits, parades,

plays and various entertainments staged by local merchants. The highlight was the Priests of Pallas parade through downtown.

Mercy Hospital used the opportunity of crowded streets – and a busy Union Depot – to raise money for its children. Carrying cigar boxes, hundreds of solicitors, many of them young women dressed in Florence Nightingale bonnets, marched into the streets of downtown seeking donations. How could you refuse? In acknowledgement of a gift – and to help donors fend off further requests from Mercy solicitors – those who contributed received a silver tag that declared, "We Help the Crippled Children." In a single day, $5,000 to $10,000 was often raised – worth as much as $250,000 in 2016.

Not everyone appreciated the approach. There were grumblings that Kansas City's many out-of-town visitors, who would spend their money in local businesses during Carnival Week, should not be "harassed" by the Mercy "beggars." Responding to the complaints, Alice was adamant about the needs of the hundreds of children from near and far cared for each year at Mercy.

In a letter to the editor in the *Kansas City Journal*, Alice wrote:

"Will you kindly allow the Mercy hospital workers to answer an often repeated question as to why we choose Carnival Week as the time for our tag day?

"Mercy hospital is not a purely local hospital. The first three years of our existence, we cared for more out-of-town children than those belonging to Kansas City. We have always taken patients without regard to their residence – the only requirement for admission being that they are under sixteen years of age and they are sick and needy. Our wards hold everything belonging to helpless childhood – Indians from the nation, Armenians, Greeks and Russians or any children from the foreign lands, as well as Kansas City's little invalids.

"We could say to any carnival visitor – 'We take children from your state' and it would be true. Just now there are in the hospital eight children from surrounding states.

"For the reasons given, we feel that we are not imposing upon our out-of-town friends when we ask them to contribute once a year to the crippled children of Mercy."

Dr. Schauffler used a different appeal for support, stressing that "good health is a national asset." In an article for the 1909 tag day, which fell on October 7, he noted that this was a time of "conservation." While Theodore Roosevelt was president, Dr. Schauffler pointed out, he had called on Americans to conserve natural resources. Others, insurance companies among them, were beginning to see that "the conservation of human life and health as an economic factor is to be given its proper importance."

"Nowhere is this terrible waste of life more striking than the mortality among infants. In New York, in the early '90s, the annual death rate was 97 out of every 1,000 children under 5 years of age.

"Aside from the suffering and grief involved, what a waste of valuable human material.

"Perhaps even more important than the death rate of the ninety-seven children is the future of the 200 others who survive the ordeal of sickness and starvation, but with weakened bodies ... [and] enter handicapped in the race of life."

Although education was considered a matter of great

*All dressed up to help Mercy ask for money on Silver Day in 1908, Sabra Julia Bellows paused to show off her doll to a photographer.*

public concern, Dr. Schauffler wrote, health care for children was not. The burden, he said, fell to Mercy.

"Behind all the work for children stands the Mercy Hospital. Here all the other institutions send their bad cases. The baby starving to death from improper feeding is here, nursed and fed back to health. The little pneumonia victims who are practically doomed at home, have here all the chance that skill and care can offer. The cases of tubercular bone disease have the light and sunshine of the broad living and sleeping porches and the best surgical attention. The children with weak eyes ... receive prompt relief. No child is too sick to be received and there is no limit to the time which they may stay if their condition demands treatment.

"The care of sick children appeals to all of tender hearts. More than that, it pays economically. To take a concrete example, here is a boy with severe bone disease in each limb. His probable fate is to have both limbs amputated in some general hospital or to die of the chronic poisoning. He is kept at Mercy Hospital a year, goes out in good general health with two sound limbs to be a useful, happy member of society instead of a dependent or a beggar. Suppose it cost $300 for his care for a year. Would it be possible to make a better investment for society, to say nothing of the individual?"

Those appeals kept awareness high of Mercy's needs year-round. But they did not completely quiet the critics, some of whom suggested that if Mercy could solicit on the streets, where would the begging end? One complaint claimed, probably with considerable hyperbole, that 99 percent of Kansas Citians were tired of it. Tag Days lasted four more years before Alice and Katharine decided to end them.

*Alice Berry Graham spent the final decade and a half of her life building Mercy from a single bed to an important Kansas City institution.*

**MERCY HOSPITAL'S HEAD QUITS.**

Illness Causes Dr. Alice Graham to Go to Los Angeles.

Mercy Hospital, the institution at 414 Highland Avenue which cares for crippled children, has lost its mother—the woman who founded the hospital fifteen years ago. She is Dr. Alice Graham. Doctor Graham left Kansas City a week ago to spend a year in Los Angeles. She was suffering from bronchitis and asthma.

Mrs. John Wagner takes the place of president of the hospital board, which was left vacant by Doctor Graham.

From a nominal institution that cared for one child in 1896, Doctor Graham watched Mercy Hospital grow to its present size. Forty-five crippled children now are being cared for. The board of education a few months ago established in connection with the hospital a public school, the second of its kind in the United States.

## "I want to work until the end"

In 1911, as Alice's health deteriorated, she resigned her position with the Free Bed Fund. She went to Los Angeles, seeking care for her bronchitis and asthma, according to a newspaper account. In Kansas City, her position as president of the Mercy board was taken by Mrs. John Wagner.

When Alice returned home she continued to publish the *Messenger*, often writing from her bed in the house on Clinton Place.

"I want to work until the end," she told a newspaper reporter. A daughter of Alice and Katharine's late sister Clara moved to Kansas City to care for Aunt Alice.

With a stenographer at her bedside, Alice dictated stories of the children who had been saved and who continued to need help. She wrote fundraising letters. Sometimes, hospital board meetings took place by her bed; other times she attended by telephone, offering suggestions on how the work should be carried on.

Alice and Katharine recognized that one of their major needs was for an even newer hospital building, a larger space and one constructed for its intended purpose. The two sisters dreamed big dreams and braced for the challenges.

Alice, however, would not be able

to participate. She died May 3, 1913, leaving a heartbroken sister, thousands of healthy children who had relied on her dedication, and countless admirers who would have to double their efforts to serve the children, their families and the community. She was 63.

"She was a woman of lofty ideals, of sublime courage, of infinite tenderness, of tenacity of purpose, of broad, deep, tolerant Christian character," one anonymous tribute declared. "Her life was that of self-sacrifice and devotion to duty."

In an article announcing her death, the *Kansas City Journal* wrote: "Doctor Graham gave up her profession and devoted her whole time and energy to helping the children. She went to live with her sister and gave up her life to the work, abandoning her profession and all her own personal desires and wants.

"Mercy Hospital and its unfortunate juveniles with their infirmities became her only interest …. She kept up her work for the children until the day she died."

R.R. Brewster, speaking to a newspaper reporter, offered a story as a testament to Alice. One wintry night, he said, she arrived at her home nearly exhausted from the cold and bruised from falling on ice.

"She had taken a crippled child to the hospital and had forgotten to save sufficient car fare," he said. "She had walked home in the dark and blizzard after performing the mission. She abandoned the story of her own plight to tell of the happiness that was in the smile of the child when it was put to bed at the hospital."

"Kansas City," Brewster said, "lost one of its best citizens in the death of Dr. Graham."

*Patients' constant companions: nurses lined up outside the hospital at 414 Highland.*

# "The worst case of abuse we have ever received."

One little girl came to Mercy Hospital in late 1915 suffering from horrible abuse. Hers is a story of the enduring spirit of children and the hospital that took care of them.

She was one of five children of an alcoholic mother who in the summer of that year had abandoned her family. The child's father, unable to care for all of his children, "fostered" the girl to a group home. Her name was Helen Keller, identical to that of the blind and deaf girl from Alabama who would achieve world fame, but no relation. At the group home, Kansas City's Helen Keller was severely beaten.

Helen's father, unaware of her treatment, made a rare visit to the home and was stunned by what he found. He called on Dr. J.E. Hunt, one of the pioneering pediatricians in Kansas City and a mainstay at Mercy Hospital, to look at Helen.

At the home, Dr. Hunt found the matter "so much more dangerous than he had anticipated and the conditions in which she was living so bad he took the child immediately in his car to Mercy Hospital," according to an account by John Arthur Horner, who works for the Kansas City, Missouri, Public Library.

One of the officials at Mercy called her condition "the worst case of abuse we ever received." Helen's case was reported in the *Kansas City Star* under the headline, "A Baby Girl of 2 Beaten."

"The doctors concluded that the child had been healthy before receiving vicious beatings," Horner wrote in his Kansas City history blog. "Her legs and bowels were paralyzed, she was badly bruised over most of her body and in many places the skin was torn off."

The operator of the so-called foster home eventually was

*Helen Keller, based on a courtroom sketch in the* Kansas City Journal.

convicted of child abuse and assault with intent to kill.

Little Helen would spend more than seven years at Mercy.

The beatings had not damaged her mind or her spirit, Katharine Richardson said. But her body was another story. She would never walk again.

"The baby is just as bright as she can be," Katharine said. "But she can hardly live. The treatment we are giving her is prolonging her life … but the chance for her recovery is so very slight it hardly can be called a chance."

In February 1923, suffering from pneumonia, Helen died. A year later in the *Messenger*, Katharine wrote:

"You will remember Helen Keller, who was so beaten and bruised that when she came to Mercy Hospital she was only half a child, but that half the very greatest and best of her.

"She was greatly loved at Mercy Hospital and during the years when she was slowly coming to life, the Hospital people longed to give her some means of getting about – some way of going down to the playroom, and out to the yard and about the house, but no wheel chair ever made was small enough or had been so built to answer the call of the tiny girl who only knew herself from the waist up and whose slowly returning life made the movements of her hands seem like the fluttering of butterfly wings.

"But someone had a thought and somebody advertised for the smallest kind of tricycle – the kind that is not now made because there are so few calls for such little carriages. However, another body's little chap had grown to real boyhood size – and among the tin soldiers and the rubber balls in the garret was just the thing that Helen Keller needed."

The owner answered the ad and the tricycle was delivered to the hospital, where it was adapted to Helen's requirements. With it, Katharine continued, "Baby Helen could go up and down the hall and out on the playground and with which she astonished everyone with her skill as a motorist.

"Hospital rules were suspended and when you wanted Helen you might look in the Laboratory or the Operating Room or the X-ray quarters or anywhere else about the house," Katharine wrote. "She was always loved, always welcomed and when she outgrew the little tricycle carriage she had gained strength and skill to manage a larger and

> The beatings had not damaged her mind or her spirit, Katharine Richardson said. But her body was another story. She would never walk again.

'more proper' one.

"After awhile, Helen went away from us and the flowers piled high about her and a pretty resting place in Forest Hill (Cemetery) told again how dear she had been to the hospital people.

"The chair – the fine, new one – was sent to Dr. Richardson's home, there to wait quietly for another time of need. After awhile, Dick Berlin came to take Helen's place – Dick with a bullet in his spinal column – and a certainty of a life span much like that of the little girl. The chair came back to Mercy and again went up and down to the school room and anywhere and everywhere the little driver wanted to send it. At first, Dick's face looked startlingly like the one that used to be seen above the handlebars and, also like that other, it slowly, slowly continued to thin and whiten.

"Yesterday, the chair came back again to Dr. Richardson's, for now Dick lies in a bed on the roof, or in the coziest and prettiest other place that can be found. He doesn't know that his small hands have done their work and that his wheel chair – his carriage – is waiting to serve some other little boy who will be given faithful loving care at the Mercy."

## Mercy's Messenger.

Published by Mercy Hospital.
"The Hospital of the Little People."

Business Manager: Ozella Wingfield.

Editor for January, 1917.
Dr. Katharine B. Richardson
121 Clinton Place.     Kansas City, Mo.

7

MERCY HOSPITAL—A FREE, NON-SECTARIAN, NON-LOCAL INSTITUTION, situated at 414 Highland Avenue. Kansas City, Mo., and devoted to the care of Sick and Crippled Children.

### Why Mercy Hospital Wants Laboratories, and Asks Your Help in Securing Them.

(1) Because modern medicine is the product of the test tube and the microscope.

(2) Because we have commercialized our scientific discoveries, our serums and bacterines and anti toxins, until they are utterly out of the reach of the people.

(3) Because the Laboratories everywhere are either strictly money making affairs, or so surrounded with an air of mysticism, and with a language so absurd and unintelligible that to the ordinary practicianer they are utterly inaccessible.

(4) Because Mercy Hospital furnishes a wonderful opportunity for the discovery of a cure for the frightful, death dealing child diseases.

(5) Because the germs of great discoveries are quite as likely to be in the brain of an obscure physician, as in that of a great savant.

(6) Because the obscure physician has no laboratory facilities at his disposal, and the best he can do is to turn his patient over to a presumably Great Specialist, and go back discredited to his practice.

(7) Because with a small Staff and a fine Laboratory Director, it is possible to welcome all honest investigators, and to so guard their work that no harm can come to the children.

(8) Because data secured by putting children under unnatural or unhappy conditions is valueless, and because Mercy can and will look to the comfort as well as to the recovery of its children.

(9) Because Mercy wants to furnish free diagnostic help to any physician whose patients are unable to pay.

(10) Because it is not necessary to have the Rockefellow millions in order to accomplish the very finest work, and because the undue prominence given t[o] this immense sum, discourages individua[l] effort, and is actually a hindrance t[o] scientific progress.

(11) Because we want to do the ve[ry] best for every little creature that com[es] to us, and because we feel that out [of] the wonderful advanages of Mercy H[os]pital should come great discoveries the actual prevention of the awful formities which at present we can little more than modify.

We take care of the Jews and Gentiles, the Italians and the Croat[s] and the Poles and the Servians, an[d] Bohemians and the Belgians, and Mexicans and the Japanese, and a[ll the] rest, and yet refuse to straighte[n] legs of the little colored people are our especial wards, and m[ore] whose delinquencies are of our m[ost] No institution, not even Mercy, right to so do, and yet be called Children's Hospital."

It only costs $1.00 a day to child in Mercy Hospital. Hund[reds of] "Clubs" meet to talk and eat forget embroidery stitches in [one] learn new ones. The membe[rs] mean to be selfish, and would feel that they are doing more helpful things, something mor[e] of progressive, motherly wome[n] they would like to put a tabl[e or] bed at Mercy, pay a dollar a Day for the care of its little occupant, and [ac]tually [do] make citizens instead of doilies.

Mercy Hospital is being constantly questioned concerning the cost of equipment in the new building, and believing that many people are anxious to help, these statements are submitted.

The New Hospital, Nurses Home and Power House will, all together, cost approximately $300,000. There is practically no Endownment, and maintenance is not provided for.

**To Endow a Bed** means to put at interest enough money to provide annually for the upkeep of a bed, which will be about $10,000. This gives the right to a Name Tablet.

**To Support a Bed** means to provide for the care of its little occupants (about $1.00 a day). This is a satisfactory arrangement for the work of individuals and small clubs. Such beds carry tablets while supported.

**To Pay for a Bed** means to furnish sufficient money to provide a bed, springs, mattress, and furnishings for one year's wear. This costs to begin with about $100.00, and the upkeep of such a bed costs about $35.00 a year. This has nothing to do with the care of the child in the bed, and does not provide for a tablet.

No beds may be marked with tablets suggesting death, as for instance, "John Brown, In Memorium." These are the inscriptions on tablets now in use:

1. Rest Well Little Girl,
   Frederick Bannister, Jr.
2. For Love of Eugene Loch.
3. League Bed No. 4.
4. Lovingly Yours, Maywood Social Club.
5. Emery, Bird, Thayer Bed No. 2.
6. J. T. Bird Bed No. 2.
7. Labor Union Bed.

Maybe when the end comes one would [kn]ow that the handles would [... ] tall young men [... ] in their

Illustrations by Archie Chapin of the Kansas City Star

"Children whose mothers toil the day for food
The while their nurslings lay at home alone
Say for the drunken sot, dead to all filial care."
G. T. Johnson.

*Messengers pleaded for money and for understanding.*

## Picking up the banner

The loss was especially hard on her sister. Not only would the burden of Alice's work fall to the younger sister now, but also there would be a void where her guidance had been. The two sisters were wonderful complements to each other. In her memoir, the former hospital manager and assistant to Katharine, Lena Dagley, put it this way:

"I saw Dr. Graham but the one time (when I was a school girl and participant in the Mercy spelling bee where Alice served as toastmaster). I have been told that she was reserved, courteous, always kind and considerate of others and knew how to get along with other people. Her sister, Dr. Richardson, was a dictator, an organizer and a fighter. Her courage and her determination were her outstanding qualities. She was very plainspoken and because of her frankness, she was sometimes considered blunt and tactless, and often made enemies for both herself and the hospital."

Alice's death was the second great loss Katharine had endured in recent years, having lost her husband, James, in 1908. But according to Dr. Dennie, who trained at Mercy Hospital in the early 1910s, the loss of Alice was one from which she never recovered. Dr. Dennie quoted Katharine as saying of her sister:

"She was always smarter than I am. I always went to her for advice and for new ideas in taking care of children and in building a hospital. Her advice was very sound and often made me change my plans. Now since she is gone, I often think when I develop a new project, just what would Alice think about this. And I place myself in her position and remember her advice and am usually successful in my undertaking."

Katharine was determined that her sister's legacy would live on.

"Some unthinking persons may not believe in the immortality of the soul," she said, "but no one, having known Dr. Graham, can doubt the immortality of a life."

## Big dreams

As the sisters discussed before Alice died, they would require a larger, proper home for the "Hospital of the Little People," as they sometimes called Mercy. Now came the need to raise money for the new hospital.

In the Mercy Hospital Annual report of 1913, Katharine made it clear that more space would be needed within a few years.

"Mercy wants to tell you," she wrote, "of its steady growth from one little white bed in a rented ward, to a small building, to a large addition to a year's work of almost 20,000 free days' treatment, to a list of waiting children still increasing demands upon its services …. We have utterly outgrown our quarters and we have neither land nor money with which to enlarge."

Roger Swanson, in his 1961 book, *A History of the Children's Mercy Hospital*, wrote that Katharine explained the value of the work this way: "Isn't it better to make a sick child self-supporting than to be taxed later for his care when he enters the poorhouse and becomes one of the great army of down-and-outs?"

Katharine and others kept busy raising money for the day-to-day operations of the hospital. At the time, about 500 patients a year were admitted to Mercy. Operating expenses for the hospital in 1915 were about $2,000 a month, and it cared for children whose homes were as far as 1,000 miles from Kansas City.

As demand for services continued to grow, the generosity of one of that era's great local philanthropists came through. Jemuel Clinton Gates, a successful real-estate operator and former footwear wholesaler, offered Mercy a two-acre tract at the corner of Independence and Woodland avenues, only a block or so south and east of the existing hospital on Highland Avenue. Gates had bought considerable amounts of land around Kansas City, much of it after the financial panic of 1873. The gift was in memory of his daughter, Lulie Adaline Gates.

*Honoring the memory of his daughter, businessman Jemuel Gates gave Mercy two acres of land on which a new hospital would arise.*

Katharine and the other friends of Mercy were thrilled and knew the time was right. They moved quickly to raise funds for a new Mercy.

One of the rules Katharine had for donations

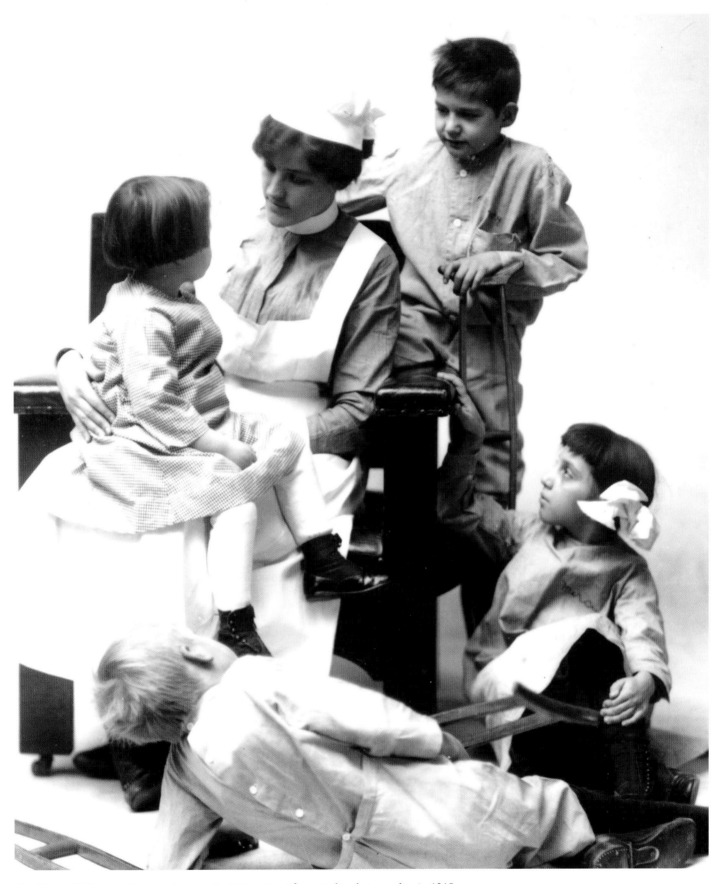

*A tableau of Mercy patients and nurse. Participants sat for a studio photographer in 1915.*

was that they be "free gifts" – free, that is, of conditions. The rule was on full display when local businessman Jacob Loose and his lawyer came to visit Katharine one afternoon. Loose, who had made a fortune manufacturing cookies and soda crackers, had heard about the hospital, knew it often begged for money and wanted to know what it cost to run the hospital for a year. At the time, Katharine told him, expenses ran about $25,000.

The story – reported in more than one account – is that Loose offered her not only enough money to run the hospital for a year, but also $1 million to establish an endowment to support the hospital in perpetuity. Katharine would never have to beg for money again. There was a condition: the hospital must be named for him.

*Katharine Berry Richardson*

Given her rule against conditional donations, Katharine declined the offer. That might have been the end of the story but Loose, who with his wife, Ella Loose, had no children of their own, remained a friend of the hospital and donated $25,000 to help support Mercy. Ella Loose also volunteered at the hospital, and the family's various trusts would contribute hundreds of thousands of dollars over the decades well into the 21st century.

## A campaign on many fronts

According to Lena Dagley's memoir, in summer 1915 R.R. Brewster gathered a group in his office at the Scarritt Building at Ninth Street and Grand Avenue to start plans to canvass for funds. Later, a larger group met at the Hotel Baltimore to organize into teams. Their aim was to raise $200,000 to build and equip an up-to-date hospital.

On July 19, 1915, the campaign was officially launched. Teams fanned out across the city, carrying an emblem of the hospital, a miniature cradle. The Mercy Hospital Club, one of many that supported the effort, served lunch each day to campaign workers. Next to the lunch room was a giant scale, which would balance only when the $200,000 had been raised.

The campaign was directed by Burris A. Jenkins, the energetic and unconventional pastor of the Linwood Boulevard Christian Church. Others intimately involved in the campaign were Peter Graves, principal of the Manual Training High School, and Granville M. Smith, president of Commonwealth National Bank. Clearly, business leaders and other powerful Kansas Citians were taking notice of Mercy Hospital and supporting its work. Newspapers reported regularly about the hospital.

As part of the fund drive, the 1891 masterpiece painting "The Return from Calvary," by the British painter Herbert Gustave Schmalz, was displayed at the Grand Avenue Methodist Church, 205 E. Ninth Street. The Rotary Club arranged the showing, along with motion pictures of children who had been helped by Mercy Hospital. Admission was 25 cents.

Lena Dagley recounted a story about yet another publicity effort, in which word was put out that a political debate would take place in the stockyards district of the West Bottoms. Politics always brought out the crowds. But the men who gathered that day were in for a surprise, Dagley wrote. Instead of partisans debating political issues, R.R. Brewster brought two of Mercy's patients to illustrate the needs – and successes – of Mercy.

One was a boy named Blondy. He was 10 and just learning how to live.

"When he first came to Mercy, he had never taken a step in all his life," Dagley wrote. "Every joint in his poor racked little body was diseased. He could never be entirely well, but it was such a great thing to him even to be able to walk (with a crutch and dragging feet) that his soul simply

> When Blondy got up on stage and sang, "It's a Long, Long Way to Tipperary," many in the audience, which ranged from office workers to tough cowboys and cattlemen in spurs and sombreros, were brought to tears.

overflowed with music and joy."

When Blondy got up on stage and sang, "It's a Long, Long Way to Tipperary," many in the audience, which ranged from office workers to tough cowboys and cattlemen in spurs and sombreros, were brought to tears. More important, they brought out their checkbooks and billfolds and made donations.

"Mercy has an idea," Brewster said, "and it is that when this fund of $200,000 is raised for the new hospital, we can plan a vocational school in connection with it so some bright little fellows like Blondy who can never be strong physically can learn to use their brains."

Already, Mercy had begun to fulfill the educational prophecy. In 1910, in a partnership with the Kansas City, Missouri, public schools, a classroom was opened at Mercy. It was only the second school in the country to operate inside a hospital. Children's Mercy would continue to provide classroom and bedside teachers for patients into the 21st century.

There was a Mother Goose Day and a parade with costumed characters carried by automobiles in a caravan through the city, soliciting funds. Children and their parents gathered to see a Pied Piper play the flute for Mercy at an estate near 51st Street and Rockhill Road. Children and parents paid $1 each to hear the magical music that, according to legend, no child could resist.

"Kansas City has a reputation for finishing the things it

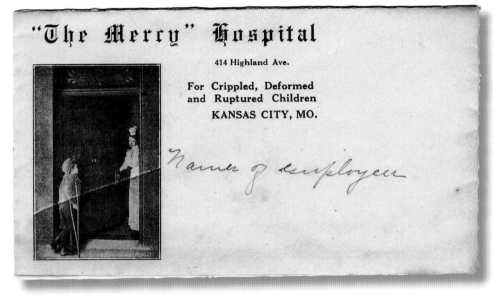

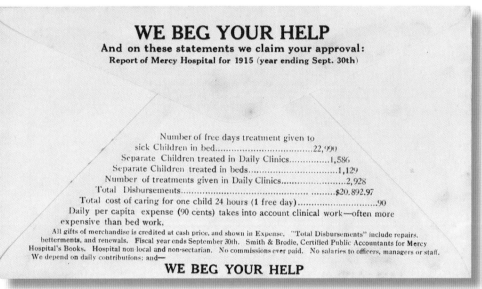

*Part of the hospital's fundraising campaign in 1915 was a message outlining the cost of care on an envelope with an image of welcome. Both were placed in the cornerstone of the new Mercy building on Independence Avenue.*

starts out to do," Dagley quoted Charles W. Armour as saying at a luncheon where he helped raise $19,000 over a single meal. "We can't fail Mercy …. The cause is worthwhile and the money is here."

Meanwhile, the architectural firm of Wilder & Wight was drawing up plans for the new building. An old residence on the Independence Avenue site donated by Jemuel Gates was demolished. E.L. Foutch, treasurer of the Board of

Trustees, announced that construction would begin as soon as possible.

By late August 1915, $100,000 had been raised, about half the original goal, and contributions continued, but the pace slowed considerably. By early October, the fund had reached only $106,000.

Even so, there were discussions about whether the planned building would be sufficient. When the campaign began, Katharine had mentioned the unending stream of needy children, and board members were concerned about whether they were building a hospital large enough. Despite standing well short of the original goal, the board decided to push for an additional $75,000 to build a bigger hospital. The "economy" of building a larger building at the outset, as opposed to adding on or starting from scratch later, persuaded the board, according to Dagley's account.

By June 1916 the fund stood at $115,000, still well short of the goal. Meanwhile, excavation had begun with the money on hand, but construction proceeded only as money became available. It had long been the practice of the hospital to assume as little debt as possible.

## A renewed effort

That autumn, the hospital's backers decided to launch a second fundraising effort, timed for the Thanksgiving season. The goal was $175,000, which would make up the deficit of the first campaign and provide for the $75,000 enlargement and more.

Dr. D.D. Munro, pastor of the Calvary Baptist Church and a member of the campaign executive council, stressed the importance of the work, according to Dagley.

"We have in this city one of the greatest women in the country," Munro said. "I refer to Dr. Katharine B. Richardson. She is doing things at Mercy Hospital that millionaires send their boys and girls abroad to have done. The institution is one of pure service to humanity, where the love of suffering little children is the mainspring. In every department of the Hospital and in all of its activities, love is apparent and paramount. Its patients must have everything that is necessary to restore them to health and strength."

That speech and more succeeded handsomely. For the 1916 campaign, the list of contributors read like a roster of

## What's in a name?

When Alice Graham and Katharine Richardson began their work caring for sick children in 1897, they organized a business entity called the Free Bed Fund Association for Crippled, Deformed and Ruptured Children.

Four years later, the association was formalized under Missouri law with the same name. According to incorporation papers dated June 18, 1901, its purpose was "by any lawful means to aid in preventing neglect of and cruelty to crippled, deformed, ruptured and otherwise afflicted children; to assist such children by surgical and or medical means, or by nursing; also to promote the intellectual and temporal welfare of children under its care."

Officers of the Free Bed Fund Association were Alice Graham as president, Florence Carpenter as vice president, Josephine C. Peters as auditor, Effie L. Stephenson as secretary, Emily T. Standeford as treasurer; and Katharine Richardson as corresponding secretary.

In 1903, upon moving into the first building that was its own, the Free Bed Fund began to go by Mercy Hospital, though there was no legal name change. It also sometimes called itself "the Hospital of the Little People" in newsletters and the blackboard in front of the hospital.

Fourteen years later, in 1917, Mercy Hospital moved into a new building on Independence Avenue. Engraved above the front-entry steps was: The Children's Mercy Hospital. But it was not until 1919 that the name became official. On July 25 of that year, papers were filed with the Circuit Court of Jackson County, Missouri, to amend the articles of agreement of the Free Bed Fund Association.

"The association and corporation will be called 'The Children's Mercy Hospital' and its location shall be in Kansas City, Jackson County, Missouri," the document reads.

That is how it has remained, legally, ever since.

In addition, the amendment added the word "sick" in front of the word "crippled" to the Free Bed Fund's name. Although already engraved on the building's cornerstone, these words were also legally added: "This association shall forever be non-local, non-sectarian and for those who cannot pay."

*Behind a row of Mercy nurses, dignitaries and other onlookers – including streetcar motormen in their uniforms and caps – watched the laying of the cornerstone at the new hospital building on Independence Avenue. The date was October 15, 1916.*

the city's bluebloods: lumber magnate R.A. Long, meatpacker Charles W. Armour, wholesaler and philanthropist William Volker, garment manufacturer H.D. Lee, physician W.F. Minor and his wife, and many, many others. As Swanson put it, "Mercy had won the heart of the community."

R.R. Brewster kept beating the drum. At one gathering of the well-to-do, he declared, "Energetic as you have been, you have not yet commenced to skim the cream of the money there is in Kansas City for Mercy Hospital." Donors increased pledges from $500 to $5,000. Others offered additional contributions if the community came through with the rest. From all quarters, generosity flowed.

A clock on the Arlington Building at 10th and Walnut streets downtown marked the progress. Shoppers and workers throughout the district watched as the campaign approached its goal. By Thanksgiving, it had come within $10,000, enough to ensure the hospital would be completed.

Clearly, Kansas City loved Mercy and its mission. Surely helping were the city's good economic times, symbolized best by the new Union Station, which had opened in 1914 and through which passed more than 200 trains in a day. Wholesale prices were on the uptick, too, thanks in part to inflation. Kansas City's wholesale businesses, then a major driver of the economy, were making money and so were many other businesses.

Construction crews went back to work on the new hospital. Mercy was on the move again. In less than two-and-a-half years, money was raised and a building put up and furnished.

## Exhausting yet exhilarating

The day before Thanksgiving 1917, the new hospital on Independence Avenue was ready. It would serve as the home of the children's hospital for 53 years.

Moving day was an emotional one for many of the staff and patients. Some of the patients were transported in automobiles, but Katharine insisted on carrying babies herself. The distance from the old hospital to the new covered less than a thousand paces. In all, 59 children were moved from Highland to Independence Avenue, along with furniture and equipment.

"This is a day we have waited for for so long," Katharine said. "I wish Dr. Graham could have seen it. But we have much work to do. There is no end to the sick children of the world."

Although Alice had not lived to experience the day, her legacy was not forgotten.

On October 15, 1916, the cornerstone had been laid with the help of four children from different states to emphasize the reach of Mercy's care. The patients – Milton Hicks from Raton, New Mexico; Thelma Butler from Appleton City, Missouri; Billy Dye from Rosedale, Kansas,

*Katharine Richardson, left; Anna Anderson, RN, second from left; Dr. C.B. Francisco, right, and children from each of four states – Missouri, Kansas, New Mexico and Oklahoma – joined in laying the cornerstone.*

and Polly Postlewaite from Okmulgee, Oklahoma – placed in the cornerstone newspapers, coins and lists of patients, board members and hospital staff.

On the cornerstone of what would soon become, officially, The Children's Mercy Hospital, were inscribed these words, at Katharine's insistence:

"In 1897, Dr. Alice Berry Graham founded this hospital for sick and crippled children to be forever non-sectarian, non-local and for those who cannot pay."

Moving day in 1917 was both exhausting and exhilarating. Although much work remained – and more challenges would inevitably lie ahead – there was no doubt that Mercy had grown up and had taken its place among the most revered institutions in Kansas City and beyond.

# A new building goes up on Independence Avenue

*October 18, 1916*

*December 28, 1916*

*January 27, 1917*

*March 29, 1917*

*May 11, 1917*

*Well before enough money had been raised to complete the hospital, Mercy's leaders set crews to work in mid-October 1916 on building the foundation, top left. A second fundraising effort beginning that fall finally accumulated enough money to allow staff and patients to move in just before Thanksgiving 1917.*

# Brady, abused and incurable

*Children with incurable conditions were often sent to Children's Mercy as a last resort and taxed the hospital's meager resources. This is the story of one of them, a child identified only as Brady. He was a victim of repeated child abuse, to whom Katharine Richardson opened her home so a bed at Children's Mercy could be open for a child with hope of recovery. It was told in Katharine's words in 1915.*

He was 10 years old when he came to Mercy and he did not know that clothes were made for little boys other than the blue overalls that had been his only covering and begged to be allowed to eat breakfast in his union suit, which seemed so wonderful to him.

I asked him if he had never had any clothes and he said: "No, except sometimes we found something in the camp after the men had gone and then I wore those things, but papa only bought me overalls and you get awfully cold in the woods when you have only overalls. I used to stay in the woods all day. I was afraid to go to the house, for the beatings hurt me so.

Curtis (a brother) was strong and it didn't hurt him much … "Curtis never struck me unless she made him. He didn't want to then, but he had to – but he always hit me light as he could. Often she tried to get Curtis to kill me.

"She used to tell him that if he let me live, he would always have to wait on me and do my work and that if he just pushed me under the water in the branch or fastened me up to a hollow log, that we could be rid of me and no one would ever know it. But I was never afraid of Curtis …"

How we grew to love him, though. Even until he died we could never wholly free him from the terrible fear that made him afraid to go out of sight of the homes he knew for fear "she" would carry out her threat to kill him. A hundred times in the night he crept from his little bed and came begging to get in with me, because the rustling of the leaves outside the window or the passing of some animal frightened him with thinking she was coming to kill him ….

Gradually, there came to him the knowledge that the whole neighborhood was watching over him …. He came to believe that education, a knowledge of books, was what had

made the difference between those people [who were caring for him] and those from who he was taken. The big sad brown eyes brightened and the little face so changed for the better that again and again our friends remarked upon its increasing beauty ….

On the shelves [of a bookcase] below his books were his "toys," not as most children want, but hammers and saws, a wire cutter and planes, all "man tools" as he called them, every one of which was as familiar to his little hands as are the sled and drum to the average boy. His tool bench had been made for him, close to the floor, and there, almost lying down, he fashioned doll's furniture, wren boxes, little wagons and dozens of other things which his Clinton Place friends received whenever an opportunity presented itself of showing his love by a gift.

Little by little, Brady grew weaker. The saw would not pass through the hard board and soft ones took their place; and then they became too much for the tiny hands to manage and cigar box lumber was bought ….

For three months before he left us, Brady was as helpless as a baby, unable to attend to his slightest wants, filled with pain and fully realizing each day brought him nearer and nearer the end. But he never made an outcry beyond the door of his own room. Many times he would say: "Sing, mother, sing quick. I'm afraid I am going to cry." And hour by hour, sometimes in the middle of the night, my tuneless voice seemed to give him strength to bear his dreadful suffering in the silence which seemed to him fitting ….

I carried his little crooked body downstairs and laid it on the white coffin. The room was filled with flowers. Carriages and motor cars brought sympathizing friends to say goodbye to the boy whom they all knew and admired. And I – I begged for help to be given me that I should so tell this story of Brady that it might be a power for good to others, like himself.

*Facing page: Standing in a window in Mercy's Highland Avenue addition was a patient identified only as Edna.*

# COMING OF AGE

*"It takes courage to grow up and become who you really are."*

— e e cummings

In every life there is adolescence, a time when growth comes quickly, inevitably and yet sometimes unexpectedly. In those uncertain years, changes can be painful and challenges can seem never-ending. Children's Mercy Hospital, as an institution, reached that stage when it prepared to move into its stately new home on Independence Avenue.

In fall 1916 war was ravaging Europe and threatening the United States. Feelings of isolationism were strong in America and the future was uncertain. That the hospital even managed to raise the money it needed was just another in a long line of wonders.

But Kansas Citians – large donors and small – came through and amassed $275,000 to build a 100-bed, three-story building at Independence Avenue and Woodland.

In 1917, on the day before Thanksgiving, the new "Hospital of the Little People," as it was sometimes called, opened for business. By then the United States had entered the Great War and much of America's focus was "over there."

*Mercy's grand new home on Independence Avenue, above, opened in 1917. Left: Among its wonders was the Junior League Play Room, complete with merry-go-round, dollhouse and pool for toy boats.*

Back here in Kansas City, moving day proved exhausting.

Some patients needing critical care were driven the few blocks from the old hospital at 414 Highland in automobiles and others were carried in staffers' arms. Those who could go home went there temporarily. Meanwhile, workmen scrambled to put on the finishing touches. Staff and patients found heating unevenly distributed in the building.

When all the children had been placed safely in their beds and the workmen had gone home, Katharine Berry Richardson had a chance to catch her breath. As she sat in solitude, it's easy to imagine she was saddened that her sister, Alice Berry Graham, had not lived to see this brand-new brick edifice they had dreamed of together.

Katharine was tired. But she knew this was no time to slow down. The new hospital featured lots of modern conveniences, yet the world outside was bringing tremendous challenges to children's health and safety.

World War I was only part of it. The next year, 1918, would be the year of the Spanish flu, a pandemic that affected 25 percent of the U.S. population and resulted in 675,000 deaths. By comparison, from 1976 to 2007 yearly deaths from flu in the United States averaged about 36,000, though the

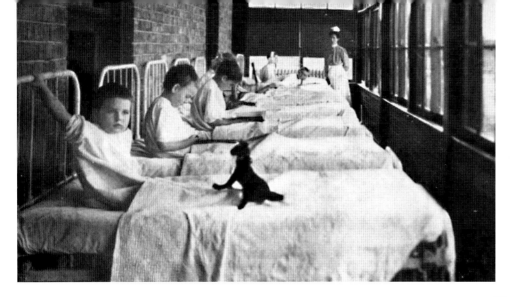

number varied widely each year.

Around the world, the 1918 Spanish flu – so-called because it received great press attention once it spread from France to Spain – killed 50 to 100 million people.

Kansas City and Mercy Hospital were not spared. The city closed schools, churches, theaters and other public places to try to stop the spread. It outlawed gatherings of more than 20 people, even for funerals. Patient ledgers from Mercy listed patient after patient with the flu. The disease affected mostly healthy young adults, unlike the traditional flu that typically threatened the very young and the very old. Most patients at Mercy survived. But the strain on the patients, staff and hospital infrastructure was undeniable.

The flu epidemic helped bring attention to the deplorable state of public health across much of Kansas City, where drinking water could still be contaminated and many lived in overcrowded housing with inadequate or no medical care. Also dangerous for too many Kansas Citians were unpasteurized milk, lack of indoor plumbing, poor storage of food and a general lack of nutrition.

The flu, then, was only one of the illnesses children faced. Dr. Charles Dennie, writing in the *Greater Kansas City Medical Bulletin* in the 1960s, recalled epidemics of measles, scarlet fever and chicken pox that forced the hospital in 1912 to

**FROM THE CHILDREN OF "THE MERCY."**

Now we have a modern home,
Where the cripples all may come,
 As they're coming right along, at The Mercy.
And the worst one of them all,
May grow straight and strong and tall,
 And send others to be cured at The Mercy.
Health and strength has come to you,
Hope and joy are just in view.
 See the little wasted features at The Mercy.
Do you dare to close your ears?
Can you disregard their tears?
 Little helpless, injured creatures at The Mercy.
You who stand with hands so strong,
That you move the world along
 Think not sorrow only lies across the ocean.
Here at home is work for all,
Here at home the helpless call,
 Here at home we claim your uttermost devotion.
But it costs to do the work,
Though our nurses do not shirk,
 And our doctors work for pay at The Mercy.
Oh, I pray you do your part,
Let the helpless touch your heart.
 We're appealing to the city from The Mercy.

*Some of Mercy's constant appeals for donations were done in verse, left. The poet referred to the "modern home" on Independence Avenue, but the image that accompanied it was made at the previous site on Highland Avenue. Above: Dr. Charles Dennie, a longtime physician at Mercy, treated victims of various epidemics in the 1910s.*

close everything except the emergency unit and outpatient clinic. Doing so forced some children to be taken to other hospitals for care, but ultimately allowed the illnesses to burn out and kept the ravages to a minimum.

Another threat to children's health at the time was tuberculosis, known as the "white plague." Syphilis also posed considerable problems and became a specialty of Dr. Dennie's. The effects of what today is called fetal alcohol syndrome led many doctors to become staunch supporters of Prohibition. Communicable diseases such as diphtheria and smallpox also threatened children in those days before antibiotics and vaccines.

No, growing up was not easy.

## Defending a sweeping vision

The cornerstone of the new building on Independence Avenue said Mercy was founded to be "forever non-

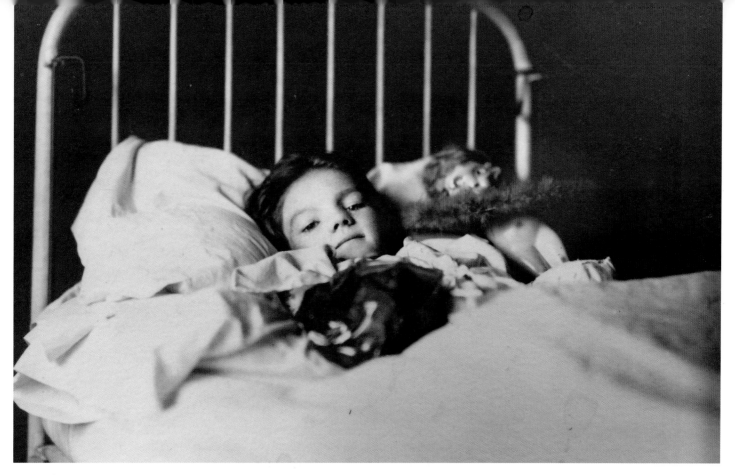

*For a girl in the 1920s, dolls improved a stay in the hospital. Right: Nurses dealt with even younger patients, some cooperative but one a bit cranky. Below, the patient totals for September 30, 1918.*

sectarian, non-local and for those who cannot pay."

Over the years, those words caused occasional misunderstandings. Some people read "non-local" to mean that Katharine and Alice would sacrifice the needs of Kansas City's own children for outsiders. Others interpreted "non-sectarian" as anti-religious. Decades after the cornerstone was laid, when Children's Mercy began to accept patients whose families could afford to pay, complaints arose that the hospital had turned its back on "forever…for those who cannot pay."

Nothing was further from the truth.

The hospital's mission was purposely broad, designed to do as much good as possible, for as many children as possible, in as many ways as possible. Those words sound like the teachings of John Wesley, the founder of Christian Methodism. Although there is no direct evidence that Katharine or Alice were Methodists, it's apparent that some of their goals were the same, and that their philosophy of life was grounded in Christianity.

Writing in the *Messenger* newsletter, first Alice and then

Katharine addressed the matter of being "non-local." There were several children's hospitals elsewhere in the country when Mercy was established, and many of them cared for "their own" children to conserve their resources. Alice and

## Once a desperate case

"Her little body was a parcel of skin and bones," an observer wrote, "her little hands and arms apparently twisted in a gnarled position before her face." She looked "for all the world like an old crone disabled and deformed from years of suffering from rheumatism."

Her name was Anastasia Roudan and she came to Mercy Hospital in 1921 at the age of 5.

Knowing of the great care that Mercy extended to all children – no matter their address, their religion or their bank account – a Red Cross nurse brought Anastasia and another child to Kansas City from a desolate area of North Dakota. Crops there had failed for six years in a row and children were living on "black bread and sour milk," according to an account by C.L. Hobert in the *Holden Progress* of Holden, Missouri. "Two more pitiful objects of humanity it has never been my lot to behold."

The result of their poor diet was a severe case of rickets for Anastasia and paralysis of the motor nerves for the older girl who traveled with her.

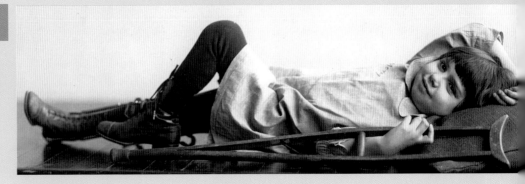

*Miss Reineke's studio in Kansas City photographed many Mercy patients in the 1920s, among them Anastasia.*

At first, Anastasia's case was desperate, and many feared it was lost. For months, she showed no sign of intelligence. She could not walk or talk and did nothing but sit and stare at her hands all day long. No one in the hospital, it was said, entertained any hope for her, mentally or physically.

Nevertheless, the staff fed her and massaged her legs and eventually straightened them. After 18 months, Anastasia was getting around on a kiddie car – not walking, but able to stand and shuffle around the room without falling.

Her face was described in the *Progress* as having "rounded out with a beautiful pink complexion. As for the gnarled arms

… we can bear testimony to their strength after an hour's orthodox hugging."

Six months later, she was ready to go home.

"Anastasia, who came to Mercy an apparent imbecile," Hobart wrote, "who could neither walk nor talk, went home, a healthy, happy normal girl."

Hobart spread the word about Anastasia and Mercy. He encouraged people to visit.

"The visit will do you good; it will be an inspiration to you in your daily tasks; and above all it will strengthen your faith in Him."

---

Katharine wanted the doors of the hospital open to all.

"A child's address should not matter," Katharine wrote.

Defending the annual solicitation of out-of-town guests in the early 1900s, Alice had noted that, in their first three years of operating a children's hospital, she and her sister cared for more out-of-town children than children from Kansas City.

As further evidence of the commitment to welcoming all, the sisters published parent education materials in several languages – English, of course, but also in Italian, Yiddish and Russian – to help those "non-local" parents, native-born or immigrant, take better care of their children.

In addition to reaching out to children across the region, Katharine made sure Kansas City knew the hospital was there for its poor children, too. In the *Messenger*, she reminded people to let friends and neighbors know about the services

available to "those who cannot pay." Her only caveat: If a child had no chance of survival, he or she should be taken elsewhere so the care of Children's Mercy could be available to those who had a chance.

As for "non-sectarian," the description meant the hospital would not support a particular sect, denomination or religious belief. Even decades later, for anyone who hears the word "mercy" and who thinks the founding sisters were nuns, this can be baffling. But being non-sectarian does not mean Alice, Katharine and others who worked at the hospital lacked spirituality or did not believe in a higher power.

The Berry sisters grew up believing in an important Christian principle: helping one's fellow human beings. By working with children, particularly poor children, they demonstrated devotion to the "least among you," as Jesus

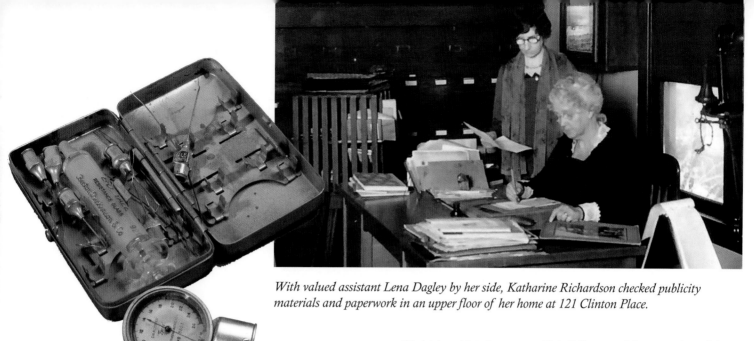

*With valued assistant Lena Dagley by her side, Katharine Richardson checked publicity materials and paperwork in an upper floor of her home at 121 Clinton Place.*

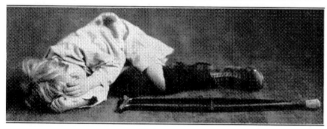

I PROMISE TO MAIL THIS MESSENGER TO SOME ONE WHOM I BELIEVE WOULD BE A GOOD FRIEND OF MERCY HOSPITAL

Forgotten ?

## Mercy's Messenger

*Published by*
The Children's Mercy Hospital
*"The Hospital of the Little People"*

July, 1923

Editor, Dr. Katharine B. Richardson
121 Clinton Place, Kansas City, Missouri

'Tis strangely fixed that what remains is only what we do when Self is not considered.

A woman in Raton, N. M., wrote and told us of a crippled child whose sister, through years of hard work, had earned enough money for a surgeon's fees. She said no good had come of all of the sister's efforts, and that uncomplaining, with her last cent gone, the girl had turned again and had taken her place to get more money to give to another man whose skill might be greater than the first and by whom the little brother might possibly be cured. It seemed a pitiful story, and we asked the pair—the boy and his sister—to let us help. She brought her brother to the Mercy and worked for him and attended him as if he were her very own. He came to be well and strong and beautiful, and one day begged us to let his friend come, too. He quaintly said "My friend," and was very insistent, and begged so hard,

orders, when a judge was wanted it was he who pronounced the sentence, and when the corner stone of Mercy Hospital was laid, Milton was one of the four who dedicated it to its work of making sick children well. Big in mind, tiny in body. One day, when the senseless words of a six-foot visitor had offered a maudlin sympathy which condemned him to patience without hope or promise, he said to me, "Are all great men big, and will I never be like that one? Can I never have a wife or children of my own like that man?" I hate the so-called sympathy that talks what it does not feel and thinks it does its duty when it only spreads out its hands and looks a benediction. That man felt virtuous as he went out of Mercy Hospital, and he had done his futile little best to cramp and wither up a growing soul. We told Milton it was **brains and heart** that ruled the world—that the biggest men and women were often the smallest—that love wins love, and keeps it, too—that beautiful spirits may live in crippled bodies—that Nature is neither a niggard nor a spendthrift, and so sometimes she gives to people lovely forms and faces in recompense for something better that she has denied them. Yesterday we received the graduating card of Milton Hicks, and from Raton comes the word that his hurdle is not holding him—bringing also the thought of the dear sister now herself advancing, and of the little brother who is keeping step, and of their connection with that other boy, who, but for

*Top, a glass syringe kit of the 1930s and a sphygmomanometer for measuring blood pressure. It was owned by Katharine Richardson. Above, in mid-July 1923, Children's Mercy illustrated its appeal for money with a melodramatic photograph and a request to send the little tract on to other potential donors.*

Christ is said to have urged his followers. Many copies of the *Messenger* and many newspaper articles mentioned the Bible or Christian teachings and ideals.

But misunderstanding evidently was hard to dispel. In the *Messenger*, Katharine wrote that ministers were welcome at the hospital as long as they were prepared to serve all children, despite their faith, and to exclude no one. No church literature was to be distributed, no church services conducted and no religious symbols displayed. Nurses would be excused, with advanced notice to make sure their work was covered, to attend church services.

Katharine's longtime assistant, Lena Dagley, recalled the reason for the non-sectarian language.

The hospital, she wrote in 1952, "numbers among its patients those of so many different faiths. Its employees are requested to abstain from all expressions or discussions which might be contrary to the religious belief of any patient in the institution, and visiting friends are earnestly requested to conform to this ruling.

"To be non-sectarian does not mean to be irreligious. We believe in God and in the Bible and we believe that worship is just as necessary to a well-rounded life and personality as is work, education, recreation, etc. We mean it is not controlled by any one particular denomination.

"We consider that Mercy Hospital is Christian in the highest sense of the word – serving sick and crippled children who might not otherwise receive care. It embraces all religions and its doors are open alike to Jews, Gentiles, Protestants and Catholics."

Further testament to that ideal came after Katharine

*The nursing corps lined up for its group portrait outside Mercy Hospital.*

died. The Central Governing Board of the Hospital published the thoughts of C.L. Hobart, a longtime supporter of the hospital. Hobart was editor and publisher of the *Holden Progress* newspaper in Holden, Missouri, about 50 miles southeast of Kansas City. He wrote:

> *"The development of Mercy Hospital from a free bed in a corner of a small hospital to its present magnificent million and a half dollar plant, in the span of a generation is an epic. In my opinion, it is the greatest philanthropy of the age. But Dr. Richardson did more than that. She left an example of virile Christianity which should be an inspiration to the Christian world. In all the years of my acquaintance, I never knew her church affiliation, but I know she was a Christian in the fullest sense of the word. Christ said, 'If any man will come after me, let him deny himself and take up his cross, and follow me.' Self denial, sacrifice and fidelity has glorious exemplification in her life … she knew what it was to be 'reviled and persecuted' but she never failed."*

Finally, Katharine thought it was important to defend the policy that the hospital's services would be free. In the hospital's formative years, some people complained that charity did no favors for the poor, that it only discouraged them from bettering themselves. Providing free care, under this theory, "pauperized" people. Katharine had this reply:

"Every time you try to argue against free hospitals, see

"They were here to serve every child, which was unique for that time in history. It didn't matter what your religious tradition was. We know from the history of this city that not all other hospitals were like that …. We know Menorah was founded really because other hospitals wouldn't allow Jewish doctors to have privileges.

"I don't interpret nonsectarian as a bad thing. I think it was their attempt to be able to make sure that there were no barriers to any child who needed to come here. And if you're affiliated with one religious group at that time that might mean not being able to serve somebody in another religious organization."

*– Dane Sommer, who became the hospital's first full-time chaplain in 1987, discussing the two sisters who founded Children's Mercy*

if your argument applies to free schools and free churches – it takes the three to make a citizen."

FOR ALL CHILDREN EVERYWHERE

## The question of race

Katharine was insistent on making care available to all children, including those of different races, but that took extra effort. Kansas City in the 1920s, like cities in much of the United States, was unapologetically segregated. More than 50 years after the end of the Civil War in 1865 and decades since African-American men got the right to vote, the United States still operated separate societies. Many white Americans – if not most – considered themselves part of a superior race.

The summer of 1919 saw race riots in dozens of American cities. One of the prime reasons for the unrest was disappointment with segregation; many African-Americans had hoped that their military service in World War I would bring them closer to equality at home. However, when the "War to End All Wars" ended and the troops returned, life in much of America settled back into the routine, systematic racism of Jim Crow laws.

At the same time, many African-Americans were on the move from the South to the North. Kansas City's black population kept growing, yet there was little in the way of health care for African-American children or adults, and what care existed was substandard. In segregated times, African-Americans were expected to care for "their own" and yet there were limited medical educational opportunities for them.

In Kansas City, African-Americans, including children, went to "Negro hospitals," according to two Children's Mercy staff members, Drs. Jane F. Knapp and Robert D. Schremmer, who did a study of the era. Hospitals for black people, however, were underfunded and overcrowded. Overall, the mortality rate for Kansas City's African-American population – 24 out of every 1,000 – was nearly double that of the country as a whole.

"Children fared no better," the doctors wrote. "The black infant mortality rate was close to double that of whites. Common causes of child death were prematurity, diarrhea and pneumonia."

A newspaper editorial at the time noted that the

*The hospital decked itself out for its 25th anniversary celebration in 1922. On the more serious side, below, a child underwent an operation surrounded by doctors, nurses and equipment in the 1920s.*

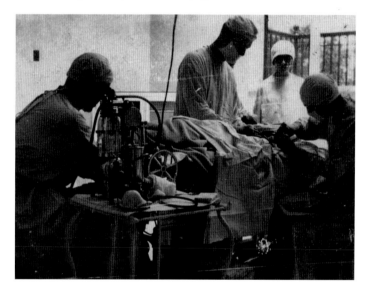

tuberculosis rate for African-Americans was 330 per 100,000 compared with 73 for white Kansas Citians.

Katharine believed it was her duty to do more.

"Mercy Hospital's only job is making citizens out of little sick children," she wrote in the *Messenger*. "It has no other reason for existence. It has in its wards children of almost all kinds … only the Negroes are excluded, but over the doors are the words 'The Children's Mercy Hospital.' The present managers want to make those words mean what they say."

Her dilemma was finding a way to do that without losing contributions from the white majority, which preferred segregation. Those contributions were the hospital's only income.

*The culmination of an early effort by Children's Mercy to care for African-American children. Dr. Robert Schauffler demonstrated pediatric techniques to doctors and nurses who began the Model Ward at Wheatley-Provident Hospital, an all-black institution in the era of segregation.*

Already, Katharine and Children's Mercy had been working to help African-American children. Katharine was among a handful of Kansas Citians who supported an orphanage at 2446 Michigan Avenue that served "neglected, abused and homeless black children." The home, incorporated under the name Colored People's Charity Association, was started in 1883 by an African-American bricklayer, Samuel Eason. When he died in 1913, Katharine and others became involved.

The question of providing health care for the orphans was crucial. Few white hospitals or doctors would care for them, and hardly any black doctors were trained as pediatricians.

Katharine turned to a friend and colleague, Dr. John Edward Perry. One of the few African-American physicians in town, Dr. Perry founded Provident Hospital in 1913. A year later, the hospital merged with a similar operation founded by Phyllis Wheatley and became Wheatley-Provident Hospital.

At the time, it was the only hospital owned and operated by African-Americans in Kansas City. Dr. Perry in 1916 arranged the purchase of an old Catholic boys' school at 1826 Forest Avenue and raised $29,000 to remodel it. Wheatley-Provident would operate there until the 1970s.

Although of different races and genders, Katharine and Dr. Perry proved to be somewhat kindred spirits. Both had suffered discrimination of different kinds and degrees, and both had been marginalized in their profession.

One of the biggest hurdles the two encountered was the lack of African-American physicians. As they worked on a way to help black children, they also found a way to train black doctors.

The 50,000 African-Americans in Kansas City wanted to be able to take care of their own, Katharine wrote. Bowing to the prevailing white view of the day, she continued: "The leading men and women see the utter unwisdom in the talk of 'social equality of the races.' They neither seek nor desire it."

*Doctors and nurses black and white surrounded Katharine Richardson, center, on the steps of Wheatley-Provident Hospital's new addition in the 1920s. Standing alone at the top was Dr. J. Edward Perry, a co-founder of the hospital on Forrest Avenue south of 18th Street.*

Instead, she said, African-Americans wanted to be able to take care of themselves. That fit the "separate but equal" philosophy that dominated race relations at the time.

By the early 1920s, she and Dr. Perry envisioned a pediatrics unit at Wheatley-Provident, where black doctors and nurses eventually could provide effective care for black children. But they could not accomplish this on their own. Like much of the story of Children's Mercy, support from the community was crucial.

In this case, white businessman Frank C. Niles supplied the foundation. Niles, president of a cigar distribution company, pledged $5,000 to establish a children's ward at Wheatley. That pledge was not all that was needed but, in a letter to Katharine, Niles made it clear there was more where

that came from.

His condition was that the care at Wheatley be provided free, just as it was at Children's Mercy, and "whatever extra

## To help the orphans

Frank Niles' contributions to Wheatley-Provident were not the end of his commitment to African-Americans and others. In 1924, he responded to another request from Katharine Richardson to help at the African-American orphanage. Niles and his wife, Emma, donated land and constructed a $60,000 mansion to house 100 children on East 23rd Street. After much growth, organization and renaming, by the 21st century this would be the site of the Niles Home for Children.

*The "No Color Line" bed, endowed by a woman from Olathe, Kansas, served the first non-white children admitted to Children's Mercy.*

expense … I will pay."

Katharine took her pleas to others, too. She suggested that, by helping improve the health of African-Americans, Kansas City could help calm the fears of those who considered the growing population and decreasing health of black residents "a menace."

"For ordinary decency's sake, let's take the burden of the superior race we claim ourselves to be and teach these colored men the way to make a sick child well," she wrote, explaining the program at Wheatley. "If you could see the surgery done at Wheatley Hospital and done by hands, the blackest of them all, you'd never ask that question again – and you'd come to bring your money and yourself to make one place in all America where any colored man might come and share the knowledge we have no right to keep from him."

The appeals worked. Donations to the Wheatley children's ward poured in from civic organizations, children's clubs and art clubs. One newspaper listed some of the contributions: needles, matches, rubber mats for baby baths, test tubes, soap, bottles and nipples. The effort was endorsed by the Council of Social Agencies, which claimed 60 organizations as members. One of the first clubs was The Mercy-Wheatley Quaker Club. Katharine wrote: "The Friends

(Quakers) have always stood by the Negro people. This last proof of loyalty originated at the pretty church at 30th and Bales" – the Friends Community Church.

Katharine asked the doctors at Children's Mercy to volunteer even more of their time to help train African-American doctors in pediatrics. Many doctors responded enthusiastically; Katharine recruited 18 white physicians for the Wheatley clinic and training program. Nurses, too, were asked to train African-American women who were interested in that career. African-American nurses were recruited through newspaper ads.

The road was not without bumps. There was, according

> "For years, the sign over Mercy – The Children's Mercy Hospital – had haunted and troubled me. I felt the sign was a lie as long as nothing was being done for the unfortunate and suffering Negro children. It is now for all children everywhere."
>
> – *Katharine Richardson*

to correspondence from Katharine, at least one white surgeon who refused to care for African-Americans. The same doctor also balked at the heavy workload doctors were asked to carry.

## The work bears fruit

Culminating the effort by Katharine, Dr. Perry and all the rest, the Model Ward at Wheatley-Provident opened on April 19, 1923. Dr. Robert Schauffler, one of Children's Mercy's first physicians, taught at the first clinic to a roomful of African-American medical students. According to the National Child Conservation League, what was being done to help African-American children in Kansas City had not been attempted anywhere else in the United States at the time.

The project was an immediate success. The American College of Surgeons in 1923 gave Wheatley-Provident a Class A rating "because the staff of the hospital lived up to the highest requirements." It was one of only three African-American hospitals in the country with that status.

In 1925, Niles and philanthropist William Volker, who had made his fortune wholesaling household items from warehouses in Kansas City, jointly donated $65,000 to expand Wheatley. That was in addition to $9,000 Volker spent to buy land for the expansion, which he also donated to Wheatley.

Although the hospital itself was owned and operated by African-Americans, the property of the hospital was controlled by an inter-racial board, made up of Niles, Volker, R.R. Brewster, Katharine, Dr. Perry and others.

The relationship between Children's Mercy and Wheatley was not formal, but Katharine pledged that "in every respect" the work at Wheatley was an extension of the work at Mercy. After a couple of years, Children's Mercy

## When the sluggers dropped in

*Babe Ruth, right, and Lou Gehrig were the brightest stars of the 1927 world champion New York Yankees when they visited Mercy Hospital. The two came through Kansas City after the Yankees-Pirates World Series of that year and played an exhibition game at Muehlebach Field as a benefit for the hospital. After the game, the ballplayers stopped by to donate a refrigerator, bringing smiles to the faces of young patients and to nurse Anna Anderson.*

and its doctors slowly backed away from Wheatley, not abandoning it but trying to remain true to the stated goal to "help the Negro help himself."

Wheatley would remain in operation as an African-American hospital for nearly 50 years.

Katharine was proud of the work she had accomplished.
"For years, the sign over Mercy – The Children's Mercy Hospital – had haunted and troubled me," she said in a newspaper article. "I felt the sign was a lie as long as nothing was being done for the unfortunate and suffering Negro

*Following pages: A place of sunlight, fresh air, tricycles and tiny rocking chairs, this balcony at the new hospital could accommodate a dozen or so patients.*

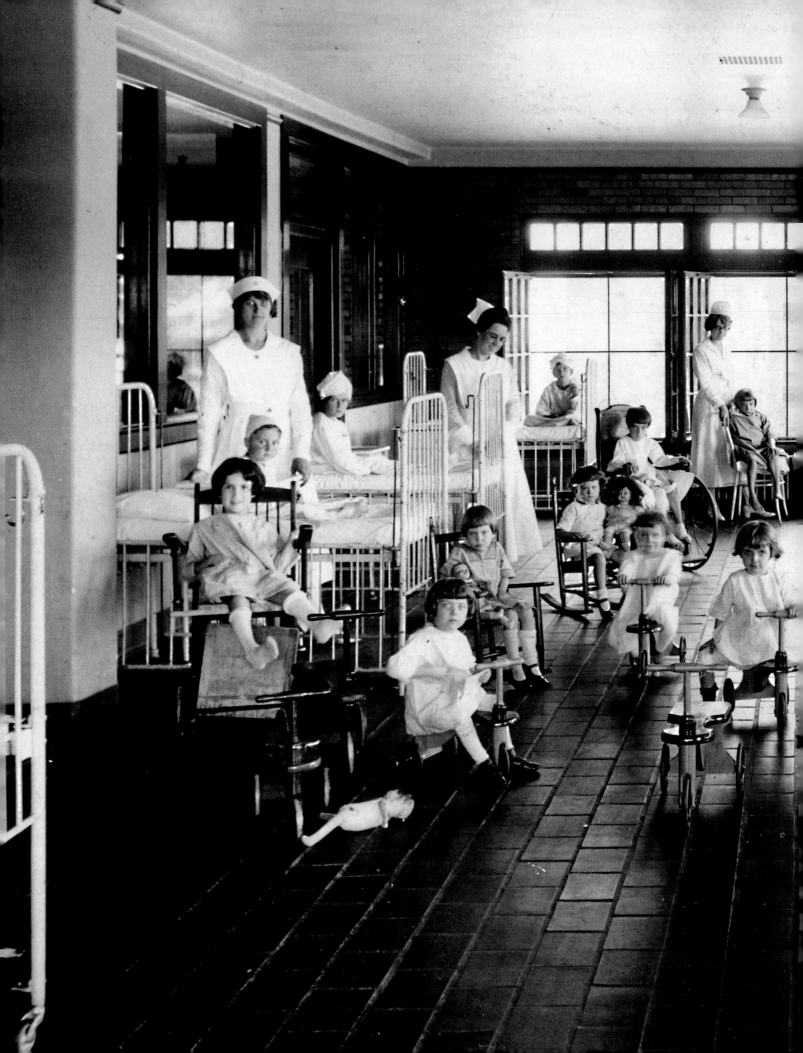

children. It is now for all children everywhere."

In 1931, a bed was endowed for children regardless of race. The donor was Mrs. Emma W. Robinson of Olathe, Kansas, who gave 100 shares of Santa Fe Railroad stock for the endowment in memory of Dr. Alice Graham "who founded and named The Children's Mercy Hospital."

According to a newspaper account, the bed was not exclusively for African-American children, but was available to them "in cases that demand the kind of emergency treatment obtainable only in such a hospital as Mercy with its elaborate equipment and large and brilliant staff of physicians." It was called the "no color line" bed for the sign that hung from its metal frame.

The newspaper described it this way: "This endowment is the maintenance – in perpetuity forever – of one free bed, to be used for any needy, sick, afflicted or crippled little child, irrespective of nationality, race, color or creed, that may require the skilled medical or surgical treatment and care of the hospital – a gift of love to its founder."

The hospital would not be fully integrated until decades later, when societal barriers were coming down.

*All bundled up against the cold and snow, infants were thought to improve with outdoor exposure, even in winter.*

declared her Kansas City's "first civic asset."

"People have varying ideas of success, to be sure," an article said. "But when a woman has devoted a quarter century to a work that belonged to the community, with the result now seen in the noble monument of Mercy; when she has been content to sacrifice the personal rewards her profession might have brought her in order that it might serve others; when she reserves for her own needs the smallest portion of her time, her skill and her energy; and yet in the fullness of her life can look upon an achievement scarcely to be matched by those of great organizations of the highest ability and greatest wealth and know that achievement as her own, she surely is entitled to feel that its success can be measured in terms of service, it is hers.

"Then Katharine Richardson, still at work and calling her task unfinished, is the most successful woman in Kansas City."

Word was spreading quickly about the good work and the open-door policy of Children's Mercy. The hospital was growing at a phenomenal rate: In 1915, it treated about 2,700 patients. By 1921, it cared for about 8,000 patients and in 1923, the number grew to 20,000. The cost of care – $2 a day for inpatients – was also remarkably small compared to $6 a day at other hospitals.

Reasons for the growth were many. The care provided by the hospital was extraordinary and innovative. Katharine

## "The most successful woman in Kansas City"

Katharine's work gained increasing notice, and in 1924 the Sunday magazine supplement of the *Kansas City Star*

herself was an outstanding surgeon, specializing in the repair of cleft palates and cleft lips. The results were life-altering for her patients. Her skills earned her induction into the American College of Surgeons, an honor for anyone, but especially for a woman in the 1920s. Other doctors and nurses on staff, too, took great measures to provide the best possible care.

In her early years as a physician, Katharine earned a reputation as an innovator. Back in the 1880s she had become an advocate for cleanliness, which from a 21st-century perspective seems only common sense. In the 19th century, however, the germ theory of the spread of disease was "new medicine." Some doctors scoffed at the notion that washing hands before operating was a good practice. Katharine saw too many women suffer and die and sided with those who promoted sanitation. (She did not, however, wear gloves to perform surgery, the cause of clashes in years to come between her and Dr. Schauffler.)

Long before the world had heard of alternative medicine, its innovations were being practiced at Children's Mercy. Katharine sent one of her staff members to the French Alps to study under Dr. Auguste Rollier, who first documented the benefits of ultraviolet rays.

"All progressive hospitals, as well as all progressive physicians (are studying) the curative action of the sun," declared the hospital's 1927 School of Nursing brochure. The rooftop on Independence Avenue contained a "sun cure porch."

In the 1890s, three new systems of alternative or "complementary" medicine opened schools and began to send graduates out into practice. Osteopathy, naturopathy and chiropractic all came into practice at a time when people were developing mixed feelings about recent advances in traditional medicine. By the 1920s, surveys showed that anywhere from 25 to 75 percent of the American population received treatments from these so-called "drugless healers," at least occasionally. Katharine was not beyond trying anything reasonable to help her patients.

Children's Mercy offered massage as another innovative

*Nurse's uniform and cape.*

therapy, along with water therapy, a gymnasium and a "curative playground."

When the hospital opened its own public school in 1910, the move testified to the belief that a strong body and a strong mind were both important to health and health care.

## A school for nurses

Despite all the advances and all the success, Katharine, as usual, was not satisfied.

Chief among items on her to-do list was a research facility. Katharine knew that advances in medicine required research and that, if the research was done at Children's Mercy, its own patients would benefit first. She also knew of bureaucratic and funding difficulties researchers faced at some of the established pediatric research centers in the eastern United States. She believed Children's Mercy could attract talented researchers because of its large number of patients. Researchers needed children to test their theories.

"Before the scientists learned that your blood could be safely injected into my veins, but could not be safely put into Tom's veins," she wrote, "experiments were carried out for 15 years and eight thousand cases were held in evidence. Finally, the thing was done and transfusion of blood is now an everyday procedure.

"But there are yet hundreds of unconquered diseases. Those of children alone would fill the wards and balconies of such places as the Mercy, where last year 20,000 young people came for help."

She made her plea for contributions to build a research laboratory and even declared: "Never in the world did Mercy want anything so much as it wants the Laboratory. Never in all its undertakings was there so great a possibility of good to be accomplished. And only money is lacking."

The hospital already was involved in research, including the use of animals, which caused some uproar. The active anti-vivisection movement opposed using live animals in research, holding that the practice amounted to cruelty. In fact, Katharine pleaded with the operator of the hospital laboratory's "animal house" to make sure the research subjects "be made just as comfortable as possible."

The estate of Joseph Tyler Bird, former president of the Emery, Bird, Thayer Dry Goods Company, offered land in July 1924 just west of the Children's Mercy building. A structure to be built on it would be "used solely for a laboratory for hospital research into the nature and causes of diseases of children and the best methods of treatment, alleviation, cure and prevention," according to Central Governing Board minutes. The building was to serve as a perpetual memorial to Bird.

However, after fundraising for the structure began, the focus shifted. Nothing in hospital records provides an explanation, but on November 24, 1925, the contract with the Bird estate was amended. Instead of research, the land and the proposed building were to be used for no other purpose than the "housing, training and caring for nurses in connection with the operation of Mercy Hospital."

Why the dramatic change? Perhaps Katharine understood that for research to be effective it needed a large patient population and that nurses were essential to attracting and maintaining that population. Student nurses were also a source of inexpensive labor; they worked for free in the hospital as part of their education. Or it could be simply that the hospital's commitment to nursing, which stretched to its very beginning, won out in the competition for limited resources. It is known that the nurses' home had long been a desire and Katharine had written that families of young women training to be nurses "demanded it."

As early as 1921, Katharine was writing to gain support for a place to call home for the nurses who trained and worked at the hospital. In a listing of needs for the building, she demonstrated that although she had refused to name the hospital after any particular donor, she was not above naming certain parts of the facilities.

She described "Special things that in our new Nurses' Home we hope will bear a name chosen by the one who brought the gift:

- A swimming pool
- A nurses library and study room
- Several large and small reception or classrooms
- A fine grandfather clock for the hall
- A beautiful stairway
- A rooftop garden where the girls may sleep or dance or dry their hair or sit and sew or read or do one of the hundred things that all young girls enjoy
- A kitchen for coffee, toast or fudge or for preparing food when the best of girls get sick and need the care that you would give your own loved daughter."

With the land secured, fundraising continued and construction began on the building to be known as Nurses Hall. Katharine was adamant in her fundraising that the time had come to provide for the nurses. A few years earlier, she had complained that Kansas City had money to build the Liberty Memorial and amusement houses and offices for big business, and yet the children and those who cared for them seemed to be a last thought.

"Mercy has waited for the war to close, waited for peace to come, waited for wages and materials to go down and it must not wait much longer," she wrote.

Katharine insisted that Nurses Hall be a proper home. It must provide room for the nurses to socialize as well as study and rest. The School of Nursing Handbook from 1927 promised that the hall would provide "those things that will make for the comfort and help of Mercy's students and to provide, as far as possible, home surroundings, with such reasonable and proper supervision as would be approved."

Katharine made sure the design included so-called "reception rooms" where the nurses could entertain guests, including male suitors. Because of the importance placed on the personal appearance of nurses, Katharine made sure there were mirrors throughout Nurses Hall.

Other touches of home that decorated Nurses Hall were hand-sewn quilts on each of the beds. Katharine remembered the Double Irish Chain Quilt pattern from her childhood home. She believed such a quilt would give the rooms a homelike quality. She spoke with the many Mercy Clubs supporting the hospital and their quilting members did the rest, piecing fabric in shades of blue and white. The blues matched those of the nurses' uniforms. So popular did this "Irish Chain" quilt prove that the First Lady of the United States ordered one in similar blue and white for her son,

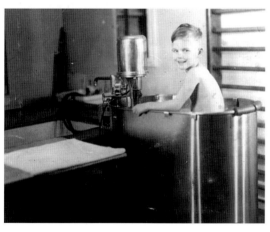

Medicine, both traditional and alternative, had a place at Children's Mercy. Children relaxed on the sun roof, top, for a treatment called heliotherapy. Above: A boy in water therapy. Right: Traditional operating room, all decked out for the photographer.

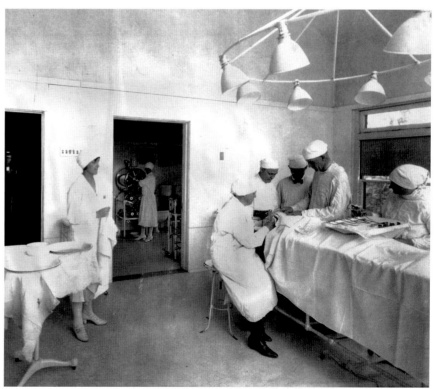

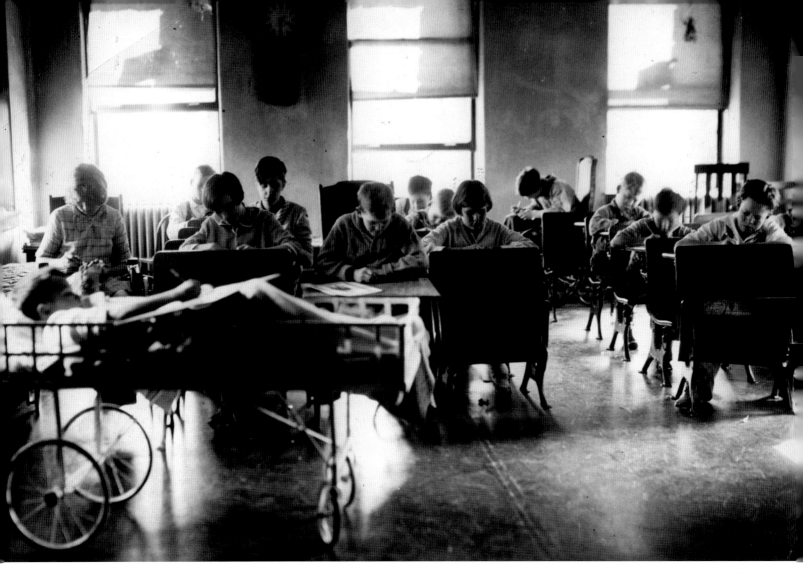

*A longtime feature for patients, the Children's Mercy school aimed to keep them up in their studies, but also to maintain a sense of everyday life outside the hospital.*

according to *The Kansas City Star*. Lou Henry Hoover, wife of President Herbert Hoover, had become acquainted with Children's Mercy on a visit to Kansas City. Well-wishers had filled her hotel room with flowers and she, in turn, sent the flowers to Independence Avenue to brighten the hospital.

Construction of Nurses Hall began in 1926. A lounge was furnished in memory of John H. Berkshire and the reading room was equipped by Mrs. J.W. Sauer in memory of her daughter. In 1927, the nurses moved in. The final cost was $185,000.

At the time, nursing school took three years, nine months of which were devoted to adult care at Research Hospital. School was not all about medicine. Dr. Richardson insisted the nurses – all young women – be properly educated in social graces as well. Afternoon tea was part of that education.

To be admitted to the school, nurses had to be:
- Nineteen to 35 years of age
- A high school graduate or equivalent
- Generally fit
- Sound of tooth
- Child-loving and conscientious

The school for nurses operated until 1938. Since then, nursing education has been provided by a wide variety of schools in and around Kansas City. In 2016, 1,400 students from dozens of nursing schools were taught and provided care at Children's Mercy. Nurses Hall continued to be a home for nurses working at Children's Mercy until the hospital moved to Hospital Hill in 1970.

FOR ALL CHILDREN EVERYWHERE

## Much-honored, yet lonely

Katharine Richardson was tireless. She devoted her life almost entirely to children and Children's Mercy. She knew there was no end to the long line of children in need of help. She begged those who read the newspapers or the *Messenger* to send patients so her surgical skills would not be wasted. At the same time, she worried about the capacity to care for all those who sought hope and healing at Children's Mercy.

Her considerable talent and remarkable perseverance earned her accolades in Kansas City and beyond. In 1931, her alma mater, Mount Union College in Ohio, bestowed on her its honorary Doctor of Law degree, its highest honor. She was the first woman to receive it. She was asked to address the students and visitors at the morning chapel exercises; at the Alumni dinner, she was appointed to welcome new members.

She was among esteemed company – Thomas Edison was there to receive the same honorary degree – yet the president of the school paid her a special tribute:

"If Union College had done nothing but turn out Katharine B. Richardson, all the sacrifice and hardships of the past would be repaid," said Dr. W. H. McMaster, as quoted in the book, *More Than Petticoats: Remarkable Missouri Women.*

He called Katherine "the guiding genius of a great house of healing in a great city where the finest medical and surgical care is given to children who cannot receive adequate care elsewhere and whose parents are not able to pay."

All the praise and all the smiling children and grateful families could not stave off loneliness. Maybe it was her relentless drive, or perhaps her off-putting manner, but Katharine had few friends. From time to time, she took children into her home, some for extended periods. A newspaper article in 1931 said Katharine "wants to adopt all the children she can lay her hands on."

In fact, Katharine did have at least one adopted son, though little is known about him or the circumstances of the adoption. She did not write about him, and more than one newspaper article written during the 1920s and '30s describing Katharine and her life failed to mention him.

Yet the 1930 Federal Census listed a 27-year-old Paul Lowell living at 121 Clinton Place with Katharine and described him as "adopted son." He is not included with her in the 1920 census, when he would have been 17 or 18 years old, suggesting he was adopted in his late teens.

Lowell was born February 8, 1902, in Tupelo, Arkansas, according to an application for a marriage license. Some believe he had once been a patient at Mercy. A newspaper article describing the trip to Mount Union College in 1931 said Katharine was accompanied by Anna Anderson, the superintendent of the hospital, and Katharine's son, a student at the University of Kansas. Paul Lowell was a member of the University of Kansas School of Medicine class of 1936.

In the 1940 federal census, Lowell was described as a doctor with the public health department. He was married in 1934 and had two daughters, Iva May, who went to Southeast High School, and Lydia, who went to Westport High. Dr. Lowell was divorced from the girls' mother and remarried in 1954 to Betty Jane Bodin, a woman 18 years his junior.

Katharine was extremely private about her personal life and her earlier days, according to Lena Dagley. She preferred the emphasis stay on children served by Children's Mercy Hospital or on others. In that way, she was much like her sister, Alice, who was often described as the more congenial of the sisters. One observer called Katharine "highly opinionated, of a terrible temper, obstinate, blunt, tactless, an enemy maker, an ardent suffragette and a dictator." Some similar qualities were attributed to her father in his obituary.

Katharine said that her frankness sometimes was considered tactless, and acknowledged she had made enemies for herself and for the hospital.

But others said those same qualities were just indicative of her passion as a person "endowed with a deep sympathy and compassion and the courage of her convictions."

"She was a wonderful teacher and a great reader," Dagley said, "an interesting conversationalist and always in demand as a public speaker."

Katharine traveled around the city and the region, making speeches to interest clubs in supporting Children's Mercy.

Her business evidently served as an antidote for her loneliness.

"I'm often invited to speak, but not invited to dinner," Katharine was quoted as saying.

In a history of the hospital published in 1961, Roger Swanson declared, "So engrossed in Mercy was Katharine Richardson that she had nothing else in life."

"Essentially she was a woman of deep loneliness when away from Mercy. In a rare confidence, she once complained of a fear of the holidays – Thanksgiving and Christmas – because of her aloneness, of no place to go and nothing to do."

During that time alone, when there were no ailing children to care for, Katharine tended to her hobbies: gardening, basket-weaving and woodworking. Examples of her woodworking have survived, including at least one chest of drawers she built that is still used in an office at the hospital. One report suggested she cultivated the hobbies in part to give her something to talk about in social circles. She worried that she was not as well-read as others because she could not afford much of a personal library.

"Please don't mind if I don't talk very much," she would say. "Just let me sit and listen."

Katharine refused to accept a salary for her work at Children's Mercy and she didn't like to share her age.

"If I can be hired, I can be fired," she said. "And I plan to work until I die. If you tell your age, they will want to retire you."

She never did retire.

## Goin' home

On the evening of June 2, 1933, while preparing her schedule, Katharine was stricken with severe pain. She

*Dr. Katharine Berry Richardson, highly regarded in Kansas City, often spent the holidays alone.*

was living in Nurses Hall at the time and was seen by Dr. Lawrence P. Engle. She died about 6:20 p.m. the next day.

According to her death certificate, the cause of death was peritonitis, probably caused by a perforated gall bladder. She had a history of problems. The doctor also noted chronic myocarditis – inflammation of the heart muscle – as a contributing factor. The death certificate listed her age as 75.

Kansas City had lost a legend. About 1,000 people attended her funeral, which took place June 7 in front of Nurses Hall underneath a favorite maple tree. Doctors and nurses and former patients attended. Her eulogy was given by Dr. Burris A. Jenkins of the Linwood Avenue Christian Church, the minister who had helped lead the fundraising campaign for the hospital on Independence Avenue. Miss M. Violet Fairchild sang "Goin' Home."

## Unselfish love

"In the death of Dr. Katharine Berry Richardson, not only Mercy Hospital, but Kansas City and the great southwest have suffered irreparable loss.... Her love and empathy for sick and crippled children knew no bounds of race or creed or color. Together with her sister, Dr. Alice Graham, she built in this children's hospital a monument to the unselfish love of devoted women for suffering little children. As long as Kansas City lives, as long as Mercy Hospital endures … the name Katharine Richardson (will) be cherished."

*– Resolution by the Central Governing Board*

Letters and poems were sent to the city's newspapers in praise of Katharine.

Katharine was buried in Mt. Washington Cemetery east of downtown Kansas City. Her sister was moved to a burial plot beside her, and they remain there today. The next year, to mark Katharine's birthday, September 28, the Central Governing Board erected a memorial seat of granite on the gravesite. As a testament to the never-ending dedication of the two sisters, the bench was engraved with a line from the poet John Greenleaf Whittier:

*"Others will sing the song. Others will right the wrong.*
*Finish what I begin and all I fail of win."*

Before she died, Katharine provided direction for those who would come after. In October 1933, the Central Governing Board published a newsletter that included part of those instructions:

"What I leave behind me will be measured by the influence left on other minds. My passing will not for a moment stop the wheels. If, by my word, I could hold to my will those who come after me, I would not do it. There are only a few things that are fundamental and if I have not been a force for the perpetuation of these, then I have been a cipher. If I have been an influence for good will, and myself forgotten, (that) will be my monument. How foolish to think anyone indispensable ....

"Our work, yours and mine, is to hold Mercy Hospital to its very best while we live, to keep fully up with all that's decent – to somehow, some way, get a Research Laboratory for children's diseases – to work as though we are going to stay forever and to realize that what is best will live on in the hearts of others."

## Hard times

Whatever darkness may have fallen on the hospital and on Kansas City at the death of Katharine Richardson was compounded many times by effects of the Great Depression. Before Katharine died, the country had been thrust into the depth of economic turmoil. In her writings after the stock market crash in 1929, it was apparent that hard times were making it harder for the hospital to raise the money it needed to survive.

*Often, Mercy Hospital solicited the public for necessities. This photo illustrated a plea for long stockings.*

After her death, the strong women of the Central Governing Board carried on despite the losses.

Kansas City may have been somewhat lucky during the Depression. Since the middle 1920s it had been Tom's

Town – its government under the rule of political boss Tom Pendergast. There has been much debate about Pendergast's role in helping Kansas City "survive" the Depression, but this much is certain: Local taxes were half what they were in other metropolitan areas and the numbers of people receiving some form of public assistance – one in 10 – was much less than other cities.

In the midst of the despair of the times, there was a flurry of construction activity and thus more chances for Kansas Citians to find work. The 29-story City Hall, Municipal Auditorium, General Hospital and the new Municipal Airport were built, among other projects. Residents approved an array of bond issues called the Ten-Year Plan to pay for it all.

Those were the work of government and political leaders, but philanthropy also played a big part. The Kansas City Philharmonic was begun and the University of Kansas City – forerunner of the University of Missouri-Kansas City – was established.

It was this philanthropic vein that Children's Mercy

*Nurses Hall, top and above: A "proper home" for student nurses, designed not only for rest and study, but also for a little social life.*

relied on. Although there was no new construction at the hospital in the 1930s – or the '40s or '50s for that matter – and a research building remained decades away, supporters

FOR ALL CHILDREN EVERYWHERE

*An early toy preserved in the collections of Children's Mercy.*

## A busy life, dedicated to Mercy

Leah Nourse – an adventuresome and persistent woman in a time when women rarely took leading roles – chaired the Central Governing Board of Children's Mercy from the later years of the Great Depression through World War II and the polio epidemic to the end of her tenure in 1956, when the hospital faced decisions about expanding services and staffing.

She also devoted countless volunteer hours and financial support, according to her family. After stepping 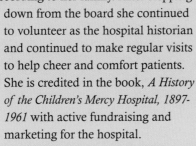 down from the board she continued to volunteer as the hospital historian and continued to make regular visits to help cheer and comfort patients. She is credited in the book, *A History of the Children's Mercy Hospital, 1897-1961* with active fundraising and marketing for the hospital.

Nourse's husband, Jack Nourse, founded the Nourse Oil Company when he was 18 years old and built it into a success. He bought two small Swallow airplanes, hired Walter Beech as chief pilot and used them to barnstorm the Midwest to promote his company and sell gasoline and lubricating oil. His airplanes rarely failed to attract attention.

Leah Nourse also became a pilot. Although her piloting days were short, she saw first-hand the importance of marketing and how that could further the reputation of Children's Mercy. She was also a member of the Salvation Army advisory board and the Women's Chamber of Commerce. Leah Nourse died in 1968.

contributed enough in time and treasure to keep the doors open and to care for as many children as possible.

The Governing Board played a vital role operating the hospital and raising money for it. Two board leaders who devoted countless hours were Catherine Bowman, chair of the Board from 1922 to 1937, and Leah Nourse, chair from 1939 to 1956. Both women were well connected to the business and social communities of Kansas City and had many opportunities to be involved in charitable causes. They chose Children's Mercy Hospital.

Bowman's husband, W.C. Bowman, owned a lumber

company. The family had a home on Janssen Place in the fashionable Hyde Park district near Armour Boulevard and Gillham Road.

In the years after Katharine's death, the emphasis was on simple maintenance. Katharine had been the driver, after all, and there was a void of strong leadership in her absence. Minutes of the Board meetings from the 1930s show a dedicated group of women doing their best, but clearly missing the strong administrative and visionary management provided by the founding sisters.

Among other things, the minutes reported, it was difficult to keep peace among the staff. That was something that Katharine would not have tolerated; she insisted on congeniality. The Board sometimes struggled to cope. Nurses and managers were fired for being "discourteous."

Pay cuts were implemented and there was discussion of canceling paid vacations. An appeal by Dr. Schauffler to the Board for permission to conduct research into osteomyelitis, or bone infection, was approved – but only if it carried no extra expense.

The medical staff still consisted entirely of doctors who volunteered their time and of moonlighting medical students. Emergency care during the after-hours was handled by medical residents assigned part-time to Children's Mercy from various metropolitan hospitals.

Doctors were urged by the Board, upon their acceptance to the medical staff, to apply "the most rigid economy in treatments, materials, supplies and length of stay of patients." At one point, the Board reduced the number of beds it

Elizabeth Martin played an integral role in the development and growth of Children's Mercy Hospital, and a look at her life makes it seem she was made for the task.

Serving as hospital administrator from 1936 to 1955, "Mercy's Miss Martin" as she was sometimes called in the newspapers of those times, guided the hospital through some of its toughest years.

Gertrude Elizabeth Martin was born July 12, 1897, in Claremont, Illinois, the third of four children of Dr. Lewis Martin and his wife, Laura Martin. A nurse was something Elizabeth Martin always wanted to become, and she applied to nursing school before she was old enough to do so.

Her father tried to discourage her, encouraging her to teach school, or work in an office or a store, or be a milliner – "something nice." But it was said of Elizabeth that the nicest thing she could think of was to be a nurse.

She tried some of the other careers her father suggested, teaching in a public school for one year. She also went to business college and worked as a stenographer, office manager, and bookkeeper. One of those jobs brought her to Kansas City. The skills she developed would be of use to her in the future, but her desire to go to nursing school never left. And so in 1921, Elizabeth entered Research Hospital School of Nursing.

Elizabeth seemed to delight in her new pursuit. In May 1921 she wrote about nursing school that she was "thrilled by the demonstrations." She was a student nurse at Mercy Hospital in 1923 and graduated the next year. Her leadership skills soon became obvious. Upon graduation she was already the supervisor of a medical-surgical floor at Research and then served as the nurse supervisor of the diagnostic department. She was named the first executive secretary of the Missouri State

*Elizabeth Martin*

Nurses Association from 1931 to 1936.

It was no surprise that Mercy Hospital came knocking at Miss Martin's door in 1936, when it was looking for an administrator. At first, Martin turned down Mercy's offer of a job. But with a bit of persuasion, she eventually accepted.

She took the helm at Mercy in a time of great uncertainty – only a few years after the death of Katharine Berry Richardson and in the midst of the Great Depression.

She worked tirelessly to keep the hospital going. One account said she often worked 12-hour days or longer. Her office door was open to anyone who had a problem or a question, but many times it was said, "Miss Martin will conduct the interview in a hallway where she is helping a crippled child learn to walk again," or "will chat with her visitor while she checks patients in a polio ward." Although she had great responsibilities in shepherding the financial and business affairs of the hospital, it was not uncommon for Martin to roll up her sleeves and tend to sick young people as a nurse when needed. Her devotion to the children and mission of Mercy Hospital was clear.

She was an engaged citizen and leader beyond the hospital walls as well. In the 1930s she was an officer of the League of Women Voters and a member of the Women's Chamber of Commerce. She never married, but she did fall in love with a 3-year-old boy in the hospital's care and adopted him, naming him Glover. She was the first single woman allowed to adopt in the state of Missouri.

After guiding Children's Mercy through the Great Depression and World War II, Martin also played a prominent role in changes in the hospital's administration, among them the hiring of the first medical director in 1953. For Mercy, those times were tough, and in 1954 there were serious discussions among hospital leaders of "reducing hospital functions and operations" because of financial difficulties. Against that backdrop Elizabeth Martin offered her resignation in January 1955. It was accepted "with regret."

Elizabeth, or "boss lady" as her staff occasionally called her, was a well-loved leader. Her resignation came as a blow to many who knew and loved her as evidenced by all of the cards and well-wishes she received. After leaving Mercy she served as superintendent of the Georgia Brown Blosser Home for Crippled Children in Marshall, Missouri, until her retirement in 1967. She died in Marshall at age 103 on November 5, 2000.

In a 1990 newspaper article, Elizabeth Martin said she didn't consider her years of service a "big deal," yet the *Messenger* newsletter described her in 1953 as "among the top contenders for the citation of working the longest and hardest to continually improve the hospital's services." Even then, they recognized the important role she would prove to have played in the history of Children's Mercy.

*Fresh air for all in the playground behind Children's Mercy, above. Kathleen H. Wilson, head of the Mercy Hospital school, worked with student patients in the 1940s, right.*

operated. An enuresis clinic – aimed at treating bed-wetting – was discontinued because of the expense. The hospital strictly enforced its age limit of 16 for patients.

By the late 1930s, when the average daily patient count was 127, the cost of operating the hospital reached about $10,000 a month. Meals for patients and nursing staff constituted a substantial outlay. Even at eight cents a meal, 8,300 meals a month added up to $664, or more than 6 percent of the hospital's monthly expenses.

At the time, income usually fell several thousand dollars short of expenses. Each year, the hospital dug a deeper financial hole. The Board of Trustees, which owned hospital property and received estate gifts – including homes, farms and businesses – was called upon regularly to cover operating costs, including taking care of building repairs.

Time and again, however, donors came through. Despite the Depression, the money collected by the many clubs supporting Children's Mercy grew from $6,471 in 1933 to $10,691 in 1935. In April 1936, the estate of Mrs. I.H.

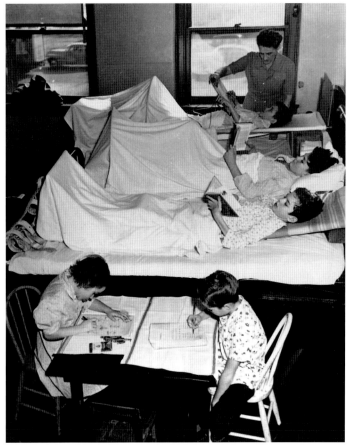

Neiman donated $10,000 to remodel the "baby ward."

A special committee of the Board was developed to put Mercy's needs "before important groups in the small towns near Kansas City." Promoting the hospital to the region outside Kansas City had been a role that Alice Graham filled when she was alive and that Mrs. Frank K. Bostick, business manager, assumed from Alice's death until the 1930s.

The *Messenger*, the newsletter designed to promote the hospital and solicit donations, had ceased publication upon Katharine Richardson's death. (It returned in the 1950s and in the 21st century existed as an electronic newsletter for Children's Mercy employees.)

With the advent of various New Deal public assistance programs in the early 1930s, Children's Mercy looked to the federal government for help in making ends meet. Yet when it appeared there could be some money from Social Security for the hospital, the Board initially declined to accept it for fear that the local Charities Bureau would reduce what it provided.

## A new leader, facing old problems

As 1936 came to a close, the Board made a decision with decades-long impact: It hired Elizabeth Martin as hospital administrator. Martin, a nurse, began work December 1 and would help lead the hospital through the rest of the Great Depression, World War II and well into the postwar Baby Boom. She would leave it poised for significant growth when she left in the 1950s.

Elizabeth Martin and Children's Mercy were born the same summer, 1897. She first encountered the hospital in 1921 when she entered training at Research Hospital School of Nursing. As a student nurse she met Katharine Richardson. Like Katharine Richardson, according to Swanson's history of the hospital, Martin was a dedicated worker.

"Kind and selfless," Swanson wrote of Martin, "she sought the best for Mercy's youngsters. Consistently, she helped to improve the quality of Mercy's care. Until 1956, when she retired, she operated the hospital with efficiency."

*Downtown Kansas City about 1940, as it looked from the roof of Mercy Hospital on Independence Avenue. The skyline featured two relatively new buildings, the Jackson County Courthouse, far left, and City Hall. Their construction provided jobs amid the Great Depression.*

The Second World War added to the hospital's uncertain future. The staff of volunteer doctors was depleted: many joined the armed forces and those who remained were overworked. Medical students from the University of Kansas were recruited for emergency room care. According to a later study of the medical staff written by Drs. Herbert Wenner and Sydney Pakula, this created concern about the lack of supervision of these late-night working student doctors. But there was no other way to keep the doors open.

Nurses were called on to do double or triple duty: sharpening needles, stretching gauze, powdering gloves, preparing infant formula and filling in for the pharmacist and switchboard operator.

At the same time, the cost of providing care increased dramatically. In 1921, the average daily cost of care was only $1.88. By 1946, after the end of the war, it would grow to $10.04. The growth would more than double again, to $24.15 by 1955. Advancing technology, new medications, higher expectations and increased staffing all contributed to rising expenditures.

To help cover costs, the Board in 1940 approved plans to appraise and review all the pieces of property it owned. Through the years, many generous people had left Children's Mercy property in their wills. As a result, the hospital owned property not only in Kansas City, but also in Taney County, Missouri; Galesburg, Illinois; Wagoner County, Oklahoma, and elsewhere. The hospital never intended to become a land baron or even a landlord but, for a while, a landlord it was – even spending money to paint properties in Kansas City.

The hospital building, by 1940 more than 20 years old, had fallen out of date structurally. Elizabeth Martin offered a plan for expansion and renovation to the Board in the 1940s, but no action was taken to implement it. The only significant renovation for decades would occur in 1948 when the isolation wards were dismantled. They were no longer needed because infection control and other treatment had improved.

The total operating budget for the hospital doubled from 1937 to 1947, when it reached $248,000. About half the revenue came from the Community Chest, according to the Annual Report. There were about 600 clubs and many individuals contributing to make up the rest of the budget. Donations of linens, clothing, food, equipment and other items were also essential.

As always, one of the largest contributions to the hospital was the free service of its doctors and dentists. All of that proved barely enough.

The number of patients increased as well. More than 2,300 would be admitted in 1946.

Children's Mercy, it seems, was just hanging on. Gifts seemed to arrive barely in the nick of time. Equipment that was hopelessly out of date usually managed not to break until the hospital could afford a replacement.

## Carrying on despite it all

Through all those trying years, the hospital continued to make friends and heal children.

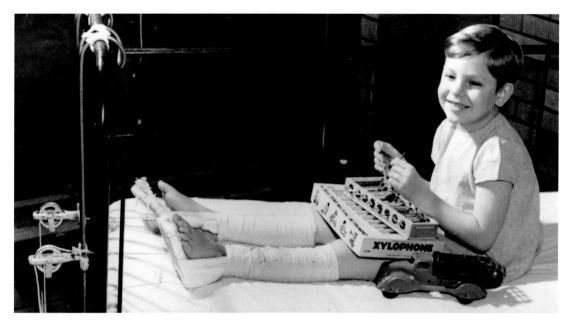

*He suffered from rheumatic arthritis, his tonsils had just been removed and this was his third trip to the hospital since September 1941, but Edward Humphrey of Kansas City still could smile at his toys in the early 1940s.*

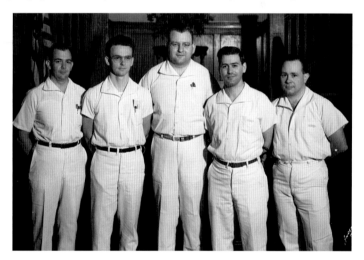

*Residents, key members of the work force, in 1947.*

In 1945, Peter T. Scott wrote in *The Kansas City News-Press* about a visit to the hospital. He met Wayne and Jerry and other patients – no last names and no addresses, he said, to protect their pride – and he left convinced the public should do all it could to support the hospital.

"I came away from Mercy hospital with a feeling of great humility," Scott wrote. "All this work and all this care and devotion being lavished on the very poor of a large city; certainly it's the American way, the Christian way, to do things."

One of the hospital's resounding success stories resulted from the school for patients that it instituted in 1910 with the Kansas City, Missouri, public schools. One of the products of the school was Joseph Marcel Vandepopuliere, who entered the hospital in winter 1944 when his rheumatic fever worsened.

According to Vandepopuliere's autobiography, he was cared for by a young cardiologist, Dr. Don Carlos Peete, who knew that antibiotic penicillin could help him, but that it was available only to the military in wartime. Without antibiotics, the recovery period was long – for those fortunate enough to survive.

Vandepopuliere, 14 when he entered, was in Children's Mercy on two occasions, once for about 5½ months. When he reached 16, he could no longer be admitted to Children's Mercy so he was seen at KU Medical Center.

While at Children's Mercy, Vandepopuliere was taught by Kathleen H. Wilson, who spent more than 20 years as a teacher and principal at the hospital. According to Vandepopuliere's manuscript, Wilson encouraged his interest in science, and he credited her with academic success that allowed him to gain acceptance into Central Missouri State College in Warrensburg. Afterward, he went to work for Ralston-Purina in St. Louis. There, he was instrumental in the creation of Puppy Chow, and later contributed to the development of Monkey Chow, which was used, among other things, to feed monkeys used in the creation of the polio vaccine.

"Without (Wilson's) assistance and positive encouragement, it is doubtful I would have gone to college," Vandepopuliere wrote. To encourage others to become teachers, he endowed a scholarship in Kathleen Wilson's name at the college in Warrensburg.

## Half a century

In 1947, Children's Mercy celebrated its Golden Anniversary. A celebration on September 28, Katharine Richardson's birthday, was highlighted by an address by Dr. Robert

*In the hard times of the 1930s, Mercy took all the help it could get. Top: Hawking salt to benefit the hospital at the 1935 Food Fair. Above: A donation of prize hogs from the 1937 American Royal.*

Schauffler, who was marking 43 years of his own service to the hospital. He called it "The Quality of Mercy is not Strained."

"The sources of Mercy Hospital power are great," Dr. Schauffler said. "The first is the spirit of the Founders. How high their ideas, how great their love …. Second, the spirit of the management. With patience and enthusiasm, they are following patterns set by the founders.

"Next, the spirit of the workers. The devotion of many of the older graduates of the training school is a beautiful

*The Children's Mercy float rolled south on Baltimore Avenue, about to cross 12th Street, as part of Kansas City's Charities Campaign in October 1942.*

thing to see …. Mercy hospital does things to people. I have seen fine doctors whom I thought rather selfish develop soft-heartedness at Mercy.

"About 500 clubs make contributions to Mercy Hospital. There are seven distinctly Mercy clubs. The Maywood Club has been on the job nearly 40 years …. Last, the love and interest of a multitude of small givers. Let me stress this. The widow's mite may carry more love and blessing than the rich man's endowment of a foundation.

"Are we delivering in full volume to our patients? On account of my 43 years of service at Mercy and the fact that former patients come to see me in their 20s, 30s and even 40s, I can testify that this ideal has been achieved many hundreds of times.

"We need many things for Mercy Hospital. They will cost a lot of money. The best way to get them is to have many warm-hearted, generous people feel assured that we will give not only efficiency of scientific service, but that the quality of mercy will be dispensed and not strained."

The hospital entered its second half-century with that mandate. The challenges it would face were many. The successes no one could have imagined.

The last half of the 20th century was a period of unprecedented and unforeseeable growth and advancement for both medicine and Children's Mercy.

# GROWN-UP DECISIONS

*"Change is inevitable. Progress is optional."*

– Tony Robbins

As the second half of the 20th century dawned, change was all around – in the world, the city, medicine, and even at 1710 Independence Avenue. The status quo, it was clear, would not long sustain the little charity hospital known as Children's Mercy.

Challenges mounted. The postwar Baby Boom exploded the ranks of children. Many of them needed care and many of their families could not pay for it. Standards for medical education rose, putting pressure on teaching programs. Epidemics of childhood infectious diseases, such as polio, spread out of control and too often without a cure. For the hospital, budget deficits only mounted. By the end of the 1950s, they would become entirely unsustainable.

At the proverbial fork in the road, the leaders of Children's Mercy faced difficult choices. Yet their community and its children were counting on them.

Real, grown-up decisions would be required. Patience and business acumen would be paramount. Change would happen, and progress would come – but none of that would be easy.

*The television age, complete with black-and-white images and rabbit-ears antenna, arrived as the hospital entered its second 50 years.*

## The pressure was on

Maternity wards overflowed; in the 1950s more than 100,000 children were born in Kansas City, Missouri, alone. New homes went up as fast as carpenters could nail up walls. A chapter about the decade in the book *Kansas City: An American Story* was titled "Churning Out Children, Settling into Subdivisions."

A single county in the metropolitan area, Johnson County, Kansas, illustrated the boom: The 1940 census put its population at 33,327; in 1950, it exceeded 60,000; by 1960, the number would jump to 143,792 and by 1970 to more than 220,000. By the 21st century it would top half a million.

Similar growth, though not as dramatic, occurred around the metropolitan area. The larger population would need more services, including an expanded and more sophisticated health care system.

Demand hit Children's Mercy hard, and its financial documents contained the evidence. In 1949, the hospital budget was $387,000. Five years later, it hit $604,000. It would exceed $1 million in 1960. Through all those years, the increases far outstripped inflation.

Increasing numbers of patients played a big role in driving operating costs higher and higher. Even in the 1950s

*Fresh air and lots of light: The sunroof at the building on Independence Avenue remained a happy place for patients and their caregivers in the late 1940s and early 1950s.*

Children's Mercy still had only a limited paid medical staff, and doctors who volunteered their services remained essential to minimizing expenses.

"The business of operating the hospital expanded," according to a later study of the medical staff by Drs. Herbert Wenner and Sydney Pakula. "An increasing need for medical and surgical services came about in both walk-in clinics and in-hospital care. New equipment was necessary."

Putting even more pressure on the budget were incredible postwar advances worldwide in health care – new treatments, new medications and new equipment. The first open-heart surgery performed with the benefit of a heart-lung bypass machine took place in 1953. The first successful organ transplant – with a kidney – was performed in 1954.

New medications became available to treat a variety of diseases, including infections. Penicillin first came into use for soldiers during World War II. The first flu vaccines also were approved for the military, and scientists were hard at work on more.

In 1953, Kansas City reported 150 cases of polio, the first widespread attack in the city. It terrified many and some parents refused to let their children go to swimming pools, among other places, for fear they would contract the disease. About 900 children in the Kansas City area – some treated at Children's Mercy – were crippled by polio in the six years before the first vaccine was announced on April 12, 1955.

Then came a measles vaccine, approved in 1958. A new rabies vaccine would arrive in 1961 and vaccines for mumps and rubella in 1967 and 1969. Medical science was making headway against childhood diseases, but the process was costly.

## Trouble making ends meet

All the while, Children's Mercy ran deficits, and they were piling up. The 1950 budget included $15,000 to cover the deficit from 1949. By 1960, deficits were running as high as $28,000 a *month*.

Clearly, increasing expenses could not be met that way forever.

The hospital dipped into its endowments, took out short-term loans and made a greater effort to raise money outside Kansas City – even if only a little bit at a time. Russell W. Preston, the hospital's "traveling representative," regularly traveled to dozens of communities in western and central Missouri, trying to generate support. He visited large and small towns, attending ice cream socials and service club meetings. By 1956, his efforts were raising $50,000 in a year for the hospital. But that was not enough.

In the mid-1950s, there was serious discussion about cutting services.

"It became obvious that some drastic steps must be taken," Roger Swanson wrote in his 1960 book, *A History of the Children's Mercy Hospital*. "Either that, or cut back on care. And nobody connected with the hospital wanted to do that."

Indeed, Kansas City community leaders and many parents wanted just the opposite. To take full advantage of the advances and provide the best possible care for the children of Kansas City, they wanted Children's Mercy to grow.

The previous couple of decades had been hard on the hospital, its finances, its staff and its ability to care for all the children who needed help. It was time, its leaders and supporters believed, to focus on the future and the best ways to provide care for all children, regardless of their ability to pay.

Leaders – both inside and outside the hospital – began to ask whether Children's Mercy could and should continue as a charity hospital dependent solely on donations. Or should it expand its decades-old mission of caring only for the poor?

## Bolstering the staff

One of the first questions concerned the medical education program. Medical students, residents and fellows remained essential to the functioning of the hospital. However, the program at Children's Mercy had "fallen below levels qualifying for residency training," according to the study by Drs. Wenner and Pakula. The problem was a shortage of teaching faculty.

As a result, in 1952 the hospital's accreditation was suspended by the American Board of Pediatrics. Without accreditation – and thus without the help of medical students and residents in patient care – Children's Mercy would be unable to care for its current population, let alone new patients that would come with an expanding population and programs.

"The time for challenge and renewal," Drs. Wenner and

*With tambourines, tom-toms, snare drums, maracas and xylophones, young percussionists took part in a rhythm band performance about 1950.*

# Mid-century doctors

The association of Children's Mercy with the University of Kansas and the work of Drs. Laurence Wayne Hart and Herbert C. Miller helped the hospital recruit many talented physicians. Those doctors, in turn, attracted others who were exceptional in their field. Here are some of the doctors instrumental in building and sustaining Children's Mercy:

**Daniel Darrow**. According to his official biography at Children's Mercy, Dr. Darrow already was considered one of the premier pediatricians and clinical researchers in the area of fluid therapy when he arrived in 1954 as one of the first full-time medical staff members of Children's Mercy. "He seemed to take the greatest pleasure in being recognized as a 'teacher of teachers' … Dr. Darrow contributed significantly to The Children's Mercy Hospital in helping to transform this institution from the status of an early 20th century charity hospital to that of a recognized pediatric education center."

**Ned Smull.** Dr. Smull began work with Children's Mercy in 1963 as a professor of pediatrics and director of the hospital. He was chosen by the Board to guide the affiliation with the University of Missouri. "From 1964 to 1977," his biography says, "a period characterized by rapid growth in patient services, changing health care regulations and rules, and The Children's Mercy Hospital's move to Hospital Hill, Dr. Smull recruited physicians in general pediatrics and pediatric specialties to form a staff and faculty capable of delivering high quality care for children while being involved in educational and research activities." By the end of his tenure, The Children's Mercy Hospital was established as an outstanding regional children's hospital." After leaving Children's Mercy, Dr. Smull operated a private pediatric practice in Kansas City.

**Stanley Hellerstein.** Dr. Hellerstein joined Children's Mercy in 1963 and was known as an outstanding teacher, researcher and clinician. He did his fellowship under Dr. Darrow at Children's Mercy, headed the Graduate Medical Education program, directed the Sickle Cell program and was the first chief of the Section of Nephrology. "His impact on the development of our institution as we know it today is unsurpassed and cannot be overestimated," according to the biography underneath his official portrait at Children's Mercy. He is "a role model that generations of physicians have looked to for guidance and the doctor that generations of patients have looked to for care and compassion." In 1979, babies in multiple hospitals in the United States, including Children's Mercy, were admitted with symptoms related to lack of appetite and development. Dr. Hellerstein discovered an issue related to the baby formula Neo-Mull-Soy. His work was instrumental in causing Neo-Mull-Soy's manufacturer to stop production and sales of the formula, saving many babies unnecessary sickness and hospitalization.

**Thomas Holder.** Dr. Holder, whose recruitment was heralded as a coup for Children's Mercy, was the first surgeon-in-chief at the hospital beginning in 1959. He is credited with elevating the level of cardiac care. He helped fashion a heart-lung bypass machine – necessary to keep patients alive when the heart was stopped during surgery – out of spare parts because Children's Mercy could not afford a new machine. Holder left for the University of Kansas Medical Center for a while and then went into private practice while also serving as chief of heart surgery at Children's Mercy during the 1970s. He was joined by Dr. Keith Ashcraft, who served as chief of urology and later chief of heart surgery and surgeon-in-chief after Dr. Holder retired. Drs. Holder and Ashcraft were the authors of the most recognized and authoritative textbook on pediatric surgery. Widely recognized as "Holder and Ashcraft," the textbook is still used to train young surgeons and is still edited by Children's Mercy surgeons.

**Herbert Wenner.** The keeper of the one-time "Fort Knox of Virology," Dr. Wenner worked with Jonas Salk in the development of the polio vaccine. He joined Children's Mercy from the University of Kansas Medical Center, where he practiced until the late 1960s. He was the first occupant of the Joyce C. Hall Distinguished Professor of Medicine chair. He was active in the development of the University of Missouri-Kansas City School of Medicine, writing a significant portion of the early pediatric curriculum. He also wrote a history of Children's Mercy that detailed much of the medical staff development. The manuscript was never published, but has proven invaluable to researchers. He collaborated on the book with Dr. Sydney Pakula, who was one of the early physician residents who trained and worked with Katharine Richardson before she died.

Pakula wrote, "was at hand."

In 1953, the hospital established for the first time the position of medical director and filled it with Laurence Wayne Hart, MD. When Dr. Hart began his job on January 1 of that year, he became the first full-time paid physician at Children's Mercy.

Hart soon arranged for Herbert C. Miller, MD, chairman of the KU Department of Pediatrics since 1945, to help him at Children's Mercy. Dr. Miller brought new attention to services needed for the care of children. He had already gathered at the University of Kansas Medical Center a capable staff of physicians in the areas of infectious disease, cardiology, psychiatry and more.

*Christmastime in the 1950s brought a big party and gifts for Children's Mercy patients. They met not only Santa but also adults who had lived through accidents and ailments of their own.*

Drs. Hart and Miller worked together for several years to restore full accreditation of Children's Mercy as a teaching hospital. Within six months of his own arrival, Dr. Hart later recalled, he presented a plan to the hospital board and to the American Board of Pediatrics to restore the training program to acceptable standards. Their work not only accomplished that goal, but also built the foundation for a world-class faculty for teaching pediatrics.

Until the appointment of Dr. Hart as medical director in 1953, all Children's Mercy physicians had served as volunteers. In 1954, the hospital added one more paid faculty position, Daniel Darrow, MD, who had been Dr. Miller's mentor at Yale. By 1968, the number of paid physicians would grow to 30. That enabled Children's Mercy to solidify the training program and to extend its expertise in various specialties.

Paid staff became increasingly important, although volunteer doctors still numbered 100 in 1960 and 180 in 1968 and would remain crucial to success.

The teaching program at Children's Mercy became affiliated with the KU Medical Center in Kansas City, Kansas, in 1953; funding was provided by the Kansas City Association of Trusts and Foundations. According to Drs. Wenner and Pakula, five young physicians were appointed for in-house training in pediatrics. Some faculty was shared between the KU hospital and Children's Mercy. The resident physicians provided much of the medical care with oversight by the shared faculty.

In addition to Dr. Darrow, other doctors who were brought on at this crucial time were Stanley Hellerstein, who trained as a fellow in pediatric metabolism under Dr. Darrow and had a long and illustrious career as a clinician and researcher at the University of Missouri-Kansas City School of Medicine after it was established in 1972; and Dr. Thomas M. Holder, a surgeon with post-doctoral training at Boston Children's Hospital, where he assisted the first-ever pediatric open-heart surgery with a heart-lung machine.

"It was a big deal when Tom Holder arrived from Boston," said Marj Trinkl, a nurse who joined Children's Mercy in 1953 and would continue to volunteer at the hospital in the 21st century.

It was a big deal because he was an outstanding physician, would elevate the hospital's surgery program and would help boost its reputation. Perhaps equally important, it signaled that Children's Mercy could compete with other hospitals in recruiting the top medical talent from across the country.

Children's Mercy also formed an affiliation with the University of Missouri. Beginning in 1956, pediatric physician residents spent two-thirds of their time at Children's Mercy and the rest at the MU hospital in

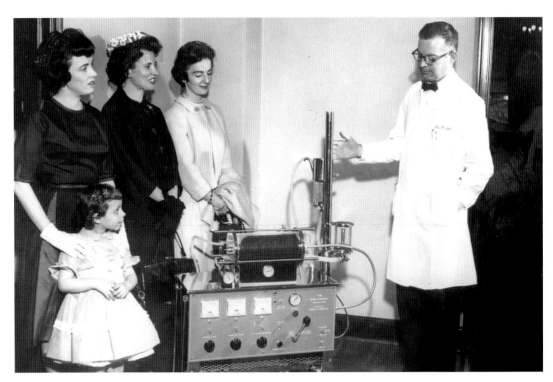

*Dr. Thomas Holder demonstrated his heart-lung machine.*

Columbia. KU continued as lead educational partner, but Children's Mercy had a large enough patient population to provide opportunities for more than one school.

Dr. Hart resigned as medical director at the end of 1958 and Dr. Miller took his place, continuing to work half-time, for three years.

By June 1959, the hospital and its training program were fully licensed to operate by the American Board of Pediatrics for residency training.

This was a crucial time. Recruitment of faculty remained a high priority and the needs of the children of the region continued to push Children's Mercy into uncharted territory.

Along the way, Drs. Hart and Miller and the board also sought more professional help to administer the hospital.

## A leadership in flux

Two decades earlier, Katharine Richardson's death had created a leadership vacuum. In his history of the hospital, Roger Swanson posed the question that faced Mercy in 1933: "Who could take Dr. Richardson's place?"

The answer, he wrote, "was obvious to everyone: no one could …. She was Mercy."

The volunteer medical staff simply carried on. So did the women of the Central Governing Board. In 1936, the board named Elizabeth Martin the first hospital administrator, and in the years she held the post much of the philosophy of the era of Alice Graham and Katherine Richardson remained.

Big changes evidently did not come easily for Martin. In the 1940s, she argued vehemently with Trustee R.R. Brewster over the possibility of accepting paying patients as a wartime measure.

The 1950s saw sweeping changes in hospital policy as the institution grew from a charity hospital into a regional pediatric medical center. Ever the loyal administrator, Martin helped pave the way for a new era of hospital management. By 1955 she decided she had given all she could. Early that year, she resigned with little fanfare. Temporarily, she was replaced by Mary Hanna, a member of the board.

Martin moved to Marshall, Missouri, where she headed a home for crippled children. Hinting at a reason for her move, Martin told a Sedalia, Missouri, newspaper that her new job would not be so large or so pressing as at Mercy.

*A tabletop doll collection represented patients, nurses and doctors of Children's Mercy as the 1962 United campaign, renamed from the Community Chest, got under way. Surrounding it were Mercy staff and supporters.*

The change in administrator represented only part of the new direction at Children's Mercy. Bylaws were changed, more responsibility was delegated to the hospital staff and for the first time men were added to the Governing Board – lumber company executive Herman Sutherland; Joseph Boon Gregg, who owned a grain company, and Bob Tureman, a real-estate executive.

In 1957, the Central Governing Board authorized the hiring of a "thoroughly trained, competent career person to handle all the new responsibilities coming up."

It chose John Stockwell, who moved to Kansas City from Rhode Island Hospital and who would work at Children's Mercy from 1958 until 1962. Stockwell was

*John Stockwell*

a graduate of Dartmouth College and had a master's degree in hospital administration from the University of Minnesota. He had been a featured speaker at hospital association conferences addressing "Training Employees in Good Attitude toward Patients."

Perhaps not coincidentally, issues of staff discord and poor attitudes had been discussed at board meetings in the years leading up to Stockwell's hiring.

"The revitalization of the quality of the care at Children's Mercy was now underway," Drs. Wenner and Pakula wrote.

It would not be long, however, before tension would develop over the hospital's home and future academic affiliations. Decisions were on the horizon that would forever alter the landscape of pediatric care in Kansas City.

## Center for children's health

At the same time Children's Mercy wrestled with increasing costs and ever more children who needed care, interest was growing among business leaders in Kansas City to develop a "children's medical center."

Views differed on exactly what that would look like, but the basic philosophy was that the children of the Kansas City region would be best served by a single exclusively pediatric medical center. The idea was to replace the existing system in which poor children were taken care of at Children's Mercy and other children were cared for in hospitals that also cared for adults.

Children's Mercy was the logical choice to provide extensive pediatric care for the metro area, but it would require a lot of help and a number of changes in its operations, its staff and its facilities.

As the Baby Boom wound on through the 1950s, hospitals across the Kansas City area found themselves caring for more and more children, yet lacking great pediatric expertise. Children, they realized, needed equipment that fit their small but growing bodies and nurses and doctors who knew that caring for children differed from caring for adults.

A comprehensive, regional children's center was desirable, but questions remained. Was Children's Mercy ready for a change in direction? Were its facilities adequate to the task? If not, what hospital would fill the void and where would it be constructed?

The leaders at Children's Mercy were ready to accept the challenge.

## To bill or not to bill

Financial realities already were forcing changes. For the first time in its history, Children's Mercy in 1955 began to charge for its care. Until then, Children's Mercy was exclusively a charity institution. In fact, Katharine Richardson had said she hoped a paying patient never got "within a thousand miles" of the

hospital for fear its mission would be compromised. But the postwar era required new approaches.

The first instance of Children's Mercy's asking families to help pay for care was mentioned in Central Governing Board minutes in July 1955:

"It was directed that a definite effort be made to collect $1 in advance for penicillin shots given to patients in the Out Patient Clinic."

Penicillin was a new "miracle" drug, one of the first antibiotics in the world, and it marked a dramatic turning point in the treatment of infectious diseases.

In months to come, there was much discussion among the medical staff and the board about whether to admit patients who could afford to pay.

At one board meeting, the minutes described how doubters were reassured that "this does not insinuate that we would diminish any of the non-paying work that we have been doing." To the contrary, the minutes continued, "since we are extending every effort to build up a top-notch medical and surgical team for work on the non-paying patient, such a team might very well be utilized to meet the demands and desires of the part-pay and pay patient."

Dr. Schauffler, the orthopedic surgeon who had been on staff since 1904, said that, even if payments were accepted,

*Dr. Schauffler: Keep the common touch.*

"We must be on guard that we do not lose our greatest asset. It must always be a hospital for the patient, a hospital for common people."

The volunteer medical staff remained adamant that physicians themselves should receive no fees "except in emergencies."

In November 1955, the board formally agreed to accept paying patients. The corporation's bylaws had to be altered to accomplish it. By the next spring a medical staff resolution stated that "simply the economic status of a patient should not be sufficient to exclude him from admission."

The move drew some opposition from outside the hospital. In letters to the editor of *The Kansas City Star*, some writers questioned whether Children's Mercy was abandoning

Calling attention to its cramped quarters in 1962, Children's Mercy commissioned a set of photographs that showed a busy room at lunchtime, above, and tight space in the outpatient offices, left. As for the X-ray lab, right, hospital leaders deemed it not only crowded but also obsolete. The problem had been growing since the middle 1950s at the hospital on Independence Avenue.

# The Halls and the hospital

Aside from the founding sisters, it's impossible to find a family more involved and more influential in the success of Children's Mercy than that of Joyce C. Hall.

Hall, the founder of Hallmark Cards, arrived in Kansas City in 1910, not long after sisters Alice Berry Graham and Katharine Berry Richardson started their children's hospital. In a way, the two, Hallmark and Children's Mercy, grew up together.

Just like Alice and Katharine's father, who encouraged his family to help others, Hall and his wife, Elizabeth Ann Hall, left a legacy of community involvement and philanthropy that has continued for generations. The name Hall is found all around Children's Mercy, and for good reason.

In the middle 1960s, Joyce Hall teamed with former President Harry Truman as honorary chairs of a fundraising drive to build a new Children's Mercy. The new building would be next door to Hallmark's national headquarters and its urban development, Crown Center. Children's Mercy opened on Hospital Hill in December 1970.

In the midst of raising money for the new hospital, Joyce Hall made another investment in Children's Mercy. In 1967 he donated the funds to establish the first endowed chair for the burgeoning academic medical center. Endowed chairs allow institutions to attract and retain the best talent by offering a permanent source of support for the chair holder. The Joyce C. Hall Eminent Scholar in Pediatrics is held by the Children's Mercy pediatrician-in-chief.

Adele Hall was introduced to Children's Mercy shortly after she joined her new husband, Donald J. Hall, son of Joyce and Elizabeth Hall, in Kansas City. Adele Hall's friend Marion Kreamer invited her to a picnic in 1954 to introduce her to the work being done at the hospital on Independence Avenue. That began Adele Hall's 50-year love affair with Children's Mercy.

In the 1960s, Adele and Don Hall helped with the campaign for a new Children's Mercy building. She also was active in transforming the scope and administrative structure of the hospital.

In the 1970s, Adele Hall could be found volunteering in the Neonatal Intensive Care Unit rocking babies; or in the follow-up clinic measuring and weighing the little ones. She was a longtime member of the Central Governing Board and its chair in 1983 and 1984. Also, she sat on the Board of Trustees, earning lifetime emeritus status on both boards. In 1980, she worked with professional golfer Tom Watson to start the Children's Mercy Golf Classic, a phenomenal success in both friend- and fund-raising, bringing more than $12 million – and the world's greatest golfers – to the hospital over 25 years. She and Don served as honorary chairs of the Healthier Ever After fund drive that launched in 2009. She served on many committees and was sought after for her counsel before many major decisions were made. When Adele Hall died in 2013, Children's Mercy lost its greatest supporter.

Randall L. O'Donnell, President and CEO of Children's Mercy, summed up her contributions: "She could bring people from all corners of the community to the table to be involved in supporting the hospital …. The strongest element that Adele represented to us can be summed up in one word, love. Adele

*Elizabeth Ann and Joyce C. Hall*

*Adele Hall*

Hall had an abundance of love."

That love spanned generations, not only of Kansas City children but also of her own family. Don and Adele's daughter, Margaret "Margi" Pence, followed her mother on the Central Governing Board, serving as chair in 2001. She and her husband, Keith Pence, have remained active and encouraged others to support the hospital.

Over the decades the Hall family, both personally and through its foundations, has donated tens of millions of dollars to Children's Mercy, often providing lead gifts to demonstrate the value of causes to others.

In late 2013, Children's Mercy renamed its Hospital Hill site the Adele Hall Campus in honor of her commitment. Other parts of the campus bearing the Hall name include the Hall Family Outpatient Center, which opened in 1995, and the Elizabeth Ann Hall Patient Tower, dedicated in 2012.

In 2004, Don and Adele Hall were honored in a private ceremony marking their 50th wedding anniversary and their love of Children's Mercy. Two "lovebird" sculptures were unveiled, sitting on a ledge high above the hospital's rotunda, looking out over the oversized hanging bird mobiles, called Spirits of the Heart, which the Halls donated. A plaque on the wall near the birds bears this inscription:

*Today, and every day, they keep a gentle, watchful eye over the Spirits of the Heart of Children's Mercy, sharing the rare unmistakable wisdom and love that only grandparents can bestow.*

its mission.

The board defended itself and assured the faithful that it remained committed to all children. Accepting payment, although controversial, would prove better than the alternative of trimming service.

Parents were asked to pay what they could afford. Initially, the income generated by paying patients represented a nominal part of the costs and operational expenses. But the change to accept paying patients and to charge for services opened the doors to a wider variety of patients and more income. The scope of services would grow to meet the needs of more children, their families and the community.

In 1957, the hospital began billing all its patients. In late 1958, it began to charge for clinic visits.

Shortly after he became administrator in 1958, Stockwell acknowledged that "ever since we started sending bills, we occasionally have calls from people who want to know if our heart is in the right place."

"Our defense is that by sending bills, we hope to make sure that health care is not given free when it can be paid for and that contributor's dollars go to those who need them."

Moreover, when it came to collecting payment, Children's Mercy was anything but aggressive. Parents were "asked if they would like to pay and if they said no, or they did not have insurance," that would be the end of it, recalled Betty Boyd, a nurse who joined the staff in the 1960s. "I

don't know how we survived."

There was no process for determining whether or not families could afford to pay; the hospital took them at their word.

If the hospital received an insurance check for a patient's care, it sent the check to the patient, according to Eric Jones, who served as hospital administrator from 1963 to 1979. The practice ended when he arrived, Jones said in an interview after he retired.

"The argument was, this is a charity hospital," Jones said. "But I told them this wasn't charity, [someone] had paid for it."

Nine out of 10 doctors who received insurance checks for taking care of Children's Mercy patients gave the money to the hospital, he said.

In one of the first years of sending bills, the hospital raised about $150,000, according to the 1960 Annual Report. That helped, yet in the same year the deficit still reached $135,000.

In 1959, Dr. Miller suggested that the hospital would have to limit the amount of free care it provided if additional revenue streams were not identified. Yet no child was turned away because of inability to pay. In the late 1950s and early 1960s, the hospital provided about $800,000 a year in free care. The policy of never turning a child away would continue. In 2015 the hospital would report providing nearly $120 million in uncompensated care.

Meanwhile, the hospital found

ways to pay for some improvements. In 1959, it used a special charity grant to begin a Department of Social Work, with a single salaried social worker helped by postgraduate students. The teaching program, which helped provide medical students and residents to work at the hospital, was supported by gifts from the Kansas City Association of Trusts and Foundations and the Joyce Hall Foundation. The gifts covered the first three years' cost of residency, which otherwise would have cost almost $100,000.

## The door opens wider

By the mid-1950s, several organizations were looking to Children's Mercy to help care for their children. The largest was the Children's Convalescent Center. The center was founded in 1948 in a large stone house at 40th and Warwick to care for children who had rheumatic fever, which could result in heart problems. After years of discussion, Children's Mercy and the Convalescent Center formed a partnership in 1957, when Dr. Miller helped secure the University of Kansas' help in providing care. With the advent of penicillin and improved nutrition and sanitation, care for these children became less complicated, yet Children's Mercy still saw a lot of them.

In 1961, the Convalescent Center moved to the ground and first floors of the east wing of Children's Mercy and its work expanded to care for children with congenital heart conditions. The center eventually was merged with Children's Mercy and became the Children's Cardiac Center. By the 21st century it would become the Ward Family Heart Center, providing the entire scope of cardiology and cardiac surgery services.

The Kansas City Cerebral Palsy Foundation began sending patients to Children's Mercy in 1955, and the hospital responded by turning over to the foundation some of its property along Independence Avenue. When the Alfred Benjamin Clinic, which cared for the indigent, lost its support from the Community Chest, it turned to Children's Mercy to treat its young patients. Children's Mercy worked with the Ararat Shrine Community Hospital, too.

In 1956, the Central Governing Board agreed to care for "colored" children who were served by Crippled Children's Services, an agency of the state of Missouri.

With that, the 1950s, which already had brought

sweeping change in financial and medical policies, saw the beginning of desegregation of the hospital. Until then, Children's Mercy had cared for black patients only through its Model Ward at Wheatley-Provident and through its one-patient-at-a-time "No Color Line" bed.

New partners, new services, new faculty members, open admissions and a growing reputation brought new patients to the hospital. In the 10 years from 1953 to 1963, the number of outpatient clinic visits increased from 13,444 to nearly 50,000. Laboratory tests doubled in the same period and surgeries increased nearly 50 percent. In one short span, from 1963 to 1965, growth was staggering. Outpatient visits jumped from 50,000 to 69,000, lab tests from 58,000 to 90,000 and surgeries from 1,046 to 1,500. There was barely room for all the work that needed to be done.

Although the number of beds remained the same, the hospital freed them up more often, providing some relief. The average length of an inpatient stay was dramatically reduced: from nearly 25 days in 1953 to 9.2 days in 1965. Yet even that was not enough to accomplish the task facing the hospital.

It was becoming clear that the hospital on Independence Avenue was not only old and outdated by modern medical standards, but also simply too small. The board and other supporters of the hospital began to wrestle with the question of what to do with Children's Mercy.

There was consensus that it should become the regional center for children's care. The questions remained: how – and where?

## What to do?

As early as 1955, discussions turned to either remodeling the existing building or building a new one.

The only significant remodeling at the Independence Avenue structure built in 1917 had occurred in the late 1940s when the isolation wards were dismantled because advances in medicine rendered them obsolete.

According to an initial report by architects, the cost to provide for a 139-bed hospital by expanding and remodeling on Independence Avenue would be $553,000. That would include new construction, general remodeling and complete gutting of the fourth floor to provide room for 24 new beds.

There were other ideas. One considered briefly was for Children's Mercy to take over the building that housed

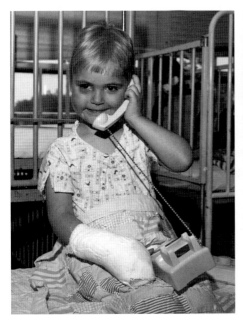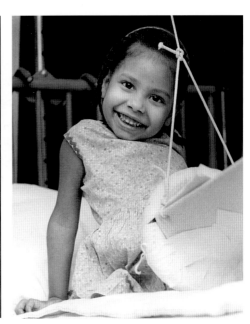

*A telephone, a tiger and traction: Three patients of the postwar era.*

General Hospital Number 2 at 22nd Street and McCoy Avenue, a block north of General Hospital. Historically, Number 2 had been used to treat black Kansas Citians, but city plans called for replacing it with a desegregated facility. Eventually, the structure was deemed inadequate for the needs of Children's Mercy.

Another idea, one that consumed much more time and energy, was to move the hospital close to the University of Kansas Medical Center, across the state line in Kansas City, Kansas. On April 14, 1959, W. Clarke Wescoe, MD, dean of the School of Medicine at KU, made just such an offer. The Kansas City area needed a regional children's medical center, he said, and KU was interested in helping develop it. Children's Mercy, he believed, was the "best and only logical answer to supplying this need in the community."

The KU offer included up to 10 acres of land for a new medical center north of 39th Street and east of Rainbow Boulevard. The land, owned by the KU Endowment Association, would be leased to Children's Mercy for 99 years at $1 per year.

Dr. Wescoe listed ways the proposal would benefit Children's Mercy and its patients:
- The land would cost Children's Mercy virtually nothing.
- KU would close its pediatric in-patient and out-patient

services at the Medical Center, sending all its private and paying patients to Children's Mercy. At the time, the KU pediatrics unit had about 80 beds and the outpatient clinics had 15,000 visits a year. As many as 50 percent of the patients were non-charity cases.
- Cost of construction and operations could be reduced substantially by integrating some services and sharing others, including the power plant, laundry, cafeteria, library and nurse's residence.
- KU and Children's Mercy also could share highly specialized equipment and treatment services.
- The idea provided proximity to doctors' offices and bus lines.

He suggested that construction costs alone could save Children's Mercy as much as $750,000. He also pointed out that other cities – Boston, Cincinnati, Pittsburgh and Cleveland – had a similar arrangement. He assured Children's Mercy that the University of Kansas would not interfere with the "policies, operation and direction of Children's Mercy Hospital."

The offer was tempting, but immediately a multitude of questions arose.

Could Missouri doctors at Children's Mercy practice in Kansas? Would the state of Missouri continue to pay for state

Crippled Children's Services patients if they went to a hospital in Kansas? What would be the effect on contributions from the Kansas City, Missouri, Community Chest? How would Kansas City public officials and residents react to the hospital's moving across the state line? Would a new children's hospital on the Missouri side be needed or desired?

Children's Mercy Trustees members were also concerned that being too closely affiliated with a university would mean a loss of control over assets and operations, according to a former Children's Mercy administrator, Richard Dreher, MD.

One of the major obstacles to the KU offer was the legality of moving the hospital to a different state. Medical licensing was one issue, although the officials at KU said it could be handled easily. More difficult, apparently, was how to use the Children's Mercy endowment funds and Missouri state public funding for a Kansas-side hospital. The corporation would have to be restructured to allow it to operate in Kansas.

Recalling the question of one state or the other, Dr. Miller, the KU doctor who served as Children's Mercy medical director for several years, wrote that for some people in Kansas City it seemed that the Civil War never ended.

Whether it was pure politics, hurt feelings, remnants of the long-ago disputes or simply logistics, the move of Children's Mercy became quite complicated.

Herman Sutherland, a member of the Children's Mercy board, recalled how the hospital was reluctant to leave Missouri:

"We had a lot of legacies that depended on the fact that we were in Missouri. We were by that time beginning to build an endowment and if we moved over there, we would have been swallowed up."

Board members and representatives from KU agreed to gather additional information and continue discussions.

In the meantime, other institutions became interested in a closer relationship

*Herman Sutherland*

with Children's Mercy. St. Luke's and Research hospitals were mentioned as partners. Menorah Medical Center awaited a decision on whether to expand or perhaps close its pediatric program, depending on the future direction of Children's Mercy.

A lot was at stake.

The Kansas City Area Hospital Association, at the request of the Community Chest, formed a special subcommittee on Children's Mercy and pediatric care. Its goal was to recommend the best way to develop a "child-centered institution with particular reference to other pediatric teaching programs in the area … the care of the indigent and medically indigent and the ability of other hospitals to accept a heavy load of non-pay and part-pay cases."

The committee in late 1959 and early 1960 gathered data and discussed issues such as the future of pediatric departments in other hospitals if a new, expanded Children's Mercy were pursued.

There was universal agreement that Children's Mercy provided an essential public service in caring for indigent patients, but that something needed to be done to protect its future. By one estimate, at the current rate of deficit spending, there was only enough money to keep Children's Mercy afloat for 18 months.

## We'll move – somewhere

By 1960 the board had decided to build a new hospital "at a site yet to be selected at a cost within a limit of $5 million." But important questions remained: Where? And with whom?

The board hired a consultant to provide a detailed study of "possible future physical relationships with the Kansas University Medical Center, Research Hospital and St. Luke's Hospital." Within months, the study was complete.

Because of "legal problems associated with a Kansas site," the

> Recalling the question of one state or the other, Dr. Miller, the KU doctor who served as Children's Mercy medical director for several years, wrote that for some people in Kansas City it seemed that the Civil War never ended.

*Patients hit the books in the 1950s in the hospital's schoolroom.*

consultant said, the Site Committee of the board should consider a place on the Missouri side of the line, but still near KU Medical Center.

Initially, the hospital considered property right on State Line Road and north of 39th Street. Yet to acquire enough land for a new hospital – three acres at a minimum – 18 different property owners would have to be negotiated with. That was distasteful because expenses could run as high as $500,000 and success was uncertain. Also, there were rumblings that a new federal highway might be built down the state line, which would make access between KU and Children's Mercy difficult and dangerous.

Instead, Children's Mercy looked to nearby sites on the Missouri side.

By the end of 1961, hospital leaders expressed interest in the old Loretto Academy at 39th Street and Mercier on the Missouri side, a five- or six-block walk from KU Medical Center.

KU turned down the idea, according to board minutes, and the board discarded the Loretto proposal, which foreclosed options for moving Children's Mercy anywhere near KU Medical Center.

"Thank God we didn't do it," Herman Sutherland said later. "It wouldn't have been adequate."

In the aftermath, Dr. Miller resigned his position at Children's Mercy and returned to KU, according to board minutes.

Children's Mercy began to look more to the University of Missouri as an academic partner.

Reflecting on that time, Dr. Vernon Wilson of the University of Missouri, who had doubted the long-term feasibility of a move near KU, said "Mercy had only one other reasonable place to locate – Hospital Hill."

## Hospital Hill

Kansas City's Hospital Hill dates to the 19th century, when the City Hospital and the German Hospital, forerunner of Research Hospital, established themselves on a hillside that swept up the south side of the valley of OK Creek. In the 1900s, City Hospital moved to a new building a block south and higher on the hill, and was renamed General Hospital, the city's charity hospital. In that segregated era, it served only white patients. In 1911, General Hospital Number 2, for black Kansas Citians, was established on the site of the first City

"In 1963, residents were few and far between ... so the nurses that were at the hospital didn't have much help, particularly at night. I learned to have great respect for nurses and always valued their opinion. It is my personal opinion that one of the reasons the hospital has been so successful is because of (nurses') abilities to care for patients.

"One of the things that is often forgotten is that physicians, when they come up through medical school and they're in training, they have a lot of book learning, they know a lot of stuff from the books, but when it comes to taking care of patients, the nurses provide the most significant help to anyone."

— *V. Fred Burry, MD. With his wife, Dr. Burry would endow a chair*
*in Nursing Advocacy and Leadership in 2015.*

Hospital. The two operations remained separate until 1957, when they were combined.

As the 1960s dawned, two men worked to consolidate and improve hospital services in Kansas City. One was Homer Wadsworth of the Kansas City Association of Trusts and Foundations and the other was Nathan Stark, a vice president at Hallmark who later would become chairman of Crown Center Redevelopment Corporation. Crown Center was Hallmark's new commercial development west of General Hospital and Gillham Road.

The effort by Wadsworth and Stark, which consumed years and seemingly innumerable possibilities, was referred to typically as "Hospital Hill." The results would be visible in the medical buildings that would sprout on the hillside.

*General Hospital, a fixture on this Hospital Hill site since 1908, agreed to turn over its pediatric treatment services and patients to Children's Mercy.*

Part of their plan was to build a full medical school on the Missouri side of the state line, not just a satellite of MU in Columbia. The prospect of a new medical school and the opportunity to be close to it and General Hospital greatly interested Children's Mercy officials. As it happened, Stark also served on the Children's Mercy Central Governing Board.

"Homer Wadsworth started to work on a medical school on Hospital Hill so we got very excited about this and said we would like to be included," Herman Sutherland recalled. "They were very happy to have us."

With that, Children's Mercy in 1963 signaled its intent to move to Hospital Hill. General Hospital, which already was situated in the area, agreed to close its pediatric beds and clinics and send all its patients to Children's Mercy. More children than ever would be cared for at Children's Mercy. The two institutions also agreed that Children's Mercy would develop a full-fledged Neonatal Intensive Care Unit, relieving General of that task and enhancing the reputation of Children's Mercy as the best place for pediatric care.

In 1963, General Hospital, Children's Mercy and the University of Missouri signed an agreement "in their concern for excellence in patient care, medical education and research." The same year, MU took control of the private, financially strapped University of Kansas City and made it the University of Missouri-Kansas City. It would be several years before a UMKC medical school would be established, but the idea was for it, too, to occupy a site on Hospital Hill. The concept of that area as the centerpiece of public health care in Kansas City was well underway.

Children's Mercy agreed to build its new facility adjacent to General Hospital and the die was cast: Children's Mercy would leave Independence Avenue and move to Hospital Hill and a more central location in the sprawling city.

"Basically, that was … the beginning of the new Children's Mercy, a new era that nobody fully realized at the time," recalled V. Fred Burry, MD. Dr. Burry joined

# The stars came calling

*Like Babe Ruth and Lou Gehrig in the 1920s, celebrities of the 1950s and 1960s dropped in to say hello to patients of Children's Mercy.*

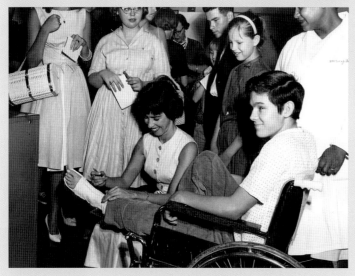

*Early 1950s television made big stars of William Boyd, above, who played "Hopalong Cassidy" and of Duncan Renaldo and Leo Carillo, top left, known for their portrayals of the Cisco Kid and Pancho.*

*Comedienne Carol Burnett drew a crowd of fans. One autograph decorated a patient's cast.*

*Clayton Moore, "The Lone Ranger."*

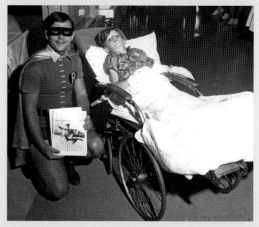

*Chiefs quarterback Len Dawson dropped in.*

*Characters from "Winnie the Pooh."*

*Burt Ward played Robin, Batman's sidekick.*

FOR ALL CHILDREN EVERYWHERE

the medical staff in 1963 and served until his retirement as executive medical director in June 2010.

It would be 1971 before a medical school would be in place on Hospital Hill, but once it was, the UMKC School of Medicine joined the Dental School, Western Missouri Mental Health, General Hospital and Children's Mercy. In 1976, General Hospital would get its own new building and a new name: Truman Medical Center. By the 21st century, the gleaming medical complex of Hospital Hill would stand as a testament to a pioneering, supportive spirit in Kansas City.

## Change and the 1960s

The politicking and discussions about the future location and direction of the hospital consumed time and effort, yet Children's Mercy continued to care for children in a world of changing dynamics.

With the dawn of the 1960s came concern about a nationwide shortage of doctors. In 1963, Congress responded, passing the Health Professions Educational Assistance Act to increase the number of medical students. Other federal appropriations in the 1960s and 1970s assisted the development of new medical schools, such as the one at the University of Missouri-Kansas City.

The new decade also brought rapid specialization in medicine. The share of doctors reporting themselves as full-time specialists increased from 55 percent in 1960 to 69 percent in 1970. As Children's Mercy worked to attract talented doctors and faculty, it found physicians flocking to the specialty of pediatrics and its associated subspecialties, such as pediatric cardiology.

The role of nurses also was evolving. Student nurses, supervised by staff nurses and a head nurse for each unit, continued to provide the majority of the care at least through the mid-1950s.

But just as other aspects of the hospital – administration, medical staff, facilities – needed to be updated, so did the role of nurses. New demands were evolving in patient care. Advancing technologies required new training, specialization and a team approach between nurses and doctors.

In the 1960s, Children's Mercy was the first hospital in Kansas City to adopt the new positions of clinical nurse specialists, which required increased training.

The drive for even greater specialization – nurses for neonatal care, for emergency care, for cardiac care – continued. In years to come, the hospital would be the first in Kansas or Missouri to win Magnet Designation by the American Nurse Credentialing Center for nursing and patient care quality.

## Gifts small and large

The backing of the community – in particular the financial supporters of Children's Mercy – remained essential in those times of "patience and optimism," the late '50s and much of the 1960s, according to William Brown, chairman of the Site Committee of the Central Governing Board.

"Mercy's friends year after year have given the hospital equipment and contributed labor and materials for improvements to wards and suites," wrote Roger Swanson in his 1961 *History of Children's Mercy*. "How long the list is!"

In the decades after World War II, thousands of clubs in Kansas City and surrounding communities continued to send in the earnings from their raffles, garage sales and other fundraisers. Western Auto and Hallmark Cards employees helped with "extensive remodeling" at the Independence Avenue hospital. Swanson credited the auxiliary of the Veterans of Foreign Wars with a donation of $70,000 toward cancer research. The Kansas City Open Golf tournament contributed $40,000 in proceeds over several years in the 1950s. The Community Chest, today's United Way, became essential. Often in times of imminent hardship for the hospital it came to the rescue with loans or new grants. Just as it has in all the years since, the hospital continued to stress the importance of all gifts, small and large.

"How, for example, can the good and loyal work of Mercy's many employees go unheralded?" Swanson wrote. "Mercy workers loved Mercy. Often they served the children's hospital at a sacrifice in pay. Their devotion to sick children is an inspiration."

Eric Jones, hospital administrator in parts of the 1960s and 1970s, said the staff at Independence Avenue "was completely one family. Everyone looked out for one another."

Volunteers also helped lift the spirits of children. Hallmark employees, and others, participated in holiday

*A bronze reproduction of the Wild Boar of Florence sits on the Country Club Plaza as a good-luck charm and collection slot for contributions to Children's Mercy. In 1965, when it was installed, appreciative onlookers gave it a once-over – more than once.*

parties for the children. Celebrities, in town for a concert, play or other performance regularly stopped by. The list was long, including stars of television and stage such as Clayton Moore of "The Lone Ranger," Duncan Renaldo and Leo Carillo of "The Cisco Kid," Carol Burnett, Ted Mack, Bob Hope and Mary Martin, and sports stars such as Ted Williams and Mickey Mantle.

The Beatles didn't visit the hospital but they did benefit Children's Mercy. Charles O. Finley, the owner of the Kansas City Athletics and a promoter's promoter, brought the Fab Four to play at Kansas City Municipal Stadium in 1964. In

a visit to the hospital to distribute baseballs, bats and plastic fireman's hats left over from a fireman's day promotion at the ballpark, Finley said that, if the Beatles' concert sold out, he would donate $100,000 to Children's Mercy. There were about 40,000 tickets for the show, costing $4.50 and up. Hard as it may be to believe today, the show did not sell out and the concert was not a financial success for Finley. He paid the Beatles $150,000 (more than $1 million in 2016 dollars) for the 31-minute performance. He did, however, donate $25,000 to the hospital.

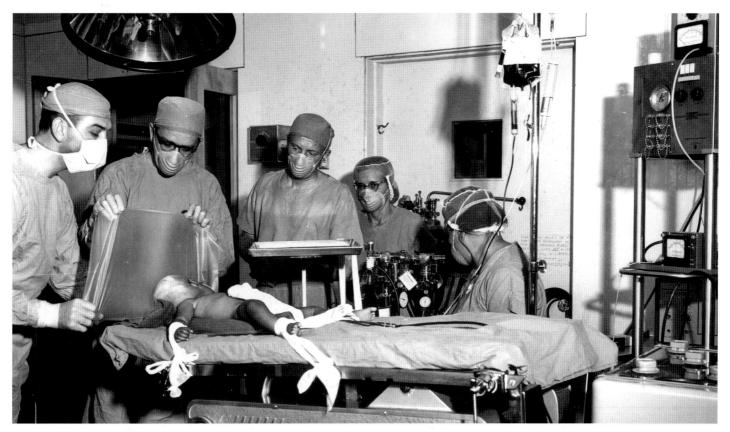

*Surgeons and nurses at work in the hospital on Independence Avenue in the middle 1960s.*

## 'No finer focal point'

That money, and much more, was needed to make the move to Hospital Hill. Estimates of construction costs alone reached $4 million.

By 1964, the community was rallying around.

"The decision to relocate on Hospital Hill was based on sound financial considerations," the *Kansas City Star* wrote. "The children of Western Missouri and Metropolitan Kansas City have a tremendous stake in the fund drive to build a new Mercy Hospital … the new hospital will be on a scale large enough (designed for 75,000 outpatient visits a year and with 115 beds) to support a children's medical center of quality comparable to the finest in the United States. The increased number of cases, both bed and outpatient, will permit an expanded teaching program. The potential for research will be substantially increased."

The *Star* and others were quick to praise the University of Kansas for its help with Mercy during a difficult time. KU

indicated it would continue to send its students to Mercy, "contingent on the quality of the Mercy staff recruited with the aid of the University of Missouri."

"It is extremely important to keep a strong working arrangement with the University of Kansas," the *Star* editorialized. "KU has made a tremendous contribution to Mercy in recent years and has the students for the essential training program. For the big job ahead, there could be no finer focal point than Mercy hospital."

Former President Harry S. Truman and Joyce C. Hall of Hallmark Cards were co-chairs of the committee to raise money for hospital construction. This was the first major, public role in Children's Mercy for the Hall family, but it surely would not be the last. In 1963, Hallmark pledged $500,000 to the cause, challenging others to raise the remainder. At the time, it was the largest gift ever to a Kansas City charity.

The money, Hall said, was to ensure that Children's Mercy could support a "truly top medical staff."

Sale of the Independence Avenue hospital would help

pay for the new facility, and there were hopes of federal help through the Hill-Burton Act for new hospital construction.

Plans progressed more slowly than anticipated. The 1964 Children's Mercy Annual Report said the move from Independence Avenue to Hospital Hill was expected in two years. By the time the 1965 Annual Report was published, ground was just being cleared and the campaign had raised only $2 million. Meanwhile, costs increased. By the end of construction in 1970, they would rise from $4 million to about $7 million.

Progress also moved slowly with the entire Hospital Hill project. Questions arose over land acquisition and financing; complicating matters were the multiple partners involved, both public and private. Plans for the building evolved, too.

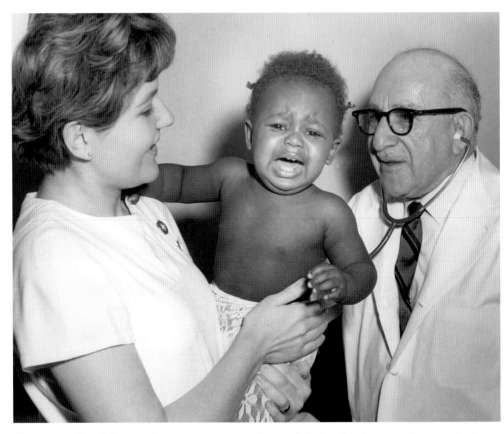

*One patient found the examination experience a bit overwhelming despite a nurse's attempts at reassurance. Two other patients – Laurie Blair and Jyme Noble – had a better time.*

Children's Mercy now planned a five-story structure with 150 beds on Gillham Road between 24th and 25th streets, and it anticipated 100,000 outpatient visits.

"One hundred of the new beds will be for patients needing acute intensive care," said a statement from John A. Kroh, the real estate executive who was chairman of the Children's Mercy building committee. "There will be 25 convalescent beds and 25 beds devoted to a 'motel' within the hospital."

Groundbreaking did not occur in 1966 as anticipated. Dr. Ned Smull, the hospital director, blamed unforeseen problems, among them a delay in getting federal Hill-Burton funds at a time when national resources were being diverted to new programs like Medicaid and the expanding Vietnam War.

Meanwhile, a growing number of patients and their needs continued to put pressure on the Independence Avenue hospital and staff. The Crippled Children's Nursery School

moved into the hospital in 1965 and remained a part of Children's Mercy until the 1990s.

Space needs forced the hospital to construct a 10,000-square-foot concrete block building between the Independence Avenue main building and nurses' home for a new clinic and accounting and records offices. Dr. Smull gave assurances that the new building would not affect plans for the new hospital on Hospital Hill.

"We have been expanding our services and badly needed additional room," he said. "We simply could not wait until the new hospital was finished."

In 1967, a grant from the Children's Bureau of the federal Department of Health, Education and Welfare made possible the Children and Youth Project, which allowed the hospital to expand services outside its walls. Children's Mercy worked with primary-care medical clinics. The program, a part of President Lyndon B. Johnson's Great Society effort, brought together various disciplines including social work, nutrition and nursing to improve the health of children and youth from poor families.

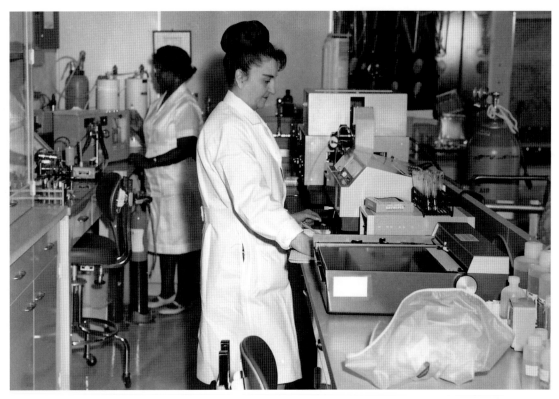

*Laboratory of Dr. Stanley Hellerstein, an expert in pediatric metabolism.*

## On a wave of optimism

In the same years Children's Mercy strove to develop its new home on Hospital Hill, Kansas City was riding a wave of optimism and good economic times. In 1966, voters approved plans for Kansas City International Airport. A year later, Hallmark announced its plans for Crown Center adjacent to the fledgling Hospital Hill development. And in 1968, ground was broken on the Harry S. Truman Sports Complex, which in the early 1970s would become home of the Kansas City Chiefs and Royals.

Amid all that, HEW in 1967 approved a grant of $1.3 million for the construction of the new Children's Mercy.

"It is one of the final steps that will allow us to go ahead," Dr. Smull said. At the time, the hospital was in the process of purchasing 4.5 acres of land from the Land Clearance for Redevelopment Authority, a co-owner of the urban renewal project of Hospital Hill.

*The Kansas City Star* proclaimed that the call for bids was near and that building could, finally, begin in late fall.

It could not happen soon enough. Conditions at the hospital on Independence Avenue were deteriorating. Staff reported regular sightings of mice and rats around the building. One nurse said before going out to the porch to retrieve oxygen tanks, staffers made as much noise as possible to scare the critters away. The neighborhood was deteriorating. When urban rioting broke out in spring 1968, staff reported hearing gunfire nearby. Workers were cautioned not to go outside the hospital after dark.

Obviously, the time for a move was at hand. The community of supporters had come through, once again, with the finances necessary to support the new dream. The educational program had been resurrected with the help of KU and now Missouri was taking the lead, with a new Kansas City-based medical school on the horizon.

It was becoming easier to recruit medical staff who wanted to be part of a new program whose leaders showed the vision "to build the finest children's medical center in the

*Hospital officials and supporters gathered at Hospital Hill on a chilly day in 1968 to join in the official groundbreaking ceremony. It marked the kickoff of construction for the hospital building that would still stand, much enlarged, in the 21st century. Below, the proposed hospital building as depicted in an architect's rendering.*

middle west."

Children's Mercy cards for the 1967 holiday season bore a drawing of the new hospital. Herman Sutherland, then chairman of the Central Governing Board, wrote a note inside one: "It's been a hard fight, but worth it. Now here we go."

Ground would be broken in the spring 1968. Brighter days were ahead.

FOR ALL CHILDREN EVERYWHERE

*The new structure took shape in the late 1960s. Because of a three-month citywide building strike and other delays, it would not be ready for occupancy until December 1970.*

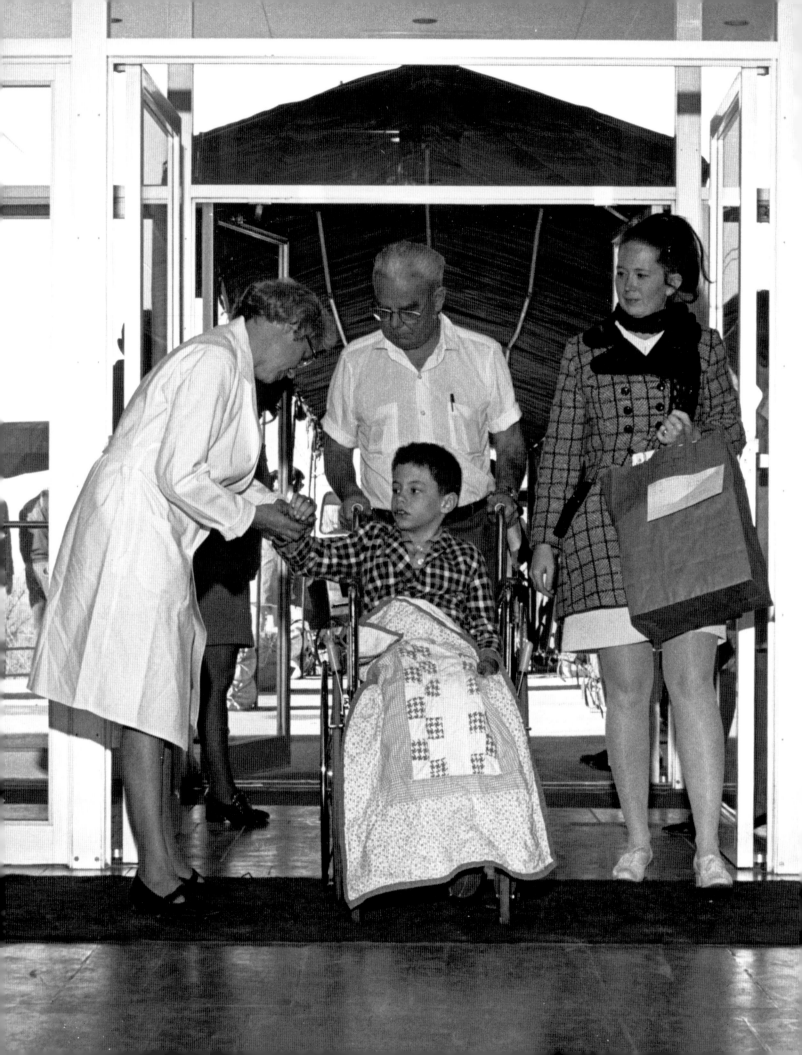

# MID-LIFE CHALLENGES AND OPPORTUNITIES

*"Coming together is a beginning. Keeping together is progress. Working together is success."*

— Henry Ford

America was at a crossroads at the dawn of the 1970s. Coming out of a decade of unprecedented social change, the country was in turmoil. Quarreling raged over the war in Vietnam and riots over race relations destroyed whole neighborhoods in some cities. Increases in government spending for the war and social programs caused concern, or anger, among many people. How could America possibly live through it all?

Yet despite the forces pulling the country apart, in the heartland of America an unmistakable resilience survived. There were riots here, too, and protests about the war. But as painful as they were, they did not completely

*Facing page: Checking into a new world, a young Children's Mercy patient passed through the doorway of the just-finished Hospital Hill building on moving day, December 17, 1970. Above: the sparkling new structure.*

discourage Kansas City. Instead the metropolitan area entered an era of remarkable optimism and growth.

In the late 1960s, planning got underway for a new airport and a pioneering two-stadium sports complex for the city's new professional baseball team and the NFL's Chiefs. Hallmark transformed the old, sign-covered hillside across from Union Station into an urban oasis called Crown Center. In the West Bottoms, there was talk of a new, architecturally unique arena, which would become home to professional basketball and hockey, concerts and rodeos. New homes sprouted in the suburbs as more and more people sought a piece of the American Dream.

Growth and change also were evident on Hospital Hill. After years of planning, fundraising, land acquisition and construction delays, the Hill was transformed into a home for public health services for all Kansas Citians, young and old.

As the 1970s dawned, Children's Mercy Hospital prepared to greet its first patients at a brand new place, 2401 Gillham Road, in the heart of Hospital Hill.

A song from the musical "Oklahoma" proclaimed, "Everything's Up to Date in Kansas City." In 1970, everything seemed to be. Powerful forces in the city came together, bringing both opportunities and challenges. As the years went by, events would test that togetherness and that march toward success.

## "We thought we were living in heaven"

For Children's Mercy, the first moving day in more than five decades finally arrived December 17, 1970. That cold morning must have seemed like an early Christmas for patients, parents and staff.

A year of planning had gone in to the transfer of people and equipment safely and efficiently from the hospital's old place on Independence Avenue to its new home on Hospital Hill. The hope had been for a springtime move, but construction was delayed at least three months by a citywide building strike. So it was not until a dreary near-winter Thursday with temperatures below freezing that the sparkling, state-of-the-art, five-story Children's Mercy Hospital opened for business. Planners called the move "Operation Santa Claus."

At 7 a.m. the emergency room at the old building on Independence Avenue closed. At the same moment the emergency room on Hospital Hill officially opened its doors.

Thirty-nine patients had to be moved that morning from the old hospital to the new. They represented a wide variety of conditions: babies recovering from premature birth, surgery and respiratory distress; burn victims; children with meningitis and chicken pox; post-surgery patients; at least one child with a breathing tube; and others on intravenous nutrition.

*A Kansas City motorcycle policeman escorted one of a series of ambulances and other vehicles carrying patients from the old hospital on Independence Avenue.*

Assisting were four field ambulances on loan from Richards-Gebaur Air Force Base and outfitted with cribs, oxygen and electricity. Each ambulance moved one child at a time, accompanied by a nurse and doctor and making as many trips as needed. Other staff stood by at both old and new hospitals.

Two mini-buses carried ambulatory patients. Nurses carried babies. At least one sporty car, a GTO with its top down, was put into service to move a tall anesthesia machine. As much equipment as possible had been moved in advance.

Kansas City police provided escorts and members of the local Jayhawk Amateur Radio Club and Civil Defense of Kansas City, Kansas, furnished operators and equipment for radio communication between the command post for dismissals on Independence Avenue and the command post for admissions on Hospital Hill.

The move of patients began precisely at 9 a.m. and finished 1 hour and 59 minutes later. Premature babies were taken to the third floor of the new building. Older children in critical condition went to the Intensive Care Unit on the fifth floor, where there was also a burn unit. Patients requiring isolation went to the fourth floor.

Fifty-five patients who could be dismissed from the old hospital without jeopardizing their care went home temporarily.

Outpatient clinics moved not long afterward, opening for business at the new hospital on Monday morning, December 28. That same day, the first surgery in the new operating rooms took place.

The chair of the hospital's Disaster Planning Committee, George W. Wise, MD, said patients were "in no way affected by the transition."

"This was an excellent trial in the movement and flow of critically ill children on a large-scale basis," he wrote. He added one last item of interest: "On this date,

## Out of the old...

*For more than five decades, this light-filled ward bustled with young patients. On December 17, 1970, its beds and equipment stood empty and dismantled and its blinds were drawn. In the hallways nurses, doctors and incubators prepared for their final hours in the old hospital. At 9 a.m. sharp, the first patient left the Independence Avenue location on the way to Hospital Hill.*

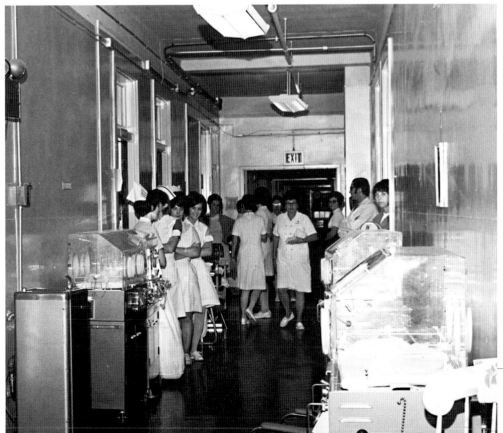

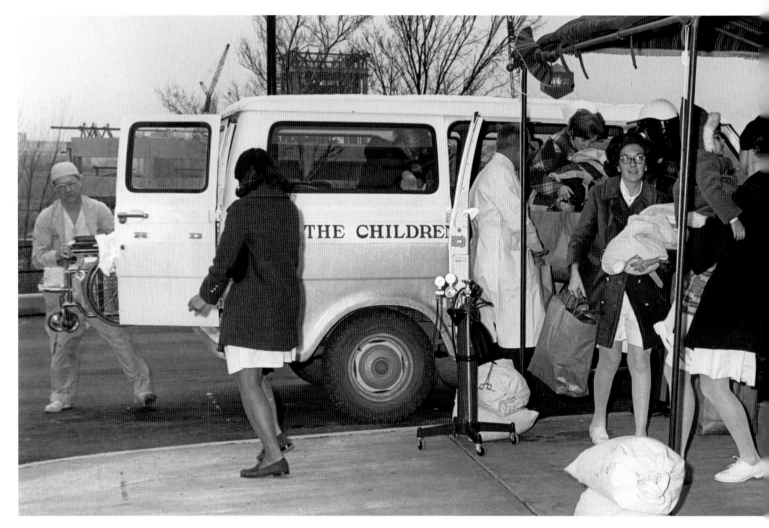

*At the new entrance on Hospital Hill, ambulances and various other conveyances finished the trip from the old hospital. They delivered patients, wheelchairs, blankets and caregivers – and accomplished the task in less than two hours.*

one of the patients moved to the new hospital had the same name (slightly different spelling) as the founder, Katherine Richardson."

Surely, Alice Berry Graham and Katharine Berry Richardson, the sisters who started Children's Mercy on its journey, would have been pleased with the new home and the expanded mission to care for even more children.

For the staff at Children's Mercy, Hospital Hill was perhaps the best present ever. Equipment and people had plenty of room. Wall outlets delivered oxygen. A cafeteria operated on site. Unlike the Independence Avenue building, paint wasn't peeling.

"We thought we were living in heaven," one nurse said.

The new building was an important part of the transition from a predominantly charity hospital. It provided more room for more patients and more attractive conditions than the run-down building it replaced.

Yet the move alone could not fulfill the vision for Children's Mercy that had taken shape in the 1950s: to become the complete pediatric medical center for all children in the region.

## "The most logical place" for children's surgery

In the early 1970s, every hospital in Kansas City had a unit where local pediatricians could send their patients for treatment. Those hospitals claimed most of the private patients

## ...and into the new

*As a film camera rolled, ambulance attendants and hospital employees lifted bedridden patients from carriers.*

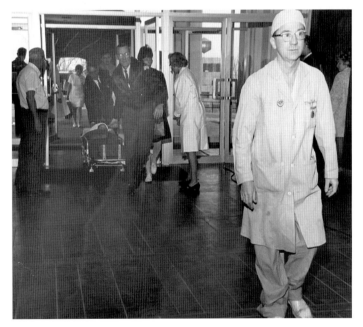

*Patients who could walk exited vans for their first look at their new hospital, left. Patients who could not, above, were wheeled through the glass-door entrance, greeted by Dr. Ruth Yohe, in white coat, and past the command center to their rooms. Dr. Elwyn Brown, foreground, led the way.*

*The new hospital's busy operating room required tight scheduling. Doctors Raymond Amoury, left, and J. Patrick Murphy checked the board.*

– children whose families had medical insurance or could afford to pay for treatment on their own. Exceptions occurred when a child's condition required the specialists available only at Children's Mercy, according to Dr. Keith Ashcraft, a former surgeon-in-chief at Children's Mercy.

Dr. Thomas Holder served both kinds of patients, charity and paying. At the time, he was the best-trained pediatric surgeon in Kansas City.

As a volunteer at Children's Mercy, Dr. Holder treated non-paying patients. For paying patients, most of his work took place across the state line at the University of Kansas Medical Center. Most private heart-surgery patients, Dr. Ashcraft recalled, were referred either to Dr. Holder at KU or to the Mayo Clinic.

When a new chief of thoracic surgery came to KU,

Dr. Ashcraft continued, he limited Dr. Holder's work, so Dr. Holder decided to leave Kansas City. In an effort to keep the respected surgeon in town, local pediatricians assured him that they would refer cardiac and other surgery patients to him if he stayed. But they had a condition.

They wanted their patients to be treated in hospitals other than Children's Mercy, because many patients' families still perceived it as a charity hospital.

Dr. Holder, however, knew that Children's Mercy had on its staff a pediatric anesthesiologist and other specialists committed to caring for children.

"This was a place where great strides were being made in anesthesiology and cardiology," Dr. Ashcraft recalled, "which made it the most logical place for children's surgery to be done."

Those points helped persuade private pediatricians that children benefited from the expertise available at Children's Mercy. In turn, Dr. Ashcraft said, private pediatricians could use the information to change parents' minds about the hospital.

In the end, Dr. Holder decided to stay. With Dr. Ashcraft as his partner, he began doing his pediatric surgery at Children's Mercy.

Performing other surgeries – for example, tonsillectomies and hernia repair – in a single place made more efficient use of surgeons' time. Drs. Holder and Ashcraft wanted to do all children's surgeries at Children's Mercy.

"When everyone understood that we treated everybody the same, if they were a private patient or a charity case, local attitudes on the part of pediatricians and parents changed a lot," Dr. Ashcraft said. "We started taking more and more patients at Mercy and word got around that Mercy was the place to go. We began to develop different (pediatric specialty) sections that all worked together to make it better. It became a major children's hospital instead of a charity place."

## Specialties and sub-specialties

To continue the transformation, Children's Mercy needed to keep enlarging the medical staff and medical offerings.

In the 1970s specialized medicine expanded greatly, spurred by a wave of new doctors. That resulted from an effort by the federal government in the 1960s to subsidize medical schools, a response to concerns about a shortage of doctors nationwide. At the same time, more foreign-trained doctors were allowed to move to and practice in the United States.

Pediatrics is a specialty all its own. In addition, there are sub-specialists, such as pediatric cardiologists, who are experts in both kids and hearts. It was in sub-specialties like those that Children's Mercy needed to establish itself if it was to become a center for pediatric medicine.

"We said, 'Let's take it up a notch,'" said Charles Roberts, MD, who joined the staff in 1980 and in 2010 became Executive Medical Director. "Let's be loved and recognized for being excellent at caring for all kids in Kansas City who need specialized care so they don't have to leave the community. That took a chance, but it was the right thing to do."

When Children's Mercy hired Dr. Roberts, he was

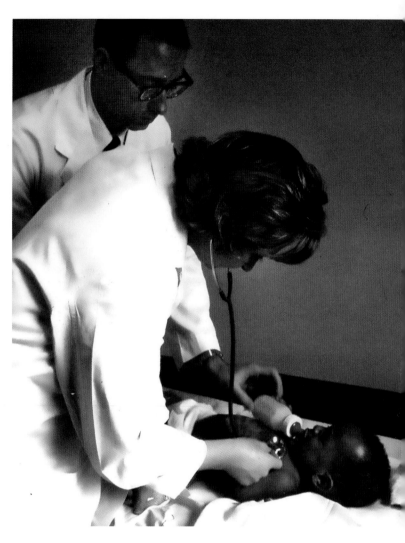

*Simultaneously feeding and checking the heart, clinic doctors attended to an infant with respiratory distress syndrome.*

the first pediatric gastroenterologist in the region. At the time, there was debate on the Children's Mercy medical staff whether there would be enough patients to keep him busy. There were. By 2016, the hospital had 23 pediatric gastroenterologists.

"In GI and lots of other specialties, we've gone from 'You're specialized in GI or cardiology,' to 'You're sub-sub-specialized'," Dr. Roberts said. "So the definition of comprehensive has changed from, 'Do you have someone in each of these specialties?' to 'Can you cover all the sub-sub specialties within those?'

"The growth has continued through today."

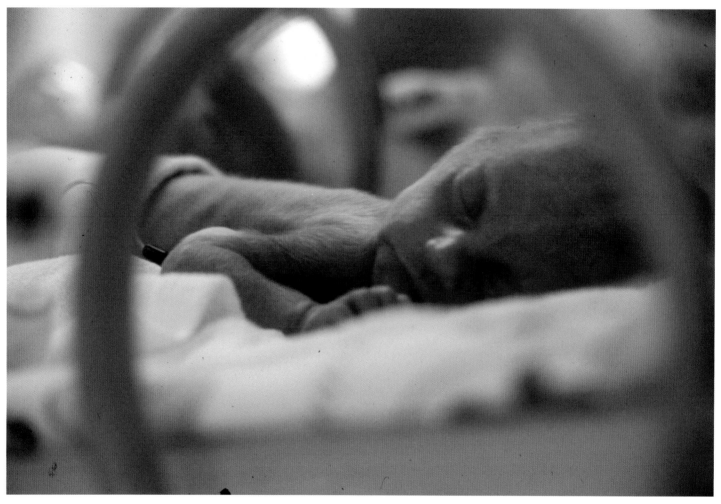

*Inside an isolette, a premature infant slept.*

Fortunately, by the time the new hospital was ready for more patients a strong foundation existed. Dr. Ned Smull, the hospital director from 1963 to 1978 and chairman of pediatrics, had begun attracting top-quality doctors who could fuel growth in the areas of medicine, education and research.

"Ned Smull was a major influence in the whole operation," said Dr. V. Fred Burry, who served on the medical staff for nearly four decades. "He knew a lot of people and when he wanted something badly enough he seemed to be able to find a way to do it."

The Board of Trustees, after Dr. Smull retired, also gave him credit, saying, "It was Dr. Smull's vision and dedication that challenged the community into action."

The education program received a boost when the University of Missouri-Kansas City School of Medicine was

established. University officials announced the decision to create the school on Hospital Hill in 1971, and the dedication took place in October 1974. Dr. Herb Wenner, a well-established infectious-disease specialist who joined Children's Mercy in 1968, was instrumental in writing the pediatric curriculum for UMKC's new, six-year, combined baccalaureate and MD program.

The school was another piece in the firm foundation being planted on Hospital Hill.

"Gradually, because of the people that were hired in the '70s, things really began to change," Dr. Burry said. "We became a major competitor in the pediatric world with KU, and I suspect to some degree with Mizzou, but Mizzou primarily had everything east of Sedalia."

Children's Mercy also grew because doctors and nurses

worked outside its walls. As early as 1964, and continuing into the 21st century, Children's Mercy provided doctors for public health clinics such as the Richard Cabot Clinic on the city's West Side, or the Operation Breakthrough child care center on the East Side. The hospital also worked with the Kansas City Health Department and the juvenile justice system.

The Children and Youth Project, made possible by a federal grant, continued to fuel growth in services. Among them were care of high-risk infants and their mothers, studies of genetics, an expanded immunization program and introduction of an adolescent clinic – the first Children's Mercy clinic outside the hospital. Federal contributions for the project diminished and eventually ended by the 1980s, but the programs spawned by the Children and Youth Project remained intact or expanded in the years to come.

## "We can do more for these babies"

The new hospital building also opened the door for a new era in care for patients less than 1 year old. The old hospital on Independence Avenue treated a few, but conditions there were far from satisfactory. With the move to Hospital Hill more space opened up for these infants, and care could be coordinated with obstetricians at General Hospital next door.

Robert T. Hall, MD, joined the staff in 1972 as the chief of neonatology and set out to establish Children's Mercy as *the* place in the region for premature infants.

"There was something in the atmosphere at Children's

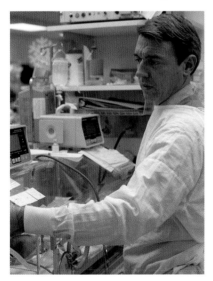

*Dr. Robert Hall*

Mercy that grabbed me," Dr. Hall said in 2015. "I had dreamed of being a small-town general practitioner, but the specialties were developing and … I was inspired to be a neonatologist."

Dr. Hall was the driving force behind development of Children's Mercy as a regional referral center for premature infants.

POISON PREVENTION WEEK

*In the 1970s Children's Mercy developed a computerized poison index, left, and promoted anti-poison displays such as a wall of student art, above.*

A colleague, Michael Sheehan, MD, who started his 41st year at Children's Mercy in 2016, said Dr. Hall knew how to work well with people.

"He could make things happen," Dr. Sheehan said. "He built the Neonatal Intensive Care Unit from nothing."

The expansion was sparked by watching too many newborns come to Children's Mercy too late.

"These babies would arrive from these small communities … at the emergency room door with the fire department and the babies would be dead," recalled Betty Boyd, a nurse who joined Children's Mercy in 1964 and would volunteer at the hospital into the 21st century. "Dr. Hall and I would look and talk and say: Something has to be done about this. We can do more for these babies."

First, other hospitals and doctors had to agree to send critically ill children to Children's Mercy and to do it before it was too late. Dr. Hall visited hospitals inside and outside the Kansas City metropolitan area, explaining the capabilities of Children's Mercy.

On one occasion, he was called to a large Kansas City

*At the moment, all eyes were on patient Pamela Whitley. The doctors, from left: Raymond Anderson, Ned Smull, George Wise and Clark Seely.*

Hall persuaded a local ambulance company to develop an ambulance from a van so that the vehicle would be large enough for a baby in an incubator and for nurses or doctors to care for the child. The improved vehicle also would have electric power for medical equipment. The company produced a prototype that became the first ambulance anywhere capable of transporting a baby in an isolette.

"This made a huge difference in our ability to transport these babies," Dr. Hall said. "It saved lives."

After a while, Children's Mercy acquired its own ambulances. Both had kangaroos painted on the side, and were known as Pocket One and Pocket Two. They were the forerunners of Children's Mercy Critical Care Transport, which eventually would operate as mobile intensive-care units by ground and air. By 2016, teams would safely transport an average of 400 children a month to Children's Mercy, some from across the United States and even foreign countries.

hospital to see a sick newborn.

"The baby badly needed help," he said. "Transferring that baby to Children's Mercy would be a big step. They had to understand we would take good care of 'their' baby – better care than they were capable of. I was able to convince them.

"The word got out that Children's Mercy could better handle the difficult cases and we started getting other consults. Next we worked with other hospitals so that we got called early in the process and could be there for the delivery."

For Dr. Hall, that meant many late nights and early mornings assisting at hospitals all around town. Eventually, other hospitals routinely asked Children's Mercy to attend some high-risk births so a neonatal expert would be on hand at the time of delivery. By 2016, two-thirds of patients referred to the Children's Mercy intensive-care nursery would be from hospitals that had Children's Mercy neonatologists present at birth.

Once other hospitals agreed that Children's Mercy was the right place for critically ill infants, there remained another hurdle: getting them to the hospital.

### Advances in transport

In the 1970s, most ambulances were no taller than standard station wagons, and they had no electricity. Dr.

Even in the new building, it did not take long for space to become a problem. The nursery on the third floor of the new hospital was designed for a dozen beds, but soon had to be expanded to 23. Isolettes stood in parallel rows about three feet apart in an open room with just enough space between them for a single rocking chair for a parent. When doctors or nurses needed to care for a baby in a neighboring bed, isolettes and the babies inside them had to be moved out of the way. Many parents avoided the unit because it was so crowded.

Of all pediatric services, neonatology showed the greatest advances in the 1970s and '80s. In that time, the nationwide mortality rate for newborns weighing two to five pounds dropped dramatically. By 1982, eighty-five percent of

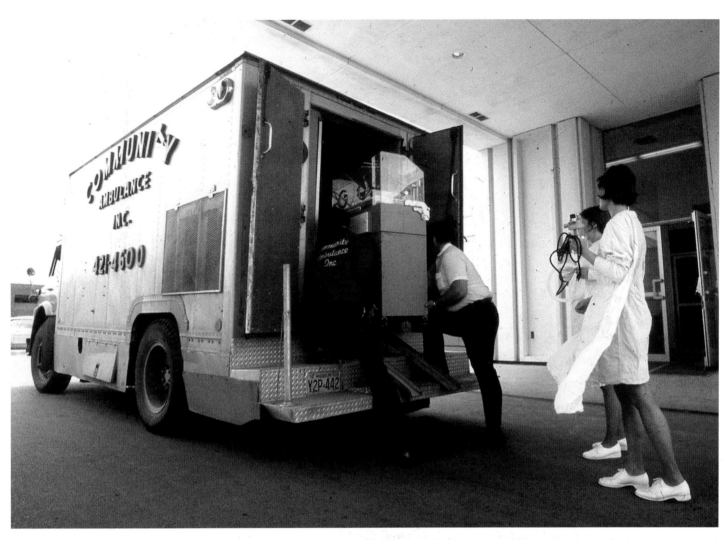

At the request of the hospital, privately owned Community Ambulance Co. assembled a then-novel ambulance big enough for doctors, nurses and a patient in a bulky incubator. Also, the company wired the ambulance for full electrical power. On this day in 1974, the ambulance delivered its patient to waiting nurses at Children's Mercy.

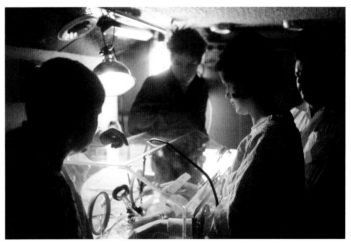

Inside the ambulance, caregivers had enough headroom to stand.

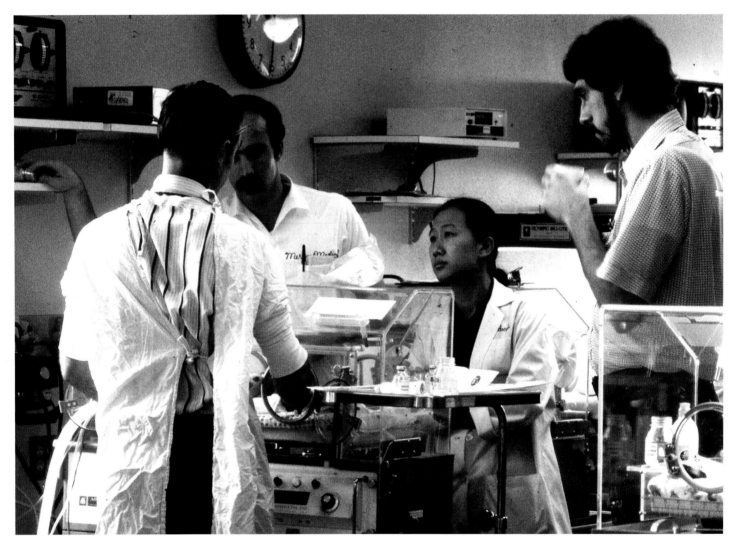

*Conferences are a constant in hospitals. In the 1970s, caregivers huddled over an isolette.*

those babies survived and went on to live healthy, normal lives.

In his early years, Dr. Sheehan recalled, "We had months in the NICU when half the babies died." From the 1970s to the 2010s, however, the survival rates for babies at two and one-half pounds, or 1,000 grams, rose from 10 percent to 90 percent.

## More and better treatments

Cardiology and cancer programs at Children's Mercy became other early leaders in its transformation into a comprehensive medical center.

The Children's Cardiac Center – which, as the Children's Convalescent Center, had moved in 1961 from its home on Warwick Avenue to Children's Mercy – flourished with the hiring of Dr. Joseph Sasano in the mid-1960s. Dr. Sasano attracted new residents and fellows to care for children with heart conditions. When Dr. Sasano left in 1974, one of his fellows, Dr. R. Gowdamarajan, was put in charge.

Dr. Rajan, as he was known, worked at Children's Mercy for decades, retiring as section chief, but remaining as a staff cardiologist into the 2010s. Dr. Holder led the surgery section of the heart program and attracted a cadre of talented cardiac surgeons.

More than once the heart program benefitted from The Children's Mercy Golf Classic, hosted by Tom Watson from 1980 to 2005.

The first specialized care for cancer patients became available with the hiring of Dr. Eugene C. Beatty Jr. When he started his clinic in 1969, the number of patients was so small it required the clinic to operate only one-half day a week. As word spread of the excellent care available at Children's Mercy, demand grew. At the same time, cancer treatment improved and became more specialized, requiring comprehensive follow-up and management. By 1974, the clinic was operating one full day a week and caring for about 50 patients a year. By 2010, that number would grow to about 2,000 patients a year, with 20 cancer specialist physicians and clinics five days a week.

In 1980, hematology-oncology was recognized as a section in the Department of Pediatrics. Dr. Donald Forgue was appointed as its first chief. In the 21st century, the section would be a partner in the National Cancer Institute's designated center at the University of Kansas Cancer Center. That designation signified excellence in cancer research. It made Children's Mercy even more attractive as a destination for cancer patients and would serve as a cornerstone of the hospital's status as a comprehensive pediatric medical center.

Other specialties developed in the 1970s and '80s. According to the 1983 annual report, Children's Mercy built the country's first comprehensive neurosciences department, which combined efforts of neurology, child development, speech and hearing, genetics and child psychiatry.

In addition, Children's Mercy began the first emergency-medicine fellowship program in the country. It built a high-caliber, full-time emergency staff after years of relying primarily on local pediatricians and residents.

In the 1980s, the emergency room was a "wide-open free-for-all," according to Jane Knapp, MD, who was the first fellow recruited by Emergency Medicine Director Bill Anderson, MD.

"It was already the largest emergency room in Kansas City (handling 30,000 to 40,000 visits a year) and it operated out of much, much smaller areas than it does today," said Dr. Knapp, who retired as director of Graduate Medical Education at Children's Mercy in 2016. "There wasn't security, the doors were wide open and people passed freely back and forth.

"The triage area was open. Sometimes parents would pass sick babies across the desk to a ward clerk to take care of; it was a busy place."

At the end of her fellowship, Dr. Knapp became head of the Emergency Department. She helped establish it as one of the leading programs in the country and the only pediatric trauma center in the region. She also worked to implement standards for Pediatric Advanced Life Support, or PALS. Through the involvement of Jim Glenski, MD; Pete Mestad, MD, and Bob Binda, MD – all members of the Children's Mercy Anesthesia Department – the hospital served as one of three national pilot sites for the program. PALS courses would continue to train hundreds of health care professionals inside and outside Children's Mercy each year.

The Emergency Room typically introduces large numbers of children and families to Children's Mercy. Some

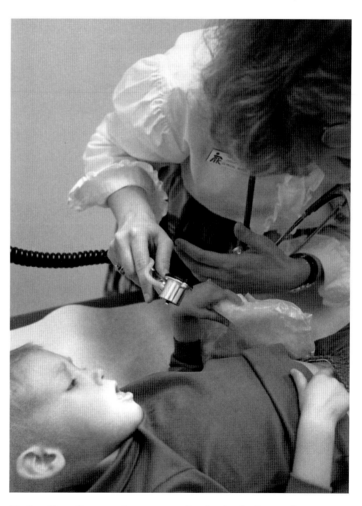

*Patient Peter Soper underwent examination in the hematology-oncology unit.*

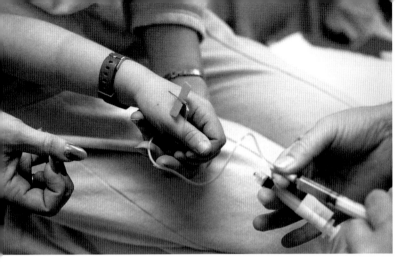

*Chemotherapy under way.*

don't need full emergency care, but because the Emergency Room is open around the clock, many families use it as a medical safety net.

"The Emergency Department serves a wide purpose," Dr. Knapp said. "Some people think of an emergency as anything that a parent thinks their child needs to be seen for. The first concern is and always will be, 'Let's see the child and find out what's wrong with them and do the best we can.' "

## Lifelong learners

Children's Mercy was successful in recruiting a talented medical, nursing and allied health staff because it was different from other hospitals in town, according to Dr. Richard Dreher, who began seeing patients at Children's Mercy in 1968 and who served as hospital administrator from 1978 to 1986.

"It was not too difficult to see what we were doing at Children's Mercy Hospital, building a new medical center, and the doctors wanted to be a part of it," he said in 2015.

Many of the kinds of doctors sought by Children's Mercy worked at large, research-oriented institutions affiliated with universities in other cities.

"One of the ways we were successful in recruiting," Dr. Dreher recalled, "is that we understood a little bit about working at universities: it's much more rigid and confining. Here, (the doctors) had a lot more liberties to set up their own programs."

In the 1970s and 1980s, Children's Mercy drove recruitment by "selling" its mission of caring for all children regardless of how their bills were paid.

"The people who go into pediatrics are different from other doctors," said Joe Galeazzi, who served in the Human

Resources Department from 1979 to 1993 and later as vice president of medical administration. "We would spend more and more time talking about the mission: that this is a place that would support them in any way to care for the patients. Everyone focuses on the patient and focuses on what the unmet needs are."

That led to continuous expansion of the medical staff and the ability of the hospital to offer more and more services, he said.

"I think a very cultural thing about Children's Mercy is that we do really encourage people to be lifelong learners," Galeazzi said. "We encourage them to find what they do best and we really focus on how that translates to the patient."

Much is made of the role of the expanding medical staff in blazing this new trail for Children's Mercy, yet nurses always have been essential, too – not only in care, but also in reputation as an outstanding pediatric center.

Children's Mercy was one of the first hospitals in Kansas City to use nurses trained specifically for the type of patients they would see, although Dr. Hall recalled considerable debate about the idea.

It adopted the "First Assistant" program, which allowed nurses to assist heart surgeons, recalled Pam Dennis, a nurse who specialized in surgery. Previously, she said, the role had been filled strictly by fellows in training.

## One of the busiest

Before moving to Hospital Hill in 1970, Children's Mercy saw about 85,000 outpatient visits a year. Its new, central location at 24th Street and Gillham Road and its growing reputation for excellent pediatric care attracted more patients, both paying and charity. Also, by 1980 the hospital provided 30 different subspecialties in addition to the general-medicine outpatient clinic and the Emergency Room.

By 1982 outpatient visits surpassed 130,000, about one-third of them in the Emergency Room. According to hospital historians Drs. Wenner and Pakula, that number made it one of the busiest pediatric hospitals in the country.

The growth in patients and staff put pressure on facilities. In 1971, less than six months after moving to Hospital Hill, the board was reviewing bids for an addition.

The administrative offices and the Neonatal Intensive

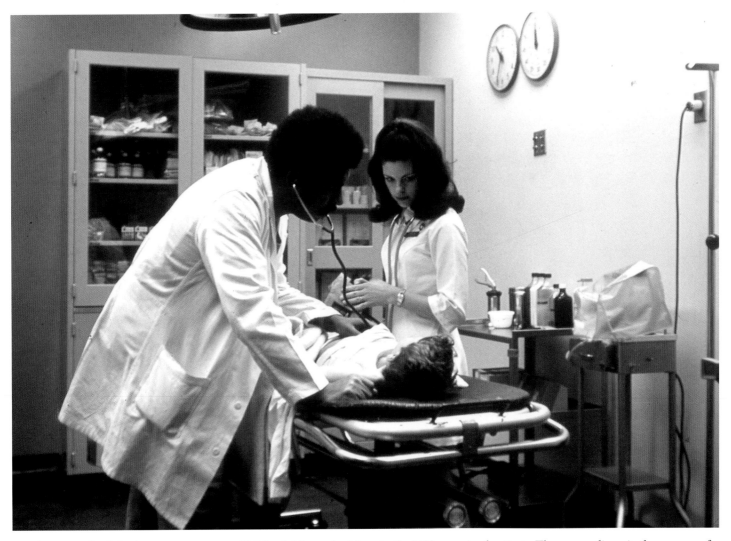

*Inside Kansas City's busiest emergency room, Children's Mercy physicians in the 1980s examined patients. The surroundings, in the memory of one doctor, occasionally proved crowded and even chaotic.*

Care Unit soon proved too small, so they were expanded. Next up, the auditorium that was scrapped from initial construction because of its cost was revived and deemed a priority for educational and general meeting space. It would open in May 1972, along with a new chapel containing stained glass from the old hospital and some furniture built by Katharine Berry Richardson. New research laboratories were added. The cafeteria was enlarged. By 1974 parking shortages led to shuttles that moved employees from parking lots near Union Station.

Much of the expansion was made possible by gifts from Gladys A. Kelce and the L. Russell Kelce Foundation. The expansion also included more space for the Crippled Children's Nursery School, which became part of Children's Mercy in the 1960s.

In the early 1980s, the Teen Clinic became the first specialty to move out of the hospital building to an office nearby. In 1985, that move was followed by the Pediatric Care Center, which operates as a general pediatrician's office, providing well-child visits, immunizations and the like. Even with those moves, space remained at a premium.

## Involving the parents

The addition also allowed space for a new concept, the Parent Care Unit, designed for children who needed hospitalization but not acute care. Perhaps they required

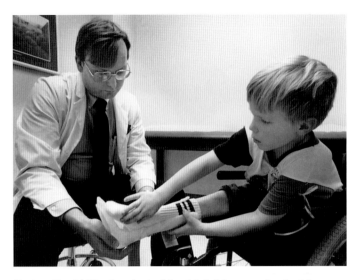

*Patient David Hosch, who had lost his left leg, was fitted with an orthopedic device by Dr. Thomas Schmidt. He learned to control his trunk, right, with the help of physical therapist Shari Adams.*

diagnostic tests or were in transition from post-operative care to discharge. Parents stayed 24 hours a day and even administered medication and checked vital signs such as pulse, blood pressure and temperature – with supervision.

When it opened in 1975, employees referred to the 22-bed unit as the "Mercy Hilton." Like the auditorium, it was planned as part of the original Hospital Hill building, but was delayed because of the cost.

An article about the pioneering Parent Care Unit appeared in the *Journal of the American Medical Association's* publication, *Medical News.*

"The facility … increases the hospital's ability to care for patients while reserving acute care beds for those more seriously ill," the report said. "The facility also encourages close parent-child relationships during a stressful period.

"Another advantage is the reduced cost to the patients' family from $87 a day in an acute care area to $47."

Thus began greater involvement for parents in the care of their children.

Although the dedicated Parent Care Unit eventually would close, parents in years to come would play an important role in their child's care. All patient rooms would become private and almost all would have beds for parents, who would be allowed to stay in the hospital around the clock.

Karen Cox, PhD, RN, who joined the hospital in 1987 and who would go on to serve as executive vice president and chief operating officer, said the national trend in the '80s was

away from involving parents.

"Many health care providers thought families got in the way and that their presence diminished the child's ability to heal," she said in 2016. "I can't believe people thought that way. They thought that the separation anxiety every time a family member left the room would be too hard on the child. It was silly."

When she was nurse manager in the cancer unit, Dr. Cox invited parents to help decorate it.

"I think that is when I really started seeing the partnership of families," she said, "not only for their own children, but for being involved in hospital operations – how we organize things; what should be important to us."

By 2016, families would play a central role in the operation of the hospital through family advisory boards (including one for Spanish-speaking families), through Family-

Centered Care Advocates on staff and through direct involvement in hospital committees and work groups. Parents influenced improvements in quality, the design of facilities and many other aspects of hospital operations. When possible, they would continue to have a direct role in the care of their children.

## Higher costs, tighter budget

All the growth at Children's Mercy came at a cost – literally.

"The major problem with doing all of this – we were building truly magnificent programs – is, How in the heck do you fund something like this?" recalled Dr. Dreher, the hospital administrator. "We lobbied the city and the county and the state and then the federal government and, of course, donors."

*For patients who did not require acute care, the 1970s saw the advent of the Parent Care Unit. Parents could stay with their children around the clock, feeding them and checking vital signs.*

As Children's Mercy attracted more patients, other hospitals in Kansas City saw fewer children and began closing their own pediatric units.

"The mindset of adult hospitals doesn't fully appreciate all it takes to take care of children," said Larry McAndrews, who would serve as Children's Mercy's first chief executive officer from 1987 until 1992. "They just don't get the economies of scale … and there are a limited number of pediatric sub-specialists."

Growing numbers of patients, new programs, new staff and equipment, new medicine, highly specialized care providers and greater demands for services all contributed to skyrocketing costs. The tab for care increased substantially. A day in the hospital cost $87 in 1975; it grew to $330 a day by 1982.

That same year, 1982, the hospital provided more than $16 million in care for which it was reimbursed nothing. That represented nearly one-third of the total cost of care for the year. The other two-thirds were paid by insurance, government

*Just like home – except for medical devices – in the Parent Care Unit.*

programs, and donors. The *Kansas City Star* saw the crisis and tried to rally the community in an editorial: "The city is on a tight budget. So is the county. So is everybody. But something must be done about Children's Mercy."

But times were tough all over. The United States had fallen into a recession and in the late 1970s interest rates reached double digits.

By 1982, Children's Mercy operated at a $2 million annual deficit. Cuts in Medicaid reimbursement contributed to the problem. Also, local governments fell behind in reimbursing the hospital for care received by their residents.

For outpatient care alone, the average cost of a visit was $60; the average amount of reimbursement was $48. The difference, multiplied by 130,000 outpatient visits a year, contributed to the substantial deficit.

For inpatients, Medicaid reimbursement amounted to only $274 of the $330 cost.

"Simply stated, Children's Mercy has experienced growing unreimbursed deficits because of the rising cost of medical care, and decreasing funding for children's health care," said Dr. Richard M. Biery, the Kansas City, Missouri, health director, in 1982. Biery headed a city-organized task force that examined the financial problem at Children's Mercy.

Hospital leaders insisted that none of the budget problems affected patient care. In fact, few people on the front lines of care even knew about the dire financial picture.

Galeazzi, the medical administration vice president, said in 2016 that he had seen 39 annual budgets and he continued to be amazed.

"As an administrator you start understanding that these things naturally play out," he said. "I spend a lot of time looking at numbers and I would say that … we spent literally every penny we could possibly spend but we spent it on the right things.

"It really is a miracle and I give credit to the community and donors and I give credit to senior leadership."

One of the ways Children's Mercy dealt with the crisis was by tapping its endowment, which was controlled by the Board of Trustees. The trustees regularly made loans to the hospital, often as an open line of credit against which the hospital could borrow whenever it needed money.

Sometimes, however, loans from the endowment went unpaid. As a result, from 1977 to 1983 the endowment's principal dropped by $3.5 million – 25 percent.

In February 1982, the hospital appealed to the Board

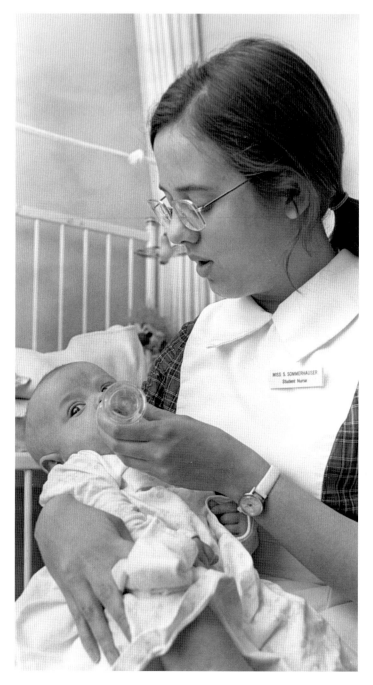

*Student nurse with infant.*

of Trustees for $1 million, saying it had an "urgent need." In addition to sudden cuts in federal Medicaid reimbursement and decreases in other government funds, Dr. Dreher recalled, collections were running behind schedule. At the same time, vendors were penalizing the hospital for not paying on time.

The trustees offered $500,000 and suggested that the

hospital find the rest of the money from spending cuts.

"The hospital is losing its shirt ..." Dr. Biery told *The Kansas City Star*. "This (borrowing from the foundation) can't go on forever. Eventually you'd have a bankrupt hospital."

Biery's task force, formed by City Manager Robert Kipp, considered several options, among them:

- More public support from outside Kansas City
- Stronger fund-raising efforts for Children's Mercy
- Possible decentralization of pediatric health care through the creation of satellite clinics.

Children's Mercy did not give up. To control costs, the hospital delayed hiring for new positions, left open existing vacancies and worked to make existing staffing as efficient as possible. No employees were laid off.

Along the way, the hospital took a controversial step, instituting an incentive plan for physicians called the Medical Practice Plan. It paid doctors based on the amount of money they billed for the hospital. The idea, recalled Lloyd C. Olson, MD, the first chairman of the Department of Pediatrics, was that doctors would work more hours and see more patients to increase their billings.

However, some doctors took offense, suggesting they were already working as hard as they could.

"We had hours and hours of meetings about this," Dr. Olson said.

Shortly after the plan was implemented, it was thrown off track by the inequality of billings among specialties. Neonatologists, with all their intensive-care equipment and staffing, would account for a large share of total billings. Psychiatrists or dermatologists, on the other hand, had a relatively small share. Dr. Olson and others decided Children's Mercy should not penalize doctors financially just because their practices weren't reimbursed at a high level. After a couple years, the Medical Practice Plan was abandoned. Other ways to increase revenue would have to be found.

The Board of Trustees, tiring of the revolving door of loans and financial crises, suggested the hospital find new and better ways to spread its message. Community support, as had always been the case, would be a key to the future. Dr. Roberts, the gastroenterologist and later executive medical director, said the hospital had not focused on telling its story.

"I don't think we did a very good job of that at the time," he said. "You can't rely on people just knowing that you need their support. You have to tell them and show them that it is important and you have to convince them to help."

## Raising money, making friends

One of the most exciting and successful new efforts to elicit support was the Children's Mercy Golf Classic. The event began in 1980 with professional golfer and Kansas Citian Tom Watson. He invited other famed professional golfers – Arnold Palmer, Jack Nicklaus, Lee Trevino and Gary Player among them – to play an exhibition round at Blue Hills Country Club. Thousands of people bought tickets to watch. From tickets sales and sponsorships, the Classic would raise more than $12 million over the next 25 years. And it would do more than that.

"It evolved into a volunteer bonanza," said Mary Jane Barnes, who volunteered in various capacities for the hospital over more than 20 years, including as chairman of the Golf Classic in 1988. "It was people volunteering who had never volunteered for the hospital before and then they would say to you: 'I would love to do more. What can I do?' It gave us a lot of free publicity."

> "In golf, most of life is played in the fairway. In life, however, things are not always fair. For many children, life is played in the rough."
>
> — *Tom Watson*

Davoren Tempel, who became vice president of fund-raising for the hospital in the late 1980s, said the event was a classic example of raising the public profile.

"Events are not fundraisers; they are friend-raisers," Tempel said. "This was a way to mobilize and have the business community embrace philanthropy and what was going on at Children's Mercy. This is a way to funnel prospects that will ultimately make investments into the hospital.

"The more you broaden the base and the more you engage people in the mission in what's going on at our hospital and changing children's lives and saving lives, the more interest you are going to have and the more gifts you're going to receive."

*Each year, Kansas City golfer Tom Watson assembled some of the game's greatest players for the annual Children's Mercy Golf Classic. It began in 1980, left, and would continue into the 21st century. In 2002, Arnold Palmer shot as Watson, second from right, watched. Also looking on: Gary Player in black shirt, Lee Trevino in blue and Jack Nicklaus in gold.*

Adele Hall, daughter-in-law of Joyce Hall, was credited with working with Watson to create the golf classic to help Children's Mercy pursue its mission.

Watson used a golf analogy to explain his commitment.

"In golf, most of life is played in the fairway," he said in a hospital annual report. "In life, however, things are not always fair. For many children, life is played in the rough."

While things were certainly rough for many children and the hospital itself, supporters always managed to come through. Sometimes it came in unexpected ways. Tempel offered a story:

"It was Christmas and we were flooded with year-end giving …. I was (in the office) late and there was a knock on the door. It was cold and snowy and this grandfather had on those farmer's overalls with these big, deep pockets and I invited him in and gave him a cup of coffee.

"(He) had a granddaughter who was diagnosed with leukemia and she was 12 that year and they spent time at the hospital …. He told me he wanted to be able to make a gift in honor of the doctors and nurses who had saved his granddaughter so that other granddaughters could be saved.

"He dug way down into his pocket and pulled out a big ol' wad of bills. It was his soybeans – money from his soybeans that he sold – and I was so touched. I thought to myself, It's not me and it's not my staff and it's not really even the doctors and nurses. It's Children's Mercy's soul that allows it to survive.

"And yes, the doctors are important in it and the nurses are important in it; the administration is important; the volunteers are important – but it has its own soul, its own spirit and it's going to live forever."

## A gift from the past

By 1982, Children's Mercy was operating not only at the limits of its financial capacity, but once again at the limits of its physical capacity. To alleviate crowding and make more room for expanding services and a growing number of patients, hospital leaders reached into the endowment for a gift promised decades earlier.

It came from the estate of George H. Sombart, the quiet and rather obscure son of the founder of the Sombart Milling Company in Boonville, Missouri. In the late 1800s, George Sombart left Boonville and moved to Coldwater, Kansas, where he went into cattle and banking. He retired in 1910 and moved to Mission Hills, Kansas. He was a Mason, a Shriner and an inveterate golfer, playing at Blue Hills and Mission Hills country clubs. He died in 1943.

Sombart's gift, though sizable, was not direct. He first left money for relatives, who were instructed to give whatever remained of it to Children's Mercy when they died. Not until 1982 did the money come to the hospital. By then it totaled $1.2 million.

A condition of Sombart's gift was that it be used to construct a building and in the 1980s money was desperately needed for exactly that. The result was the Sombart Building, constructed just north of the existing structure.

At the groundbreaking on June 30, 1982, *The Daily News* of Boonville, Sombart's native town, acknowledged that not much was known about Sombart "or why he wanted to leave the money to the hospital in the first place." But the newspaper offered a clue, quoting Sombart's sister-in-law as saying, "Since he died a bachelor with no children, I think

maybe he left the money to the hospital because he never had any children."

Whatever the reason, Children's Mercy was bursting at the seams and the Sombart Building helped solve the problem. It connected the 1970 hospital building with the former nurse's residence of old General Hospital, which housed several outpatient clinics and a few doctors' administrative offices.

The new building provided space for administrative operations and expanded laboratories. It freed up space in the main hospital for new specialized surgical and cardiac services, as well as room for library facilities and offices for medical residents.

Until the mid-1990s, the Sombart Building served as the main entrance to Children's Mercy. In 2017, it would still be in use as the main entrance for same-day surgery patients and families.

## Patient care, research, education – all three

With a bit of breathing room in the matter of space, if not finances, the Central Governing Board decided it was time to consider the hospital's future. Higher health care costs – brought on by new medical technology, advanced treatments, new pharmaceuticals, inflation and greater expectations and demand – put continued pressure on the budget. Marion Kreamer, Adele Hall and other board members thought it was time for professional strategic planning.

As the first order of business, the board in 1982 formed a Role and Mission Committee to consider overhauling the hospital's administrative operations. Board member Jerry Smith, a Kansas City auto dealer and philanthropist, chaired the group, which consisted of hospital staff and board members.

With the help of a facilitator from the University of Missouri-Kansas City, the committee discussed what kind of a medical center Children's Mercy wanted to be.

"What is the Number 1 priority of the hospital: Patient care, education or research?" the committee's notes asked. Leaders pondered the future and how to continue evolving from a charity hospital to a comprehensive pediatric medical center.

"Children's Mercy has been ambivalent about its

primary role," the notes continued. "We can't be all things to all people."

But in the end, after months of meetings, the committee and ultimately the Central Governing Board voted to be just that. The hospital would embrace all three roles of education, research and patient care. The Role and Mission Statement adopted in March 1982 stated:

> *The Children's Mercy Hospital is a regional medical center dedicated to providing the highest quality comprehensive care for children from birth through adolescence. A full range of pediatric medical and hospital services is available to all children regardless of race, religion, residence or ability to pay. Patients and their families are treated with consideration and understanding in a patient-centered environment .... The education, teaching and research activities ... are essential to attaining the goals of quality care and in advancing the knowledge of child health.*

Within a few months, Children's Mercy launched a new capital campaign, its first since the 1960s. Called "Continuing the Commitment," the aim was to raise $12 million "to keep secure the institution's status as a high-quality and stable facility," according to a *Kansas City Times* editorial. Jerry Smith, who had led the Role and Mission Committee, and William P. Harsh, a Hallmark executive, served as campaign co-chairs.

*The hospital leadership often called on Jerry Smith to head committees.*

Much of the early focus of the campaign was low-key and aimed at large donors.

Dr. Hall, the neonatologist and a member of the campaign steering committee, recalled an early meeting of the group, which included directors, trustees and donors. Jerry Smith, he said, stood and stressed the importance of Children's Mercy to the community and how the campaign would be the community's chance to show it.

According to Dr. Hall, "I remember Jerry saying ... 'We need this hospital, and the good news is we've got the money

and it's right in this room!'

"I'll never forget that, what a great line. And they did; they ponied up."

Board support demonstrated to foundations, corporations and other major prospects that the hospital's leadership was committed. The campaign teamed up doctors and board members to call on business leaders and other wealthy Kansas Citians for help. The emphasis was on face-to-face solicitation, not over the phone, through the mail or media advertisements. There were no longer parades or Mother Goose days, as in earlier times.

Hospital needs to be met with the additional funding would include $6 million for building and renovation, $3 million for equipment and $3 million for "people needs," including a family support fund, education and research money and the endowment.

Rising health care costs were on everyone's mind, and the hospital addressed the matter.

"Efforts include cooperative agreements to share services with other hospitals, improved billing procedures and development of variable staffing levels during different periods of patient occupancy," a campaign worker notebook said.

Children's Mercy was also working to open new clinics or to expand existing ones.

With the money sought by the campaign, outpatient clinics would be consolidated in the former General Hospital nurses' residence, now a Children's Mercy annex. The main hospital would then be remodeled, the operating rooms expanded and the Sombart Building connecting the hospital to the annex would be expanded. The neonatal unit also would be renovated. Ten of the rooms in the old parent care unit would be remodeled to become private rooms instead of shared rooms. According to Dr. Dreher, parents' expectations for privacy were increasing.

Surgery continued to drive growth. More than 3,000 surgeries took place each year in three operating rooms at Children's Mercy. With the complexity and the volume of outpatient surgeries increasing, the need for additional rooms was urgent.

Raising money for the endowment also was considered essential. Nationally, it was estimated that 50 percent or more of the future financial support of charitable organizations would come from endowment income and not from insurance or government, according to campaign materials. In the case of Children's Mercy, the endowment would be the largest source of income to pay for care not covered by family or insurance.

At the time, the endowment, at $17 million, was "still far below the amount needed to provide quality health care to all children in need," campaign material stated.

Not long after the campaign was launched in late 1982, donors responded. Near the front of the line was the Hall family and its company, Hallmark. Also, Children's Mercy became the first charity to receive a donation from the estate of Hallmark founder Joyce C. Hall.

A $1 million gift from Hall's estate was announced the same day the Hallmark Education Foundation said it would chip in $2 million for the overall campaign. The money from Hall's estate was used to permanently endow the Joyce C. Hall distinguished professorship in pediatrics, which is held by the hospital's chief of pediatrics. The endowed chair was first established in 1969 with a $500,000 gift from Hall, who had served as campaign co-chair for funding to build the initial Hospital Hill campus.

The two gifts brought to $5 million the total raised in the first month of the campaign. About six months later, more than $9 million had been raised, including nearly $2 million from the hospital boards, more than $250,000 from physicians and nearly $100,000 from employees. The list of contributors was like a *Who's Who?* of Kansas City philanthropists: Hall, Kemper, Sosland and the Kansas City Association of Trusts and Foundations.

By May 30, 1984, the campaign announced it had

*Dr. Richard Dreher, hospital administrator in the late 1970s and early 1980s, received a check from George Brett, the star of the Kansas City Royals, who were in their early heyday.*

reached a grand total of $12,664,483. The goal had been met and surpassed.

Just in time, too: The inpatient census was running from 85 to 100 percent of available beds.

## A divisive plan for expansion

As exciting as things were on the heels of a successful capital campaign, challenges remained. With the completion of the Sombart Building, the hospital found itself mostly landlocked. The UMKC Dental School stood to the south. Truman Medical Center and the UMKC School of Medicine stood to the east. Crown Center and Hallmark lay across Gillham Road to the west.

Hospital leaders looked north, to the nearly deserted building of old General Hospital.

When the city opened Truman Medical Center on Hospital Hill in 1976, it mostly abandoned the buildings of the old General Hospital. The City Health Department still operated in one of the wings, but the buildings of the old

hospital, which opened in 1908, had fallen into poor shape.

Together, Children's Mercy and Truman officials asked the city to raze the buildings. To make room for its own new building, Truman Medical Center had torn down the old German Hospital, which had become Research Hospital before Research moved south. Demolition of aging structures on Hospital Hill was not unprecedented.

However, historical preservationists, including some from outside the city, had other ideas. What transpired over several years beginning in the mid-1980s became one of the darker chapters in the Children's Mercy story. This time, instead of the community rallying around, strong divisions emerged.

In 1985 the City Council appointed a special General Hospital Task Force, which concluded that much of the old General Hospital structure should be saved and used for new purposes. One proposal called for it to be converted to low-income housing. Of particular importance to the task force and the preservationists was saving the imposing north and west facades of old General. Standing as they did on a hillside, the structures had for decades presented a striking appearance.

The past president of the Historical Kansas City Foundation, Linda Gill Taylor, chaired the task force. She insisted that its recommendation to save the buildings was based on economic, planning and architectural criteria, not simply the wishes of preservationists.

Children's Mercy disagreed. The hospital already had shown an interest in and the ability to use an old building; the old General Hospital nurses' residence already was being remodeled for Children's Mercy outpatient services. But the rest of General Hospital was a different story. Children's Mercy consultants concluded that it would be too expensive to renovate the building and that its design was simply outdated and not adequate for the medical needs of the times.

The dispute would go on for years.

## New chief in a new job

In 1986, the Central Governing Board decided that the complexity of operating Children's Mercy required the

*Facing page: Old General Hospital, mostly vacant since Truman Medical Center opened, became the center of a long dispute.*

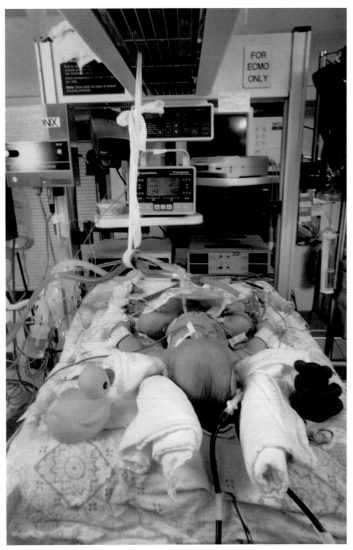

*A baby's heart was monitored and his heart and lungs helped along in 1989 by a machine called ECMO – Extracorporeal Membrane Oxygenation. The device is used to take over some of the body's work and give the patient a chance to rest and grow.*

leadership of a chief executive officer. Acknowledging the work of administrators dating back to the 1950s, the board noted that they had not been trained in the manifold problems facing hospitals in the 1980s, among them finance, dealings with insurers, medical staff development, government affairs and community relations.

Chosen to fill the new job of CEO was Larry McAndrews, who had served as administrator at Prentice Women's Hospital and before that, of the Institute of Psychiatry – both components of Northwestern Memorial

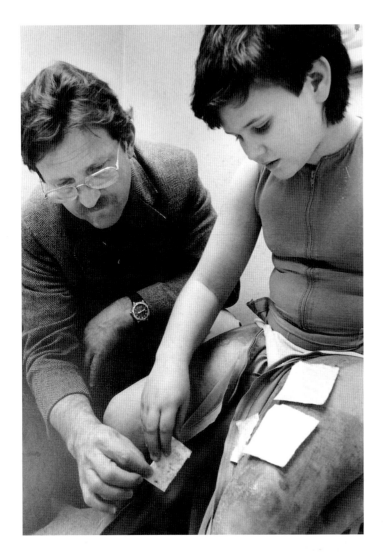

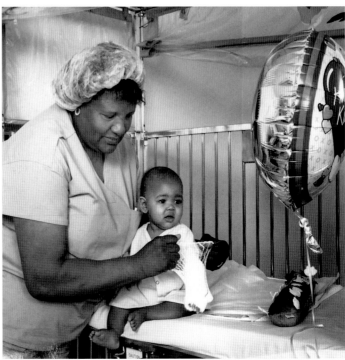

*Caring for severe burns: Nurse Bertha Clifton comforted 8-month-old Penny Johnson, above. Dr. Ronald Sharp worked with patient Timothy Boydston, left.*

Hospital in Chicago, the teaching site for Northwestern University.

Embarking on the new job June 1, 1986, McAndrews took up the first assignment handed him by the Central Governing Board: Put the hospital's financial house in order. He intended to do that, in part, by offering more services, expanding current ones and improving physical conditions.

All the while, patient growth continued. To meet that demand and to put the hospital on more sound financial footing, plans were already being made to double the hospital's size in 10 years.

That had led to the fight over old General Hospital, and to the conflict that right away put the new CEO on the hot seat. Fund-raising grew increasingly difficult because the future of the hospital was uncertain and many donors opposed

re-use of the old General Hospital building.

"Restoration of a deteriorated building, however otherwise desirable, is not seen as part of our mission," McAndrews said in a memo to employees three months after he took over. "To raise future funds for this purpose would divert money from meeting the needs of sick children."

There had even been discussion about moving the hospital to another part of town, but McAndrews said remaining on Hospital Hill was the best option, considering the central location and the huge capital investment already in the property.

A stalemate ensued. In summer 1986 the City Council, despite the recommendation of its task force, voted to tear down the building. Three months later, the council reversed course and decided to save it.

Demolition opponents kept the issue alive with petition drives, vitriolic comments at public hearings, accusations in letters to the editor and accusations aimed at leaders of Children's Mercy and at its important ally, Hallmark.

Part of the furor stemmed from the fact that the building

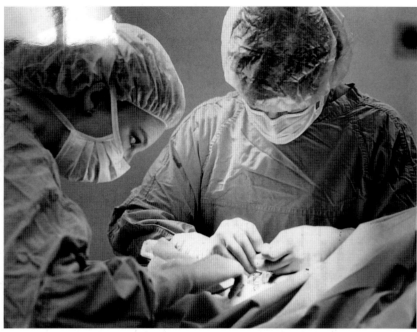

*Healing arts in the late 1980s: A mentor, left, worked with "Joey" to help apply glitter to his handiwork. In the operating room, above, all was concentration.*

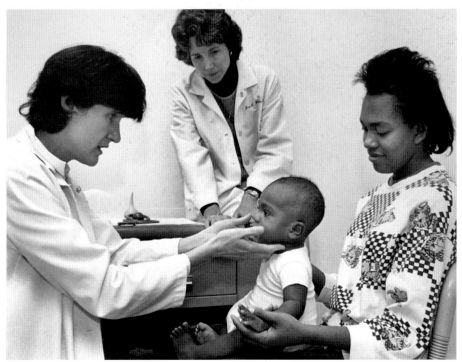

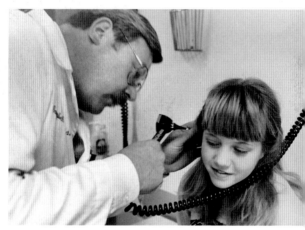

*Getting the once-over, carefully and clinically, patient Jason Stubblefield sat on his mother's lap as Colleen Ryan checked him. Dr. Jean Barton, background, looked on. In the Endocrinology Unit, above right, Dr. Campbell Howard examined a girl's ear. A cancer patient put pencil to paper, right, helped by a Children's Mercy nurse.*

# Beyond spina bifida: A patient's father tells his son's story

The genetics counselor handed my wife a business card. It belonged to Dr. Fred Hall, head of the Spina Bifida Clinic at Children's Mercy Hospital.

"I know this is difficult news," the counselor said. "You should call Dr. Hall. He can help you understand what to expect."

We had just received a diagnosis that our unborn son had spina bifida. In 1989, pre-natal testing was new, but a blood test flagged that something might be wrong with our first child. A level II ultrasound confirmed that there was an opening in the lumbar region of his spine. We left the doctor's office for what was to be an emotional afternoon. We went home and cried. We contemplated our future with a child whose disability we knew nothing about. Kim called Fred Hall's office. He could meet with us later that afternoon.

Dr. Hall's calm demeanor minimized our uncontrolled emotions. I began to think his business card should read "Zen Master." We told him, getting upset, that we didn't know anything about spina bifida, and the doctor we consulted told us there was a possibility of severe brain damage. Our son might never recognize his parents.

"I see a lot of children with spina bifida," Dr. Hall said. "And those children are bright, compete academically, play sports and have full lives. If you treat any child like a china doll they are going to become a china doll. The children I see aren't like that. You get what you expect."

We walked out of Dr. Hall's office with confidence that we could manage the challenges in front of us.

A few months later, Eric Nicholas Ratliff was born on the coldest day in Kansas City history. Fred Hall was in the delivery room. Later that day, Nick was transported to Children's Mercy Hospital to have a shunt inserted and closure surgery on his back. That was Nick's first trip to Children's Mercy.

Over the next 18 years, there would be many others – visits to the spina bifida clinic and a handful of surgeries. Along the way, we worked with fabulous doctors and staff such as Drs. Ann

*Infant Nick Ratliff in the Neonatal Intensive Care Unit, upper left, and then atop a pony. Years later, above, he smiled at life.*

Modrcin, John Patrick Murphy and Nigel Price, who performed an extraordinary 17-hour back surgery when Nick was a teenager. Carol Hafeman was the nurse at the Spina Bifida Clinic during the 18 years he went there. Over the years, I left many messages for Carol about one concern or another. They were all answered promptly and cheerfully. No question was too foolish or indelicate.

Nick graduated from high school and from Children's Mercy. He went on to graduate from KU and get a driver's license. Now, he has a full-time job.

Thanks, Children's Mercy.

*Jon Ratliff, Nick's dad*
*December 2016*

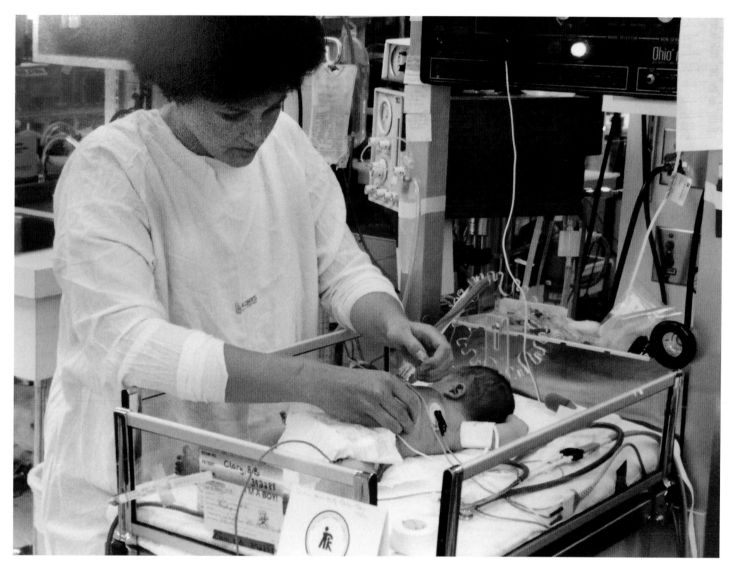

*Baby boy Clary received treatment in the Neonatal Intensive Care Unit in the late 1980s.*

targeted for razing housed the City Health Department. As the *Kansas City Business Journal* noted: "The Health Department's patients include some of the city's poorest citizens, AIDS victims among them, which has lent emotional resonance to the controversy over the structure.

"Some preservationists hint darkly that the hospital's stance has nothing to do with (General Hospital) per se, but with proximity of the Health Department to the hospital and apprehension that it may scare paying patients away. They point in particular to powerful neighbor Hallmark Cards Inc. and the Hall Family Foundation, one of the hospital's principal benefactors, as the instigators."

According to the opponents' theory, the *Business Journal* said, "Hallmark ... wants the area bounded by 23rd and 24th streets, Locust Street and Holmes Road, to remain as a buffer for Hallmark and the nearby Crown Center retail and residential complex."

As accusations and arguments flew in public, the hospital, the university and the city quietly worked on a compromise. At one point, the hospital Board of Trustees forwarded the city $350,000 to pay three-fifths of the cost of demolition. But as the city wrestled with balancing the interests of many constituents, old General Hospital remained standing. The money was returned to the trustees, albeit temporarily.

## A move into the marketplace

Apart from the protracted controversy over old General Hospital, the 1980s marked the arrival of "managed care" as a model for insurance reimbursement. In the world of managed care, companies like Blue Cross Blue Shield contract with hospitals and other providers to accept reimbursement at a discounted rate. Insurance companies then assign patients to one of the contracted providers or network of providers. The insurers pay providers in the network when patients use their services. If insured patients receive care outside the network, the insurers pay less – and in some cases nothing.

"The idea behind managed care is that the insurance company can drive a population of patients to you, but in return, they want a discount on charges," explained Jo Stueve, who started at the hospital in 1988 and would work in managed care until becoming executive vice president and chief operating officer in 2006. "When we started to contract with all the managed care plans … we became more of a provider for commercially insured children. That's when we really started seeing more and more children with all kinds of conditions. This allowed us to expand our scope of business."

Then-CEO McAndrews recalled that time in a 2015 interview: "We knew we could add value to health care for all children. We navigated between the two competing networks. We had some competition for neonatal (babies), but no one could compete with us for the other specialists … so we were able to survive."

*Larry McAndrews*

Yet the Central Governing Board wanted more than survival. Its members had big dreams. As health care and health care finance evolved, the hospital needed to be adaptable and, if necessary, play hardball.

"We had some challenging years," said Mary Jane Barnes, who was chair of the Central Governing Board in 1990 and 1991. "We had to get more contracts and we had a heck of a time."

Other hospitals in town, she said, did not want more commercially insured patients going to Children's Mercy because it would mean less business for them. Commercial insurance pays at a higher rate than Medicaid. The little

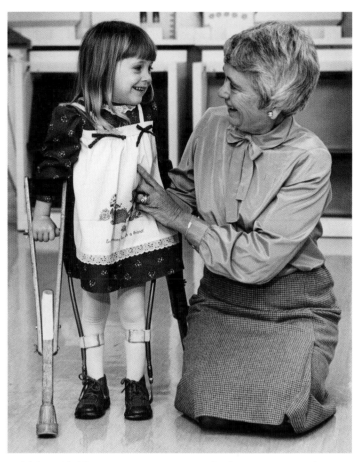

*A lifelong Children's Mercy supporter and volunteer, Mary "Shawsie" Branton helped a little girl with braces and crutches.*

charity hospital would have to push back.

Weathering tough negotiations and agreeing to discount charges, Stueve said, the hospital affiliated with more providers and thus more networks. That opened the doors to more children whose doctors had been reluctant to refer them "out of network."

"It was very competitive for a while with different models, different reimbursement mechanisms," Stueve recalled.

In the face of the competition, Stueve and her team worked diligently. Slowly the "market share" of Children's Mercy began to grow. That not only helped feed the bottom line, but also helped build the hospital's reputation as a full-service medical center.

"Before this time, we weren't participating in the marketplace," said Dr. Karen Cox, who came to work at Children's Mercy in 1987 and would become executive vice

## Surviving, practicing and prospering

When Angela Myers was 16, her knee began to hurt. Doctors found bone cancer. At Children's Mercy, Angela had chemotherapy, then surgery to replace her knee.

She lost her hair, but not her sense of humor. On Halloween, Angela dressed up as "Mr. Clean." She decided to be a doctor. Even though the cancer came back and she had treatments during college, she kept going.

She became the first Children's Mercy Holiday Hero in 1995 as part of a campaign to support the Cancer Center.

*Age 16, Halloween garb.*

"My family wanted to show how important the Cancer Center had become in our lives," said Angela, who is now known as Dr. Myers. In 2016 she was practicing medicine at Children's Mercy, the institution where she received care, and serving as the Director of Children's Mercy's Infectious Diseases Fellowship Program.

*As an adult, she is now Dr. Angela Myers.*

president and chief operating officer. "The only way patients got here was if they were really sick or on Medicaid or self-pay.

"It is important to us, to our mission, to always take care of those children," she said, "but we know we have to do well across the board and take care of all the kids to be able to take care of the kids that can't afford it.

"It's also important that we see lots of children. Volume matters. What some hospitals see only occasionally, we see all the time. We are the experts. You can't do half as many heart surgeries as we do and be as good as we are."

Some signs emerged of better days ahead. From 1984 to 1989, the hospital experienced an 11 percent increase in outpatient visits and a 7 percent increase in admissions. The hospital's share of pediatric patients in the Kansas City area reached about 55 percent.

The financial situation of the hospital also improved. Of the hospital's $51.4 million budget in 1987, patient insurance covered 71 percent. Twelve percent came from Medicaid. The hospital's endowment contributed 6 percent.

In November 1988 a Missouri income-tax increase was approved to help hospitals. In February 1989, Kansas City, Missouri, voters approved a local tax for the Health Department, Truman Medical Center and Children's Mercy

By October 1989, Children's Mercy was reporting a "positive financial situation" – and balanced budget.

### Strong feelings, and finally a solution

Still waiting on a decision about the fate of the old General Hospital building, Children's Mercy considered other options for expansion.

Both Research Medical Center and St. Luke's made overtures about partnerships or mergers at their properties.

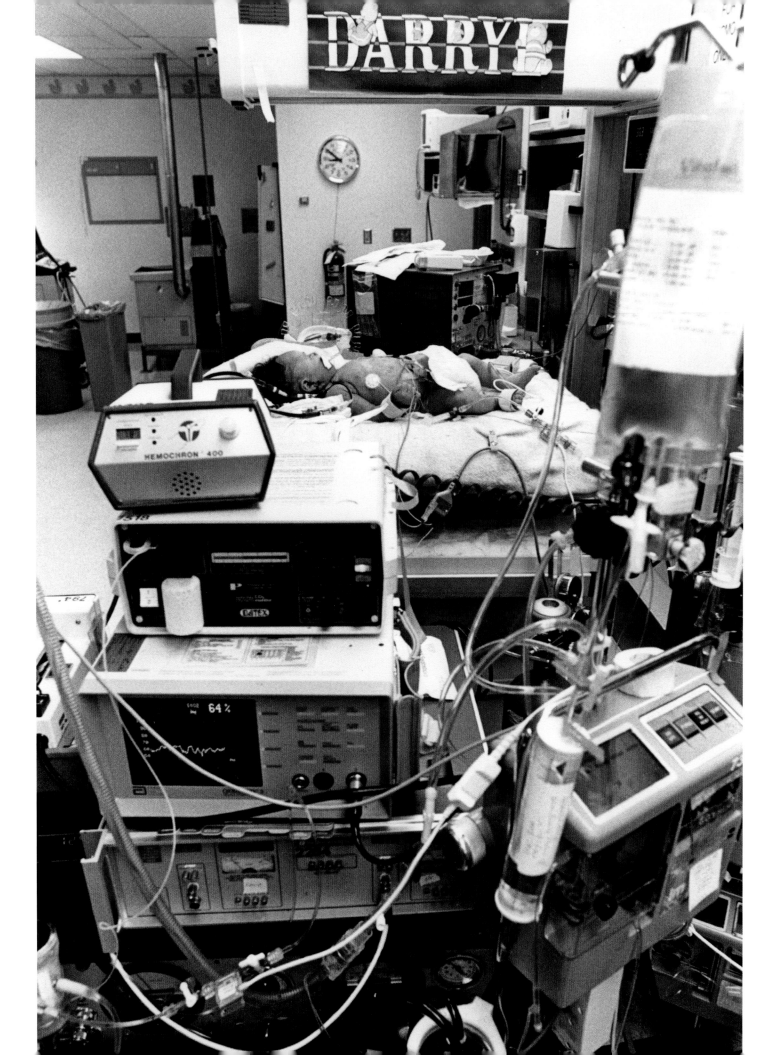

The desire to remain independent swayed hospital leaders to reject those offers. Children's Mercy also considered building in a different part of the city, including along Interstate 435 in the growing southern part of the metropolitan area.

Some people called talk of a move a "threat" if city leaders of Kansas City, Missouri, failed to provide the hospital expansion room on Hospital Hill. Children's Mercy replied that it was necessary to ensure that the hospital continued to meet the needs of the region's children.

All the while, hospital board members and other officials worked behind the scenes on a resolution of the quandary over old General Hospital. Mary Jane Barnes, Adele Hall, Herman Sutherland, Marion Kreamer and others visited with city leaders away from the limelight. Hospital employees were encouraged to write Mayor Richard Berkeley and the City Council, explaining the need for Children's Mercy to expand.

By the early 1990s, tempers were flaring and the fight was very much public.

A *Kansas City Business Journal* article in November 1991 put it this way:

"To the preservationists, the debate is over who runs the city and whether a private institution, however worthy, should be able to run roughshod over an agreement (from the Council-appointed pro-preservation Task Force).

"To the hospital, the issue boils down to nothing less than a choice between preserving an old decaying building and preserving Children's Mercy's vaunted reputation as one of the foremost pediatric hospitals in the region."

Linda Gill Taylor, the lawyer who chaired the task force, said: "This is not about the hospital's expansion plans or square feet. It's about the arrogance of power. These people are used to getting their way and they're mad. The fundamental issue is: Who's going to control what our public facilities look like – a small clique of people, many of whom live in Kansas, or our elected government officials?

"They believe their values are the only ones or are superior ones and frankly, that is not the case."

The hospital's CEO, McAndrews, rejoined: 'We don't

*Facing page: There was little doubt about the name of this patient. "Darryl" lay hooked to a breathing apparatus and various monitors in 1990 in the Neonatal Intensive Care Unit.*

## Casting the net

Having created the CEO position in the mid-1980s, the Central Governing Board, in another nod to the needs of the growing hospital, created the position of executive medical director as the administrative leader of the medical staff.

Dr. Marvin Kolb was the first to hold the job, beginning in 1992 after serving at Mercy Center for Health Care Services in Aurora, Illinois, and as chairman of pediatrics and director of medical education at the University of North Dakota.

*Dr. Marvin Kolb*

At Children's Mercy, he said years later, much of the focus was on pediatricians in private practice. For decades those pediatricians volunteered their time and had been crucial to the operation of Children's Mercy. As the hospital became more specialized and employed more of its doctors, the relationship with private pediatricians changed.

"As our specialties grew," he said in 2016, "we needed to build collaboration with the community pediatricians. We needed to bring them into the fold, to make them a part of the family."

While he was executive medical director from 1992 to 1994, Dr. Kolb helped spearhead the Night Clinic in Overland Park to foster a closer relationship with those doctors. At the time, other health care systems – St. Luke's and Health Midwest – were trying to attract more doctors into their networks.

The effort would remain important to Children's Mercy in the 21st century. The Physicians Relations Department would promote Children's Mercy among and improve ties with private pediatricians and family practice doctors. In early 2017, Children's Mercy would announce creation of Children's Mercy Affiliated Practices, community pediatric practices closely aligned with Children's Mercy to provide integrated and comprehensive care.

think you can entomb the spirit of caring in a mausoleum … the only people who could possibly justify this are those who put preservation ahead of everything else."

But just as tempers appeared to boil over, calmer minds worked out a compromise. The day after the *Business Journal*

*As the hospital expanded, administrative offices moved into a line of construction trailers.*

## All around the town

With that controversy finally solved, Children's Mercy could focus on its future. As part of its work in the mid-1980s on its mission and goals, the hospital developed a master plan that envisioned new buildings and services, not only on Hospital Hill but also in the growing suburbs.

Pediatricians around the area, and particularly those in southern Kansas City and Johnson County, suggested that many of their patients and families were reluctant to leave their suburban communities to travel to Hospital

article appeared, an agreement was announced. Under it, the City Health Department would move from General Hospital to the UMKC Health Sciences building at 2220 Holmes. For its part, the Children's Mercy Foundation would contribute $1 million to pay for moving the department. In a bow to preservationists, it also agreed to provide money to renovate the historic Blossom Mansion at 1032 Pennsylvania or another "equally historical building located in downtown Kansas City."

The hospital also agreed to preserve the iconic frieze above the entrance of General Hospital, some of which stands today at a monument near 22nd and Holmes.

Mary Jane Barnes, chair of the Children's Mercy Central Governing Board, was glad the battle was over.

"We know Kansas Citians want us to get on with the care of our children," she said, "and our expanded hospital will enable us to do that. We feel all participants are happy. Of course, the children are the real winners."

Hill. So in 1987, the hospital arranged for authorization to do business in Kansas and opened specialty clinics in Overland Park near I-435 and Nall Avenue. Specialties were based on recommendations of those same pediatricians.

The Specialty Center turned out to be wildly popular. It opened the door to many new families in the growing southern reaches of the metro area and also helped the image of Children's Mercy. Specialties expanded and, after a few years, the Pediatric Night Clinic opened, offering after-hours urgent care for illnesses that were short of life-threatening.

*Ceremonial shovel was used at groundbreaking for the new hospital in 1968 and for expansion in 1992.*

"When the lights go out at the pediatrician's office, the lights go on at the Night Clinic," said the Children's Mercy 1993 Annual Report. "This co-op of Johnson County pediatricians and Children's Mercy nurses keeps kids who need medical attention out of costly emergency room situations. A telephone triage line helps parents decide whether to come in or treat children at home."

The Night Clinic was staffed primarily by pediatricians in private practice and was marketed not as competition but as a complement to primary care doctors. Reports on visits to the Night Clinic arrived in the primary care doctors' offices the next day for follow-up.

An Overland Park outpatient surgery center opened in 1988. That and the specialty center were the predecessors of what became Children's Mercy Hospital South, later renamed Children's Mercy Hospital Kansas.

"We had to move forward," Dr. Roberts said. "Part of the motivation for that was there was growing interest in our pediatric specialists. Adult specialists in the area were calling us and wanting to know what to do with a 5-year-old or an 8-year-old.

"Families at the time were not comfortable with coming down to (Hospital Hill) so they preferred to see an adult specialist. And the adult specialists were calling us. So we knew these kids were not getting the care they should. We were going to have to leave 2401 Gillham Road and be more available in the community if we really wanted them to be able to access that specialized pediatric care."

Meanwhile, with the growth in the suburbs and the plans for growth on Hospital Hill, leaders began to think about another capital campaign. The 100th anniversary of the founding of the hospital was approaching, and Children's Mercy created a Centennial Fund with plans to double its size by 1997. To do so, it needed at least $70 million and approval from the state of Missouri, which evaluates the need for new hospital beds under its Certificate of Need program.

Much had been achieved in the hospital's first 100 years, yet it now envisioned even greater accomplishments. A new day was dawning. A new era was on the way.

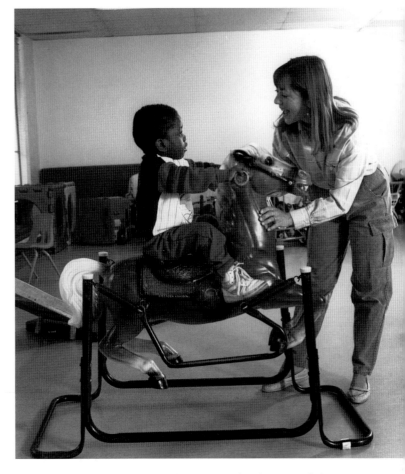

*Above: Riding the range on a hobby horse in the playroom of the Critical Care Nursing Unit. Below: Phillip Blewitt, 4, filled his menu request in the Hematology-Oncology Unit.*

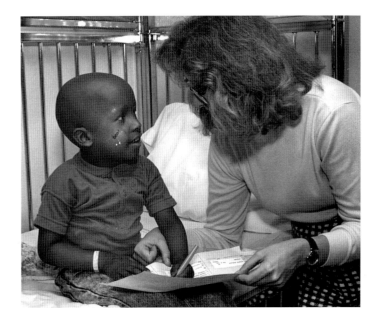

# A NEW CENTURY DAWNS

*"It's kind of fun to do the impossible."*

— Walt Disney

With the centennial year of its founding fast approaching, as well as a new millennium, Children's Mercy in the early 1990s had big dreams and momentum. After years of struggling with finances and space to care for the increasing multitudes of children needing help, its fortunes were turning around. Kansas City was on the cusp of being home to a world-class, comprehensive children's medical center.

Leaders at Children's Mercy focused on the hospital's vision – without forgetting its mission to take care of children regardless of a family's ability to pay. In the 1990s they would adopt strategic plans calling for new buildings, new programs and new locations.

They imagined how their young patients would approach the challenges and opportunities: Children would be relentless. Children wouldn't quit. They would keep dreaming. They wouldn't know the word "impossible."

*Facing page: Checking eyesight in a specialty clinic.*
*Above: A child's question became the inspiration for a marketing campaign.*

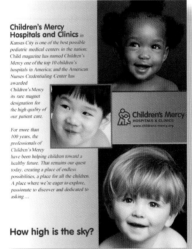

**Children's Mercy Hospitals and Clinics** in Kansas City is one of the best possible pediatric medical centers in the nation: Child magazine has named Children's Mercy one of the top 10 children's hospitals in America; and the American Nurses Credentialing Center has awarded Children's Mercy its rare magnet designation for the high quality of our patient care.

For more than 100 years, the professionals of Children's Mercy have been helping children toward a healthy future. That remains our quest today, creating a place of endless possibilities, a place for all the children. A place where we're eager to explore, passionate to discover and dedicated to asking ...

**How high is the sky?**

The slogan of an early hospital advertising campaign – itself a new phenomenon of the 1990s – posed a child's simple question: "How High is the Sky?"

And the adults were compelled to seek answers. After all, they believed, the sky was the limit.

## "We can be the best. We must."

Change was all around. The Centennial Campaign of fundraising had begun with an eye toward doubling the size of Children's Mercy on Hospital Hill.

In 1992, Larry McAndrews, the CEO who endured the rough-and-tumble battle over the old General Hospital structure, resigned. He moved east to take over leadership of the National Association of Children's Hospitals and Related Institutions, headquartered in Alexandria, Virginia. McAndrews served that organization until 2012, when it merged with another group and was renamed the Children's Hospital Association.

Before he left Kansas City for the East Coast, McAndrews secured from the state of Missouri a key item: a certificate of need, which helped pave the way for Children's

Mercy to expand.

Hospital leaders believed exciting times lay ahead. To replace McAndrews, they undertook a national search. Mary Jane Barnes, chair of the Central Governing Board in 1991 and 1992, said the board saw an opportunity to think big.

"We needed someone who could develop a vision for the hospital and lead us to it," Barnes said. "We had a strategic plan, but it seemed we were always driving away from it to handle problems or issues or challenges. We were reacting."

The search led Children's Mercy to Little Rock, Arkansas, where the CEO at Arkansas Children's Hospital for the past 9½ years had been Randall L. O'Donnell, PhD. Although he was not actively looking to move, Dr. O'Donnell agreed to consider Children's Mercy. Among other things, living in Kansas City would put him and his family nearer relatives in Des Moines, Iowa.

The attraction, on both sides, was nearly immediate.

"I could tell, the first time I spent the morning with him," Barnes said, "that he had a vision. He could walk it, he talked it and he could do it. That is what we needed."

Others didn't have exactly that reaction. But they came around.

"The first time I heard him speak, I thought he was crazy," recalled a smiling Dr. Karen Cox, Chief Operating Officer of Children's Mercy. "He said we were going to be the best children's hospital in the world and I thought somebody in the interview process didn't give him the whole scoop.

"But after I saw some of the things he did ... I began to believe."

Dr. Marvin Kolb, the medical director, summed up his first reaction succinctly: "Hang on!"

Leland McGinness, who had hired Dr. O'Donnell as his successor at Arkansas Children's and then followed him

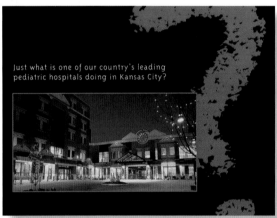

Just what is one of our country's leading pediatric hospitals doing in Kansas City?

*Construction on the Hospital Hill campus and expansion throughout the metro area marked the 1990s. Left: Longtime supporter James B. Nutter sponsored a mailer aimed at raising the hospital's profile nationally.*

to Kansas City to serve as his chief of staff, smiled when he remembered that reaction. McGinness, during a couple of decades in the Air Force, learned to strive for excellence in everything. He tried to pass that drive along to those around him.

"There is no obstacle too big to overcome," McGinness said in 2016. "We can be the best. We must. We can't cheat the children."

Dr. O'Donnell, in a 2016 interview, said simply: "I didn't want to be anywhere where I didn't feel the hospital could achieve that pinnacle of being the best. It's the only place I ever wanted to be. I saw that the roots were already in place for that here.

"I knew it was poised for significant growth, but there was a lot to be done and it wasn't going to be a small challenge. I love a challenge."

Dr. O'Donnell arrived early for the interviews and walked around the hospital by himself. His first impression

*Young patients listened as nurse Kimberly Reid shared a children's book with them.*

was of a helpful, cheerful staff.

In addition, he said, "I knew there were construction plans and I had a good feeling. I had dinner by myself .... I watched the sun set and I'm looking at Children's Mercy. There were a bunch of trailers circling the hospital (used for offices) and I thought, well, there's a plan of action here. We could do good here."

## Dreaming bigger and better

Plans took off after Dr. O'Donnell came to work for Children's Mercy in January 1993. By then, the Centennial Campaign fund drive was in full swing and construction had begun on a new Outpatient Center where General Hospital once stood.

The hospital's endowment fund, which a decade earlier was being used as an ATM for hospital operations, was within about a year paid back in full, and had grown to $55 million. Wise investments and a new, concerted philanthropic effort boosted the bottom line. Also, Children's Mercy began receiving substantial funding each year from federal and state subsidies for taking care of a "disproportionate share" of poor patients. These meant the hospital had less need to "borrow" from the endowment.

Having boosted the bottom line and with leaders ready for bold action, Dr. O'Donnell almost immediately began dreaming bigger and better. He pushed to add two floors to the Outpatient Center; he called for expansion of the neonatal intensive care unit and for more inpatient beds. He didn't do it alone, of course. In addition to the leadership already in place at Children's Mercy, others who came with Dr. O'Donnell from Arkansas Children's and made great contributions were McGinness, Jerry Blouin, chief operating officer, and Dwight

Hyde, chief financial officer.

The Philanthropy Department was working overtime. The Centennial Campaign had raised $52 million in 1992 and 1993, at the time the largest single capital campaign in Kansas City history. The money came from 1,200 donors. Gifts ranged in size from $1 to $20 million, the largest from the Hall Family Foundation. That money would help double the size of the hospital, from 320,000 square feet to 640,000 square feet.

The very next year, 1994, hospital leaders extended the campaign to raise an additional $15 million for the extra floors, beds and services. That drive lasted until 1995 and attracted gifts from 4,000 donors. The largest was $5 million from the Hall Family Foundation in the form of a challenge grant, payable only when the rest of the money was raised.

The dizzying growth, not only in buildings but also in programs – especially research – caught some people by surprise.

"Rand knew how to run a children's hospital," said Dr. Robert Hall, the former chief of neonatology at Children's Mercy. "His vision far exceeded mine. I did not and would not perceive a children's hospital in Kansas City progressing to the level that it did.

"Rand took some bold risks and initiatives and they always came up smelling like roses. I think he has been a terrific leader and he has been able to step out and do things that might have been perceived as too risky for some."

Dr. O'Donnell is quick to pass the credit to others:

"I don't say it lightly that the people who work at Children's Mercy are my heroes. They do incredible things and they take care of people in outstanding ways."

Still, there are few who doubt Children's Mercy would be where it was in the 21st century without the vision and the leadership of Dr. O'Donnell, who by 2017

had served as head of the hospital for 24 years. That is longer than anyone other than the Berry sisters, Alice and Katharine, who served from the founding in 1897 until Katharine died in 1933. (Dr. O'Donnell said he had no plans to try to break the record of 36 years.)

"He has a tremendous gift for dreaming and visualizing where we ought to go and how we ought to do it," Herman Sutherland, chairman of the Board of Trustees, said in a 1993 *Kansas City Star* article after Dr. O'Donnell's hiring. "He's good with the public; he has a sweet way about him. We just want him to run … a good hospital."

The time under Dr. O'Donnell's leadership turned out to be a whirlwind of building activity, expansion of the hospital staff, increased attention to medical research, extended community outreach efforts and collaborations with partners near and far. The work was happening simultaneously. Children's Mercy was transforming from a sometimes-overlooked children's hospital into a valuable community asset and a crown jewel of the metropolitan area.

## Bigger, better …

Change came quickly. The Hall Family Outpatient Center opened on Hospital Hill in September 1995 with dozens of specialty clinics ranging from orthopedics and cardiology to dentistry and developmental and behavioral health. Thousands of Kansas Citians, including many children, attended an open house that included costumed characters, ice cream and other treats, and a scavenger hunt that encouraged visitors to make their way through the entire five-story clinic building. Barely more than a year later, the Herman and Helen Sutherland Patient Tower opened, providing a new Pediatric Intensive Care Unit, Neonatal Intensive Care Nursery and private rooms for other patients.

*Articles marked the arrival of a new CEO.*

*Talking medical things over in the Pediatric Intensive Care Unit were Dr. Gerald Woods, third from left, and others, above. Also important was keeping a young patient's feet warm, right.*

Dr. Cox, who by 1995 had become a vice president for Patient Care Services, said that the new space, although much needed and appreciated, created demand for even more.

"The minute that tower opened," Dr. Cox recalled in 2016, "it was a crisis. The building was full and I spent a large part of my time dealing with complaints from families who were in the (older part of the hospital) because we didn't have private rooms.

"Imagine if you went to check into a hotel and they said, 'We have your reservation and you'll be sharing a room with somebody.'"

As a result, yet another new patient tower was added to the ever-evolving, ever-growing, never-ceasing wish list.

The new spaces were different in other ways. Gone were long hallways and rooms with drab green-and-white walls. Instead, bright colors and drawings of fanciful characters covered the walls and windows were built so the outdoors could be seen from a child's height. Mobiles hung from the ceiling and kaleidoscope designs enlivened the carpeting.

In the rotunda off the main lobby a spectacular star field of lights brightened the domed ceiling. On the wall nearby was a panel of buttons. When pushed, they changed the color of lights in the ceiling from red to blue to green or various combinations. The artist who designed the dome, Italian inventor Remo Saraceni, put in a shooting star that caught viewers by surprise and delighted children as it sailed across the "sky."

In front of the hospital the Sybil Silkwood Nutter playground – named for the little girl and her friends who put on plays to raise money in the early 1900s – was added in 1999. Built into the sidewalk was the largest working piano keyboard in the world, also designed by Saraceni, who devised the giant keyboard that actor Tom Hanks danced on in the movie "Big." An in-house artist, Donald "Scribe" Ross, joined the Children's Mercy staff in 2003 and added whimsical characters and bright colors to everything from hallways to ambulances.

Without a doubt, this was a place for children. A sign above the entrance to the Hall Family Outpatient Center proclaimed: "The Children of Missouri and Kansas Welcome You to Their Hospital."

*Northward expansion in the early 1990s. A lively entrance took shape, below right. Meanwhile, buses dropped off employees at the old one.*

*The Neonatal Intensive Care Unit, extensively equipped and colorful, inside the Herman and Helen Sutherland Patient Tower, which opened in 1996. Below: Caring for a patient in the Pediatric Intensive Care Unit.*

## Branching out

By the 1990s, Kansas City had more interstate highway miles per resident than any other metropolitan area in the United States, and still kept spreading south, north, east and west. By some estimates, it was the most sprawling city in the country. That growth and the distances involved put pressure on businesses: How to serve a population that lives and works farther and farther from downtown? Children's Mercy was no different.

In 1987 the hospital opened an outpatient Specialty Center with pediatric specialty clinics at 5520 College Blvd. in Overland Park, Kansas. An after-hours Urgent Care Center was added in 1993. The Specialty Center saw more than 15,000 visits a year and the Urgent Care Center nearly 7,000. Also in 1993, an outpatient surgery center opened near 87th Street and I-35. In 1996, 475 surgeries took place there.

Population in the southern part of the metropolitan area continued to increase. After talks with area pediatricians about

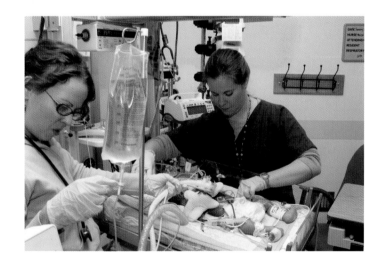

the growing demand, Children's Mercy officials decided it was time for something new.

In August 1995, Children's Mercy purchased the building of The Kansas Institute, a closed psychiatric hospital,

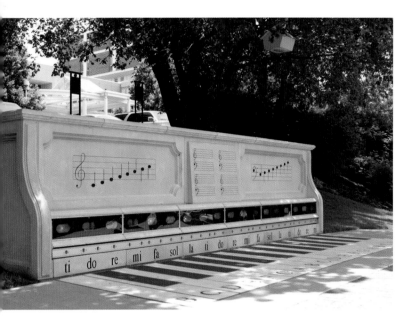

*Outside the hospital: The biggest keyboard that there was – and it worked, left. Above, the Sybil Silkwood Nutter playground was named for the little girl who put on neighborhood plays to support the hospital in the early 1900s. Sybil's children and grandchildren have continued her spirit of giving into the 21st century.*

at I-435 and Nall Avenue in Overland Park. About a year later renovations began, transforming the space into a new kind of community hospital, one just for children but without intensive care or emergency services. In September 1997, Children's Mercy South opened.

"We are excited to be ... taking a more visible, active role in the communities we serve in the south metropolitan area," Dr. O'Donnell said in a press release at the time.

The three-story brick building offered expanded access to an array of pediatric services, including:

• Sixteen outpatient specialty clinics in addition to the ones already operating nearby at College Boulevard and Nall Avenue.

• Two outpatient operating rooms, replacing the surgery center on 87th Street.

• An after-hours Urgent Care Clinic, to treat illnesses or injuries that are not life-threatening.

• Radiology and laboratory services.

• A short-stay inpatient unit.

Children's Mercy was the first children's hospital in the country to open a short-term inpatient unit – with stays limited to two or three days – at a satellite campus. The untried idea was risky, Jerry Blouin, chief operating officer at the time, acknowledged. But both families and physicians in the southern portion of the metro area indicated they wanted care closer to home. The bet paid off, and today the number of beds at what is now called Children's Mercy Hospital Kansas has more than doubled, to 54. Children's hospitals in other cities, including Dallas and Cincinnati, have followed the Children's

Mercy model.

Another innovative program at the Kansas hospital was the introduction to the Kansas City market of a new pediatric specialty – hospitalists. Hospitalists are doctors trained in primary care and based full-time at the hospital. They care for patients only during their stay, reducing the demand on pediatricians in the area. Those pediatricians can refer their patients to Children's Mercy Hospital Kansas and not have to take time away from their private practice. The hospitalist concept succeeded and eventually spread to Children's Mercy Hospital on Hospital Hill and to other hospitals.

The campus at I-435 and Nall proved an immediate success. The after-hours clinic had 14,263 visits in 1997, double the number experienced the previous year at the earlier location at 5520 College Boulevard.

Visits to the outpatient clinics rose 15 percent over the previous year. Less than a year after the I-435 and Nall campus opened, plans got underway for expansion. Adjacent land was purchased from Sprint in 1998, bringing the total to 12 acres. The next year, plans were presented to the city of Overland Park to add as many as 200,000 square feet to the site, including a new Children's Mercy building. It took several years, but in 2004 Children's Mercy Hospital Kansas opened a four-story addition, providing expanded room for surgery, urgent care and outpatient clinics. The hospital also continued to operate clinics at the building at 5520 College Boulevard, at its intersection with Nall Avenue, where the original Specialty

*Inside and all around, visual excitement – in the cafeteria, in midair inside the lobby, above, and at a nurses station, where shelves held lots of books and games.*

Center was situated.

The Kansas hospital, McGinness said, positioned Children's Mercy strongly in a growing part of the city.

"We are responsible for the kids and if the kids aren't going to come downtown they ended up in adult hospitals," he said. "We needed the satellites to be accessible for all children

*The hospital opened its first clinic in Johnson County at College Boulevard and Nall Avenue, top, in 1987. Ten years later, the south campus opened nearby.*

and all of their needs."

It was that same thinking, he said, that led Children's Mercy in 1998 to purchase the private practice of two Wyandotte County pediatricians, Drs. David M. Porter and Stephen P. Schaum. The two doctors had worked together for 25 years, serving primarily poor families in central and western Wyandotte County. The Children's Mercy employee newsletter, the *Messenger*, described the new partnership:

"For Drs. Porter and Schaum, it is an opportunity to ensure long-term accessibility to high quality pediatric care for their patients. For Children's Mercy, the change allows the hospital to work with well-respected community pediatricians to further extend the hospital's resources to an underserved area of the community."

On January 4, 1999, the office opened with the same staff – including the two doctors – and a new name, Children's Mercy Parallel Parkway Office, at 4517 Troup Avenue, just west of I-635 and Parallel Parkway. The Parallel Parkway office grew considerably and in 2007 moved to a new building at I-635 and State Avenue. It was renamed Children's Mercy West – The Cordell Meeks Jr. Clinic. Meeks was chairman of the hospital Board and a Wyandotte County judge when he died in 2006. In 2016, the clinic would see 17,000 patient visits a year.

This was the second doctor's office Children's Mercy purchased. The first was acquired from Blue Cross Blue Shield and folded into the Pediatric Care Center, which serves mostly children whose families have

*Murals made to capture the imagination at Children's Mercy on the Adele Hall campus. The hallway leads to surgery rooms.*

Medicaid insurance. The Pediatric Care Center has operated in various places – near 31st and Main streets, inside the Children's Mercy Clinic and Research Building on Hospital Hill, and, since 2011, at 31st Street and Broadway. In a letter to pediatricians in 1998, Dr. V. Fred Burry, the executive medical director, said that "as primary care in both Missouri and Kansas has evolved into a managed care model, it has become essential that we have a strong network of primary care providers who are geographically distributed in order to serve the Medicaid pediatric population."

## Promoting research

One part of Katharine Richardson's vision that she did not live to see fulfilled was a comprehensive research program to combat childhood disease. Although research had long been a part of Children's Mercy, hospital leaders unveiled their first comprehensive and detailed Research Vision in 1995. It began to crystallize with the hiring of Dr. Ralph Kauffman on July 1 of that year.

Children's Mercy declared its intent to build, staff and support a top-quality pediatric research program and stressed what it would mean for children. The scientists would work in state-of-the-art laboratories. With its connection to Children's

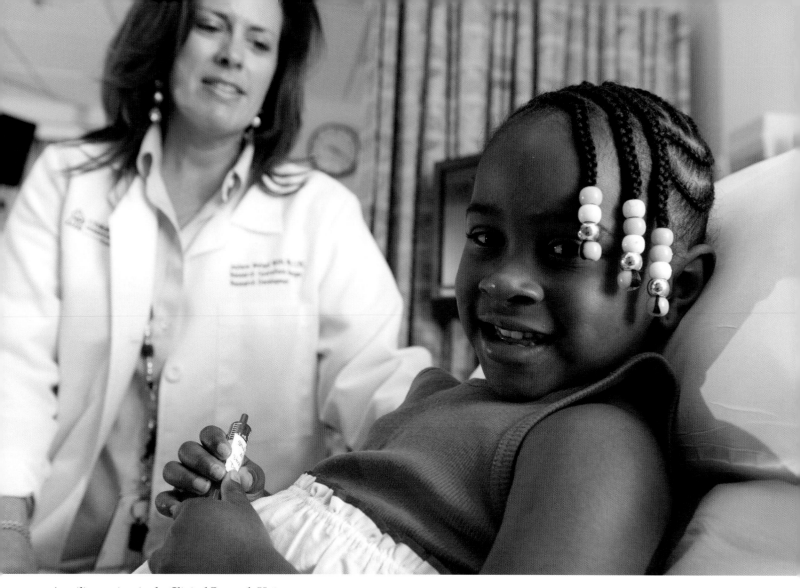

*A smiling patient in the Clinical Research Unit.*

Mercy patients and families, the research program would offer unrivaled pediatric "bench to bedside" opportunities.

Dr. Kauffman was an established researcher in clinical pharmacology and immediately began to assemble a team of respected scientists to continue that work. Much research had been done on pharmaceuticals for adults, but little on most of the medications given to children. The Clinical Pharmacology lab Dr. Kauffman established at Children's Mercy in 1996 was one of only seven funded by the National Institutes of Health in an effort to close that gap.

In addition to Clinical Pharmacology, the Research Vision included genetics and "core laboratories," defined as work with the best chance to be developed quickly and taken directly to clinicians and children.

Continuing the research effort, the second of the two towers resulting from the Centennial Campaign opened in 1999, named for philanthropists Paul and Betty Henson. Henson had led the telecommunications company that became Sprint. The new tower included not only the largest pediatric clinical pharmacology lab in North America, but also a unique Clinical Research Unit containing patient rooms and equipment to carry out a variety of research studies in a safe setting. Research was taking its place as a part of the hospital's foundation.

That same year, the hospital launched the Discovering Tomorrow campaign to support research. By 2001, under the leadership of Dee and Fred Lyons, Discovering Tomorrow reached its goal of $34 million.

Fred Lyons was an executive at Marion Merrell Dow, successor to a pharmaceutical firm, Marion Laboratories, that had been started in Kansas City by Ewing Marion Kauffman. Kauffman, best known by most Kansas Citians of the late 20th century for founding and owning the Kansas City Royals, also created the Kauffman Foundation. The foundation, headquartered near Kansas City's Country Club Plaza, focuses on entrepreneurialism and education.

Lyons and another Marion executive, Ed Connelly, persuaded the Kauffman Foundation to endow the first of several research chairs at Children's Mercy. Dr. Ralph Kauffman, no relation to Ewing Kauffman, became the occupant of the Marion Merrell Dow/Missouri Chair in Pediatric Medical Research. There is also a Marion chair in clinical pharmacology, and Fred and Dee Lyons personally endowed the Dee Lyons chair in pediatric genomic medicine.

Children's Mercy was one of the founding partners, in 2001, of the Kansas City Life Sciences Institute, a collaboration of hospitals and teaching institutions in the metropolitan area focused on bringing bioscience research and its benefits to Kansas City. Children's Mercy doctors have a long history of research collaborations and teaching affiliations with strong academic partners. That helps provide a foundation to attract highly qualified scientists and clinicians.

## Comfort for patients and families

Dr. O'Donnell's vision went beyond new buildings and groundbreaking research. As a student in hospital and health administration at the University of Iowa, he was the first PhD candidate anywhere to prepare a dissertation on the benefits of "psycho-social" care of children. The essence of the concept was that children recovered faster if all their needs, not just medical ones, were addressed. Dr. O'Donnell, writing in 1977, titled his dissertation "The Psychological Effects of Childhood Hospitalization: Implications for Pediatric Health Care Delivery." He was one of the early advocates of what today is commonly referred to as patient-centered and family-centered care.

Some of the programs that formed this kind of care were not new to Children's Mercy. From the earliest days of the hospital, sisters Alice Graham and Katharine Richardson knew their patients needed special care because they were children. In the 1920s, Mercy opened a playground at the

*Westward into Wyandotte County.*

hospital to help kids heal. It also started a school to help make its patients' environment as normal as possible.

"Children are not small adults," is the credo for this style of comprehensive care. Psycho-social programs include chaplaincy, child life, social work and others that empower patients and families in decisions.

Children's Mercy hired its first chaplain, Dane Sommer, in 1987. Despite the fact that a volunteer network of chaplains existed at the hospital part-time, he recalled, many people were unsure of his role.

"When I got here, there was really a big question about what you are supposed to do with a chaplain," said Sommer,

*In the radiology department, a Child Life specialist talked things over with a patient, a play replica of the scanner close at hand.*

who would still be at the hospital in 2017 as head of Spiritual Services.

One of the reasons it could be difficult for people at Children's Mercy to embrace the concept of chaplains is the hospital's nonsectarian heritage. The founding sisters were adamant about supporting all children, regardless of their faith – or lack of it.

Over time, chaplains were embraced throughout Children's Mercy. They serve not only patients and families, but also staff. There was a small chapel in the hospital both on Independence Avenue and on Hospital Hill, complete with donated stained glass windows and pews made by Katharine Richardson. The small Hospital Hill chapel still exists, but a newer, bigger space was opened in 2012, the Lisa Barth Chapel.

"We have a place where all people are welcome," Sommers said, "where people of faith, people with a religious tradition or people who would describe themselves as non-

believers or non-religious can come together and have a place they can go and … kneel and pray or they can go sit in quiet or they can read a book, listen to music – a gathering place."

By the early 1990s, chaplaincy and social work were well-established.

The Child Life department, on the other hand, was in its infancy. Child Life works to make things comfortable for patients and families by helping reduce stress, helping children cope with their emotions and encouraging them to learn and grow during their stay.

Children's Mercy had long recognized the importance of "letting kids be kids" and had a Patient Activities Department. But Stacey Koenig, hired in 1993 as the first child life specialist, said there were opportunities to expand the program.

"One of the very first things we did was to schedule play sessions," she said. "It was purposeful play, therapeutic play that had some medical sense around it. We got out syringes and bandages and all those things that kids were experiencing in the hospital and we started playing with them and children got to express their anxieties and their fears through play. Things that were unknown to them, we worked through it."

As with chaplaincy, some medical professionals doubted the value of Child Life. But Koenig and her team, backed by the CEO and other hospital leaders, persisted.

She recalled a watershed moment with Dr. Stanley Hellerstein, the kidney specialist who had been on the staff since the 1960s.

"Dr. Hellerstein was working on a procedure where the children had to give a urine sample and they would just freeze," Koenig said. "They couldn't get the kids to do it because they were scared. They felt such a loss of control."

Child Life specialists went to work, helping the patients understand that they had a job to do, and that there would be a beginning and an end to the process. It worked and it helped the doctors and other staff get their jobs done, too. Dr. Hellerstein reported the success to the medical staff.

"He said, If you are doing a procedure on a child and you don't have Child Life there, you aren't doing the procedure right and you're not doing the child right," she said. "Those were the Ah-ha! moments that allowed us to do our jobs and help the children."

Child Life grew to include other kinds of therapy, some involving music and even dogs.

Koenig also helped boost the hospital's volunteer and family-centered care programs. Along with Dr. Cox, who saw firsthand the value of parents as partners in the cancer unit in the late 1980s, Koenig pushed to establish the Family Advisory Board. It took a sales job to convince some of the staff who, she said, did not see families as partners in care.

"The Family Advisory Board provided timely and important information to our staff so we could do things better for patients and families," Koenig said. "And it all started through volunteerism. If we hadn't opened the door for some of our parents to come back and volunteer, we would have completely missed out on some great strides."

Today, there are several family advisory groups – among them Consejo, an advisory group for Spanish-speaking families – as well as a Teen Advisory Board of patients. Parents serve on committees throughout the medical center and there are two former Family Advisory Board members who are full-time Children's Mercy staff members, working as advocates for the families' interests.

## Solving finances

Access for all children, opening new buildings, hiring more staff and responding to change in the health care insurance industry complicated the hospital's financial picture. All the while, Children's Mercy worked to remain nimble and innovative.

In 1998, Children's Mercy joined Truman Medical Center to form Family Health Partners, a managed-care network of physicians for Missouri Medicaid patients. Financially, it worked this way: FHP received a payment from the state to cover the cost of care based on the number of patients enrolled in the plan. If the patients were healthy and needed little or no care, FHP kept the money and the profit. If the younger patients were sick and needed care or hospitalization, Children's Mercy would provide the care and be reimbursed by FHP.

"It allowed us to do the right thing for the children and their families," said Bob Finuf, who was president of Family Health Partners.

When families chose an insurance network, nearly half of those in the Kansas City region picked the Children's Mercy/Truman plan.

Not all other health plans included Children's Mercy and coverage was denied to some patients. Children's Mercy still pledged to take all children regardless of their ability to pay, but it also fought to be included in more plans.

Some insurers complained about the cost of care at Children's Mercy. Indeed, because of its extensive specialty and support services, it was not the cheapest option. Yet doctors and supporters spread the word to business leaders – whose choice of employee benefits would influence insurers – that Children's Mercy remained the best option. They pointed to facilities, expertise and ancillary programs such as Child Life. The bottom line, they said, was better care.

About the same time, President Bill Clinton sought to expand health insurance coverage. Although his broad attempt at health care reform was squashed in 1993, Clinton and Senator Ted Kennedy of Massachusetts kept trying to find

*A research program, one of the founders' dreams, got a boost in the early 2000s.*

ways to help struggling families. The result, in 1998, was the State Children's Health Insurance Program, which basically expanded the Medicaid program to more families. That meant more Children's Mercy patients had at least some way to pay for their health care, lessening the hospital's reliance on other sources.

Meanwhile, Dr. O'Donnell worked with the National Association of Children's Hospitals and other children's hospital CEO's to expand support for children's hospitals that trained medical residents and fellows. Medicare reimbursed adult hospitals for training but not children's hospitals, for the most part. In 1999, Clinton included Children's Hospitals Graduate Medical Education Funding in the federal budget.

*Facing page: As part of the tradition established by the hospital's founders, the Lisa Barth Chapel serves all creeds, believers and non-believers.*

The result was about $5 million for Children's Mercy. Dr. O'Donnell was in Washington standing next to Clinton when the bill approving the funds was signed.

Although Children's Mercy was never flush with cash, said Joe Galeazzi, the vice president of medical administration, "we never went into what I would call lockdown mode." Doing so might have entailed layoffs, spending freezes or, even worse, denial of services.

"It is a real testament to the belief and trust in our employees," Galeazzi said, "that if they said a patient needed something, we trusted that was what was best for the patient and we'd figure out how to pay."

Dr. Charles Roberts, executive medical director since 2010, agreed, saying:

"If the kiddo needs a test, give him the test. If he doesn't, don't do it. Don't worry about the money."

As some hospital administrators worked tirelessly to

*The Child Life department
works to ease the stress of
hospitalization – with the help
of musical instruments, top, by
discussing treatments using dolls
and toys, above, and by explaining
procedures to children old enough
to understand.*

FOR ALL CHILDREN EVERYWHERE

shore up finances, others continued to work on expansion plans for new programs and buildings. McGinness said the hospital was rolling the dice – in a calculated way.

"We believed that if we did the right thing in the right way, the community would respond."

And it did.

## Spreading the word

Children's Mercy "sold" its expansion ideas, in part, by making a more concerted effort to tell its story. Within a few months of arriving in Kansas City, Dr. O'Donnell recruited one of his former Arkansas Children's Hospital colleagues, Barbara J. Mueth, to establish a larger public relations and marketing program. The hospital hired its first advertising agency, Kansas City-based Bernstein-Rein, and the public began to see billboards and TV commercials promoting Children's Mercy. Hospital advertising – like legal advertising – was a new phenomenon nationwide in the early 1990s.

Public relations staff was hired to ensure the hospital's story was told in newspapers and on television. A weekly

## Relieving pressure on the emergency room

The cost of medical care has been a concern for decades. Part of the reason for higher costs is that medical care has simply become better, and with improvement comes cost. Among other things, medical progress involves advanced equipment, more and better-educated staff, larger rooms and more precise pharmaceuticals. Government regulations and patient expectations also contribute to higher costs.

Another part of the complex cost equation is the use – sometimes warranted and sometimes not – of emergency rooms that must be prepared for everything. Not every child who shows up in the emergency room is a true emergency case. But all are taken seriously at Children's Mercy.

"I try not to look at the fact that these cases aren't really an emergency because there's a reason they came here," said Laura Fitzmaurice, MD, head of the Emergency Room, in a 1995 KMBC-TV documentary "Angels of Mercy." Her comments rang true in 2017 as well.

"Perhaps the parents perceived it as an emergency," she said. "Maybe they don't have a physician. If somebody comes, we have to treat them. And after hours, in the evenings, there aren't a lot of other places for them to go."

As part of its efforts to rein in costs, Children's Mercy took steps to provide care without relying unnecessarily on a highly trained, fully staffed and equipped regional pediatric trauma center open around the clock.

Children's Mercy established the Medical Clinic in the 1960s to provide routine care for children who might otherwise seek it in the Emergency Room, or not at all unless it became serious – and thus more complicated and costly to treat. By the middle 1970s the Medical Clinic became the Pediatric Care Center, which was one of the busiest clinics in the hospital. The Center's aim was to provide a medical home for children and to give them preventive care, too.

In the 1980s a fundraising campaign sought, among other things, to increase the availability of primary care offered by private family doctors and pediatricians or through the Pediatric Care Center. Later in the decade, an appeal for more local government funding again included seeking outside partners in primary care.

The Pediatric Care Center has expanded several times, moving to larger locations near 30th and Main streets, inside the Clinic and Research Building on Hospital Hill and, finally, to the Clinics on Broadway in 2011. It operated 56 exam rooms on two floors at 31st and Broadway in 2016, mostly serving children with Medicaid. Children's Mercy West in Wyandotte County is also a primary care clinic. In Fiscal Year 2016, the primary care clinics had a combined 77,899 visits.

Children's Mercy also established a metropolitan-area network of Urgent Care Centers to treat children when their primary care doctors are unavailable. Urgent Care is for conditions that need prompt attention yet are not life-threatening. The cost of an urgent care visit averages only one-third the cost of a trip to the emergency room. Insurance coverage varies.

The first Children's Mercy urgent care, called the Night Clinic, opened in 1993 in Overland Park. Today, Children's Mercy operates urgent care centers at Children's Mercy Northland, East and Blue Valley. In Fiscal Year 2016, the urgent care centers recorded 82,277 visits.

Meanwhile, Emergency Rooms at Children's Mercy Hospital and at Children's Mercy Hospital Kansas kept plenty busy. In Fiscal Year 2016, the two ERs had 109,223 visits, about one every five minutes of every day.

*In the 1990s, First Lady Hillary Clinton visited patients at Children's Mercy as part of a national tour on behalf of children's reading.*

"Healthy Kids" news release on timely children's health topics was printed by dozens of small-city papers throughout Kansas and Missouri.

More people than ever saw the Children's Mercy name and the message that it represented the sensible choice for children's treatment. The message pointed to the hospital's vast expertise – more staff pediatricians than all other hospitals in the region combined – and its ability to handle nearly any challenge. Children's Mercy representatives continued to carry the same message face-to-face to large employers to make sure their company-sponsored insurance plans included Children's Mercy.

Staff also began appealing to national media. Perhaps the biggest public-relations coup of the time happened on the cusp of the hospital's centennial celebration when *Child* magazine in its February 1997 issue named Children's Mercy one of the top eight children's hospitals in the country.

"We have long known we were one of the best," Dr. O'Donnell said at the time. "We are all working hard to make this the best children's hospital in the world and it is a credit to all of the employees and the medical staff to make the *Child* magazine list. Our children and families deserve the best – and we give it to them. Now, this is no longer our secret."

*Child* continued to rank hospitals for many years and Children's Mercy remained on the list even as its ratings questionnaire grew more complex and comprehensive.

*U.S. News & World Report* magazine also ranked hospitals then – and still does. Until 2005, however, its rankings for children's hospitals were based strictly on reputation among a group of about 100 pediatricians, who worked predominantly on the East Coast and had a preference for research institutions. Children's Mercy was not mentioned. But when *U.S. News* began using a qualitative and quantitative survey that hospitals across the country were invited to fill

# How to make it happen? Listen, lead, learn

In a decade beginning in the mid-1990s Children's Mercy, the struggling little hospital-that-could, became a health care juggernaut.

Besides new buildings, new programs and new staff, the hospital experienced a cultural shift – a change in attitude. First came what some considered an absurd proclamation – our institution will be the best children's hospital in the world. That became a rallying cry. Staff and others began to believe it. A vision of what could be and what should be captured the attention of those inside and outside the organization.

In 2005, the Robert Wood Johnson Foundation asked

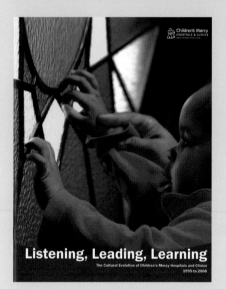

Children's Mercy to chronicle its cultural transformation, its success in going "from good to great." It was one of 10 hospitals in the United States chosen to document its effort, and the only children's hospital in the group. Children's Mercy was singled out as a model for improving culture to more effectively meet the needs of patients, to promote a positive work environment and to support the goals of the organization. The aim was to provide a tool kit for other hospitals that might want to follow suit.

Over a year, project managers interviewed dozens of hospital employees and community members and looked at data from a variety of sources. The result was a booklet, written by CEO O'Donnell and COO Cox, "Listening, Leading, Learning," which outlined the steps Children's Mercy had taken from 1995 to 2006, and gave concrete examples of changes and improvements.

The authors of the study found measures to gauge success everywhere: over the decade the number of beds doubled, as did the number of employees. Net revenue more than doubled and charity care as a percentage of total charges

## The findings

| Facility/staff size | 1995 | 2005 |
|---|---|---|
| • Bed count | 167 | 310 |
| • Employee (FTEs) | 1,768 | 3,511 |
| • Annual employee turnover | 15.7% | 12.2% |
| • Medical staff | 350 | 528 |
| **Financial** | | |
| • Net revenue | $137 million | $382 million |
| • Patient charges | $209 million | $673 million |
| • Charity care* | $19.9 million (1996) | $13.4 million |
| • % of patient charges | 9.5% | 1.9% |
| • Medicaid patients | 47% | 45% |
| • Foundation | $144 million | $212 million |
| • Annual giving | $4.4 million | $15.9 million |
| • Capital campaigns | $68 million (1992) | $120 million (2001) |

* Does not include shortfall from Medicaid not covering costs.

declined. Patient satisfaction rose. The endowment grew substantially, annual giving increased nearly four-fold and research funding increased to twice what it had been.

"Listening, Leading, Learning" credited a six-step process for the hospital's success:

- Articulate a bold vision – in this case, to be the best.
- View all employees as essential contributors.
- Expect excellence and encourage it.
- Place patients and families first.
- Reposition the organization externally.
- Stay open to failure and responsive to change.

Among the lessons leading to success:

- Organizations can be moved by lots of little changes, such as the decision to hire co-managers in nursing units or to tell all employees their job was patient care, combined with big changes, such as creation of a world-class Child Life Department or hiring previously contracted medical staff.

- Staff at all levels of the organization must be involved in projects that aim to affect the entire organization. Change can be initiated anywhere in an organization, but to be truly effective it must be pursued at all levels.

The report summed up the steps and the advice this way: Aim high. Hire talented people. Let them lead.

"A dramatic change had taken place at Children's Mercy over the past dozen years," the summary continued. "Patient and employee satisfaction is up; the financial picture is as bright as it has ever been; employees and the community are rallying around a vision to provide the best possible pediatric care in the finest environment. Quite simply: to be the best children's hospital in the world. We're not just talking the talk, we're walking the walk."

out, Children's Mercy cracked the list. By 2010, it was ranked in the Top 50 of all 10 specialties the magazine compared. Children's Mercy has remained ranked among the best ever since.

Magazine rankings were not the only national recognition for Children's Mercy. But they were a tangible and public measure of success. Among other things, they were aimed at increasing employee satisfaction, improving recruitment opportunities and bolstering community support. Other recognition for Children's Mercy followed, locally and nationally, as one of the best places to work, as an adoption-friendly workplace and as a company that welcomed and supported diversity.

## State of the art

As more and more parents wanted their children at "one of the best," Children's Mercy once again needed to make room. In 2001, the hospital, capitalizing on the success of the Discovering Tomorrow research campaign, launched yet another capital campaign. This campaign, named Destiny, sought more than $100 million, including:

• $32.7 million for a new four-story Clinic and Research Building atop a parking garage on the north side of the campus.

• $15 million for expansion at Children's Mercy South

• $6.2 million for what would become the Ward Family Heart Center

• $25 million in unrestricted endowment

• $15 million to cover the cost of uncompensated care and to support programs designed to improve the quality of care in such areas as asthma, diabetes and kidney disease.

• $9.9 million for a new floor in the Henson Patient Tower, which had just opened in 1999.

The capital expenditure budget for 2002 estimated more than $60 million in new construction in the next five years and $67 million more after that. In addition, there were millions in remodeling and millions more for equipment.

The Clinic and Research Building – containing "sparkling, state-of-the-art laboratories" on its top two floors – opened in 2004. It represented what the hospital termed

"a dramatic expansion of the research program at the region's only pediatric medical center."

Other parts of the Destiny campaign were equally successful. Davoren Tempel, the vice president for fundraising during this time of strong growth, described how the campaign approached potential donors:

"We had to talk about what all this would mean for the children. We had people at Children's Mercy with passion for what they did and we needed to connect them with the right donors. People give to other people, not to organizations."

Within a few years, the campaign ended after raising $120 million.

## It "woke everybody up"

Children's Mercy always had committed itself to high-quality care, yet achieving that goal had not always been easy. To address the need to improve meant raising the question of medical errors or system malfunctions. Few in health-related fields – and fewer lawyers who represented them – wanted to admit mistakes.

But the landscape changed in 1999 with the release of a study called "To Err is Human" by the Institute of Medicine, an arm of the National Academy of Sciences. The study estimated that as many as 98,000 people a year in the United States died as a result of "preventable medical errors."

Among those errors nationwide: giving the wrong kinds or wrong amounts of medication, conducting too many blood transfusions and patients being infected while under care.

# A new medication, a new life

Sick from the day she was born, Jenny Ray McGee saw more hospitals and doctors in her first 16 years than most people see in a lifetime.

As an infant, she couldn't eat, she couldn't sit up and she couldn't hold up her head. Doctors were at a loss. Her parents, Debbie and Mike, were told to make her comfortable because she would not live long.

Yet live she did, although her life was defined by a baffling neuromuscular disease. Doctors in Kansas City, at the Mayo Clinic and at Washington University in St. Louis all tried to help. They could provide only temporary relief, and her family kept searching for answers.

Her muscular weakness and lack of energy kept her on the ropes, overpowering the medicine and the transfusions she was receiving. She spent much of her time in a wheelchair and in braces. The hospital bills reached stratospheric heights, even omitting the cost of the family's moving to Minnesota or to St. Louis for weeks or months at a time. The emotional drain was immeasurable.

Then a Children's Mercy specialist took a chance. As a result, Jenny Ray's life filled with joy, and plans for college and medical school.

"She refused to give up and we refused to give up on her," said Debbie McGee. "She is our miracle baby."

In late 2005, Jenny Ray and her family went to see Dr. William Graf, who had just become chief of neurology at Children's Mercy. He decided to try something new. He

suspected Dopa Responsive Dystonia, or DRD. He was right.

DRD is a condition that usually begins in childhood or adolescence with progressive difficulty in walking and, in some cases, spasticity. Other symptoms can include developmental motor delay, tremors, muscle stiffness, abnormal tongue and mouth movements and Parkinsonian symptoms.

Jenny Ray had some of those symptoms, but not all. She also was sick from the time of birth. DRD often mimics other conditions such as muscular dystrophy or cerebral palsy so it is difficult to diagnose. Dr. Graf also said the diagnosis of DRD was made after treatment, not before.

"As physicians, we're used to making a diagnosis and then offering a treatment," he said. "But in this case, you give the medication [ levodopa ] – it does no harm to administer it – and if it is successful, you know you've found what it is."

Dr. Graf said discovering children with this readily treatable condition was one of the most rewarding experiences in the practice of pediatric neurology.

In the case of Jenny Ray, the effect of the medication was both immediate and amazing. The year 2006 was one of intense therapy, physical and psychological. After her graduation from high school, she hoped to begin a journey through medical school and specialty training to become a pediatric neurologist.

The reaction from the health care industry, recalled Dr. Cox, a chief operating officer at Children's Mercy, was disbelief. It wasn't that no one thought errors happened, but that so many deaths resulted from them.

"The IOM report woke everybody up," she said. "There were a lot of things, frankly, in health care that we thought were the price of being sick. You were at risk for infections: yes, that's true. And yes, there are some things that happen. But they just happen. That was the attitude.

"One thing a lot of people said was that it really can't be that bad, that there can't possibly be that many deaths. But my comment back to them was, what if it were only 10 percent of that? Would we be OK then, if errors only killed 9,000 people a year?"

The Institute of Medicine report said most of the errors resulted not simply from individual providers' doing something wrong, but from systemic problems in health care.

It concluded that everyone, not just doctors, needed to be encouraged to speak up and to ask questions as their part in keeping patients safe. Hospitals, including Children's Mercy, needed to become more transparent and to share information both within and outside their own organization. That led to collaboration among medical centers – like the kind represented by the Solutions for Patient Safety by the Ohio Children's Hospital Association – that extended well beyond Ohio.

In 2001, the Institute of Medicine followed up with a new report, "Crossing the Quality Chasm." It outlined six aims for improvement with an acronym, STEEEP: Safe, Timely, Effective, Efficient, Equitable and Patient-centered.

Children's Mercy embraced the goals and formed a new department, Quality and Clinical Safety, to integrate those

## About the name…

Although the official, legal name has not changed since 1919, Children's Mercy has used several different names to distinguish itself over the years.

In the early 1990s, as the hospital established itself as a comprehensive academic medical center with multiple locations, promotional materials, news releases and marketing tools began calling it "Children's Mercy Hospitals and Clinics."

About 20 years later, acknowledging its recognition in Kansas City and with a nod toward a growing national and international market, it dropped "hospitals and clinics" and began using "Children's Mercy Kansas City" outside the metro area and simply "Children's Mercy" in the metro area where the brand was well-known and beloved.

*1969*

*2002*

*Mid-1980s*

*1982*

*2013*

*Late-1990s*

*2013*

*OK, now ... Ah--h-h! Dr. Jay Portnoy worked with a patient in the Allergy Clinic at Children's Mercy.*

principles throughout its operation. Rapid Response Teams, which were to react within minutes to even subtle changes in a patient's condition, resulted from that work. Patient safety was redefined as everyone's responsibility.

"The most important thing in ensuring a culture of safety is that people can speak up," Dr. Cox said.

Checklists were created to guide procedures, as were clinical-practice guidelines, which used data collected over treating many patients to suggest treatments most likely to succeed. Before the guidelines, doctors relied primarily on their own experience and the experience of a few close colleagues.

The guidelines, also known as "evidence-based medicine" were discounted at first by some doctors who called them "cookbook medicine." They feared the guidelines would detract from their ability to provide care they thought best.

But Dr. Lloyd Olson, chief of pediatrics for 22 years before retiring from Children's Mercy in 2007, looked at it another way: "It asked the question: What is the evidence

that you have for making that decision?" Dr. Olson became a champion for evidence-based medicine for 10 years before he retired.

The first set of guidelines developed by Children's Mercy was for asthma patients. Too many were seen regularly in the emergency room, and they had come to be called "frequent flyers." A team reviewed literature to determine best practices and established the guidelines – which helped doctors know what to prescribe and how to help patients and families follow a treatment plan. The move led to a significant reduction in emergency room visits and hospitalizations. That initial team was led by Dr. Jay Portnoy, Chief of Asthma, Allergy and Immunology. Jackie Bartlett, a PhD and registered nurse who had helped Dr. Portnoy, was recruited to coordinate new clinical guidelines for other diseases. Today, Dr. Bartlett is director of the nationally recognized evidence-based practice program at Children's Mercy.

The quality of nursing care also helped increase recognition for Children's Mercy. In 2003, Children's Mercy

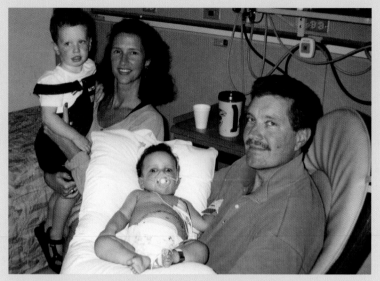

*When he was only 11 months old, Luke Harbur received a liver transplant at Children's Mercy, above. Two decades later, he was grown up and going strong, below.*

"Your child needs a liver transplant or he will die by the age of two."

Those 15 words changed the life path of our family.

In 1994 our first son, Cole, was born perfectly healthy. Sixteen months later, the birth of our son Luke was a very different story. Luke was born with liver disease and received a life-saving liver transplant at the age of 11 months – all because another family said "yes" to organ donation.

Luke's donor was Aaron Drake, an 8-year-old boy from Olathe, Kansas, who died from an allergic reaction while on a family vacation. In 1996, Luke became the recipient of one of

the first liver transplants performed at Children's Mercy Hospital. The place became our home for health care for the next 19 years.

Today, Luke is a thriving young adult and his medical team will forever be remembered. And Children's Mercy will always be a part of our hearts as a special place that gave us hope when often we felt that hope was not possible.

Because of the gift of organ donation that our family received we founded Gift of Life, a nonprofit organization in Kansas City. Gift of Life educates high school students about donation and supports families as they wait for a transplant.

Children's Mercy Hospital saved Luke's life, and in a different way we are saving lives too.

*– Nate and Kim Harbur*

became the first hospital in Kansas or Missouri to receive Magnet designation from the American Nurses Credentialing Center for quality of nursing and patient care. Only 6 percent of hospitals in the United States met the rigorous standards for that honor. Children's Mercy has earned the Magnet designation every three years since the first recognition.

In its 2005 visit to Children's Mercy, the major hospital accrediting body, the Joint Commission on Accreditation of Healthcare Organizations (later renamed simply The Joint Commission) delivered stellar marks to the hospital for meeting all the National Patient Safety Goals, such as improving effective communication and reducing infections. At the time, Children's Mercy received full accreditation with no recommendations for improvements, its highest ranking ever.

Since then, Children's Mercy has continued its efforts. Employees are regularly encouraged to look for new ways to improve care. As part of a project called "Listening, Leading, Learning," hospital leaders acknowledged that the system was not perfect:

"Steps are taken. Mistakes are made. Learning happens. When you champion the value of individual leadership, you have to accept the risks along with the rewards…. Children's Mercy must remain adaptable."

## North side, east side, all around the town

It's said that the only thing constant is change, and change was, indeed, constant at Children's Mercy in the 1990s and 2000s. There was no finish line, it seemed. Nowhere was that more obvious than in new buildings that accompanied the growth of clinical and research programs.

In addition to its operations in Overland Park and Wyandotte County, Children's Mercy in 2003 opened clinics and an urgent care center in the northern part of the metropolitan area. Children's Mercy Northland operated in a remodeled single-

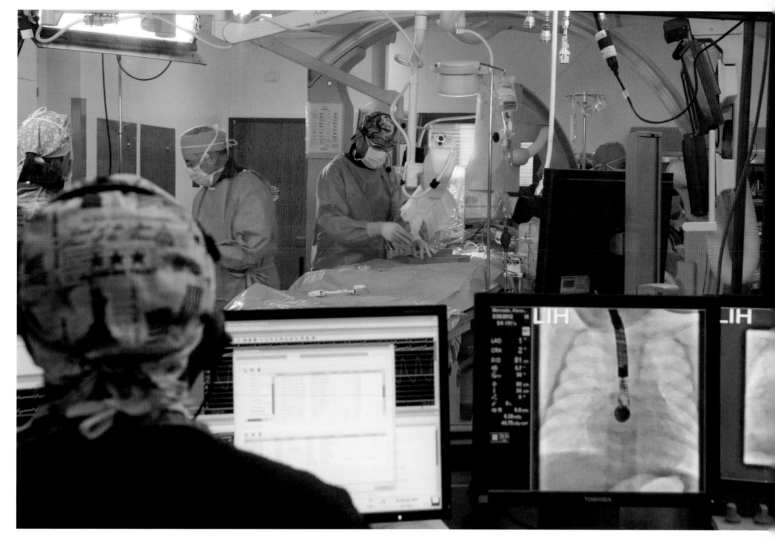

*Catheterization lab in the Ward Family Heart Center.*

story shopping center at Barry Road and U.S. 169. Laboratory and radiology services also were available at Northland, which became a popular destination for families from outside the metropolitan area who prefer not to make the drive into downtown Kansas City.

Reaching out farther than ever in 2003, Children's Mercy established a sister hospital relationship with Guangzhou Women and Children's Hospital in China. The hospitals share staff, education and information. Children's Mercy has since established similar relationships with another hospital in China and hospitals in Mexico and Panama.

In 2007, the Don Chisholm Center opened at 23rd and Holmes streets, just north of the Hospital Hill complex,

to provide office and education space for hospital employees and patients. It also houses a day care center for employees' children and the Center for Healthy Lifestyles, a collaborative research program in conjunction with the University of Kansas. Meanwhile, more employees began to work from offices in the nearby Crown Center complex.

In 2010 the hospital purchased out of foreclosure a 10-story office building at 31st Street and Broadway Boulevard and the next year opened Clinics on Broadway. The operation houses a variety of outpatient clinics, including the bustling Primary Care Center and the Teen Clinic.

In 2012, the final piece of a "circle of care" for children in Kansas City opened. Children's Mercy East occupies a three-story brick building at Little Blue Parkway and I-70 in Independence, Missouri. It includes the Edward G. and Kathryn E. Mader Urgent Care Center and more than a dozen specialty clinics to serve the families of eastern Jackson County, Missouri. Radiology and lab services are available. And there is vacant ground for expansion.

Outreach clinics in regional cities have been a part of Children's Mercy for more than 20 years. In 2012, Children's Mercy took a bolder step outside the Kansas City metropolitan area and established a permanent clinic for several specialties in Wichita, Kansas. It has since been expanded. A year later, similar clinics – staffed with specialists chosen specifically to meet the needs of the children in those cities – were established

in St. Joseph and Joplin, Missouri, in partnership with Mosaic Life Care and Freeman Health, respectively. Telemedicine services – through which doctors and others can see patients over a video connection – help expand the reach of the hospital by eliminating travel time when appropriate.

As the metropolitan area continued to grow, Children's Mercy Blue Valley opened in 2013 at 135th Street near Metcalf in south Overland Park. It provides urgent care and offers the expanding practice of sports medicine.

Pressure to control costs continued to grow, too. Children's Mercy branched into home-based care in 2003 with the purchase of a private-duty nursing agency that eventually became Children's Mercy Home Care. The service includes nursing, nutrition, medication and medical equipment services for patients in their homes throughout 33 counties surrounding Kansas City.

Serving a larger region became more feasible with the sophistication and expansion of the transport service, which was started by Dr. Robert T. Hall for infants in the 1970s. Children's Mercy Critical Care Transport provides more

*Helicopters and fixed-wing jets, along with ambulances are part of Children's Mercy's award-winning Critical Care Transport unit.*

than 5,000 ground and air trips a year and has been named Transport Program of the Year by the Association of Air Medical Services. The ambulances, helicopters and airplanes, both propeller and jet, are mobile pediatric and neonatal intensive care units. Specially trained nurses, respiratory therapists and emergency medical technicians accompany every trip. Patients are transported routinely within a 175-mile radius of Kansas City, and international transports have occurred.

## Helping in a hurricane

Perhaps the most dramatic transports happened in 2005, when Hurricane Katrina forced New Orleans Children's

*Children's Mercy reaches far and wide across the metro area. Clockwise from left: The Center for Sports Medicine on 135th Street in Overland Park; the Clinics on Broadway on 31st Street near downtown Kansas City; East at Little Blue Parkway and I-70 in Independence, and Northland at Barry Road and U.S. 169.*

Hospital to evacuate patients. Dr. O'Donnell worked quickly with his counterpart in New Orleans, as well as with U.S. Senator Kit Bond of Missouri and Governor Matt Blunt, who helped secure the aid of the Air National Guard based in St. Joseph.

The effort culminated in the largest single pediatric medical transport in history. Children's Mercy received 24 patients and their families from the Gulf Coast, flown 800 miles aboard two C-130 military transport planes. The Children's Mercy transport team also took several patients to other children's hospitals.

"When children are in need, you reach out and help," Dr. O'Donnell said at the time. "That is what we've been doing for more than 100 years in Kansas City. We could not sit by and wait."

Neither could other Kansas Citians. Not long after the children arrived, calls came to Children's Mercy from people who wanted to help. With patients ranging in age from three months to 23 years, suffering conditions such as cystic fibrosis, kidney failure and broken bones, Children's Mercy had the medical care covered. The total cost amounted to about $1.8 million.

Many families arrived in Kansas City with only the clothes on their backs. Some stayed at the hospital and others were put up for free or at discounted rates at area hotels. The Ronald McDonald House helped. Children's Mercy directed donations to the Family Support Fund, which helps families in out-of-the-ordinary situations.

*After Hurricane Katrina devastated New Orleans and the Gulf Coast in 2005, two dozen children and their families were airlifted to Children's Mercy for treatment, below. "We could not sit by and wait," said the hospital's CEO. Meanwhile, Kansas City kids raised money for them, above.*

In all, about $700,000 was raised for the 24 children and their families. The money came from 3,000 donors, of whom 2,150 gave to the hospital for the first time. Donations ranged in size from $1 to $60,000. Donors also gave other items such as toys and toiletries. Children's Mercy coordinated the shipment of truckloads of toys to Louisiana and Mississippi.

"Money was not part of the discussion," Dr. O'Donnell said. "We'd worry about that later. First we had to do the right thing and help save these children and families. I'm so proud of our community."

## More adventures

Throughout its history, Children's Mercy has appealed to its community so it would never have to let down the children. The same was true again in 2007, when leaders embarked on another ambitious plan of expansion. Called Healthier Ever After, plans called for new programs, new buildings, new staff and new endowed chairs.

Costs were almost mind-boggling, even for an

institution that had been growing constantly for nearly 20 years: hundreds and hundreds of millions of dollars over a dozen years with a second and third phase of unknown cost. Expectations were that spending could reach $1 billion.

The case for the expansion was made, in part, by the numbers. In the dozen years before 2007:

• Outpatient clinic visits rose 104 percent to more than 400,000 a year, including 133,000 Emergency Room and Urgent Care visits.

• Admissions increased 100 percent, to more than 15,000.

• Average daily census of inpatients went up 65 percent to 214.

• Surgical procedures rose 142 percent to nearly 16,000.

In 2007 alone, visits to the emergency room and urgent care increased by 12 percent, intensive-care nursery visits by 23 percent and critical-care transports by 18 percent. Projections were for growth of the pediatric population in the Kansas City region, and the hospital's service area expanded as well. Eighteen counties formed the primary service area for the hospital and Children's Mercy routinely saw patients from about 140 counties in Missouri and Kansas. Children's Mercy also faced more demand for space for intensive care and the need for a fetal health program for mothers with babies at high risk from congenital conditions; in response it opened the Elizabeth J. Ferrell Fetal Health Center. For the first time in its history, deliveries were performed at the hospital, bringing immediate help to high-risk babies. The 500th birth was recorded in 2016.

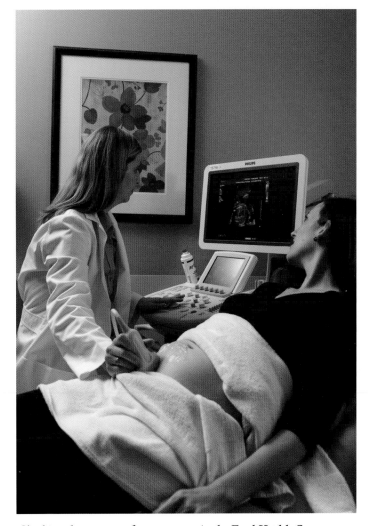

*Checking the progress of a pregnancy in the Fetal Health Center.*

## New designations

The era of change was marked not only by expansion but also by the restructuring of the Central Governing Board and the Board of Trustees, both of which had existed since not long after the hospital established itself in the early 1900s. In 2003, the Central Governing Board became simply the Board of Directors and the Board of Trustees became the Foundation Board of Directors.

The big dreams of Healthier Ever After faced rapidly shifting economic conditions as the United States entered the Great Recession. The health care industry was also in upheaval over rising costs and attempts at reform. After passage of the Affordable Care Act in 2010, political debate turned deeply partisan for the rest of the administration of President Obama. After he left office in 2017, discussion focused on ways to replace the act. While the debate raged, health care providers faced fiscal uncertainty and – at least for Children's Mercy – a seemingly unending stream of children in need of care.

Throughout it all, the hospital's Healthier Ever After campaign soldiered on. Appeals for the $100 million-plus fundraising campaign were presented with fairy-tale images

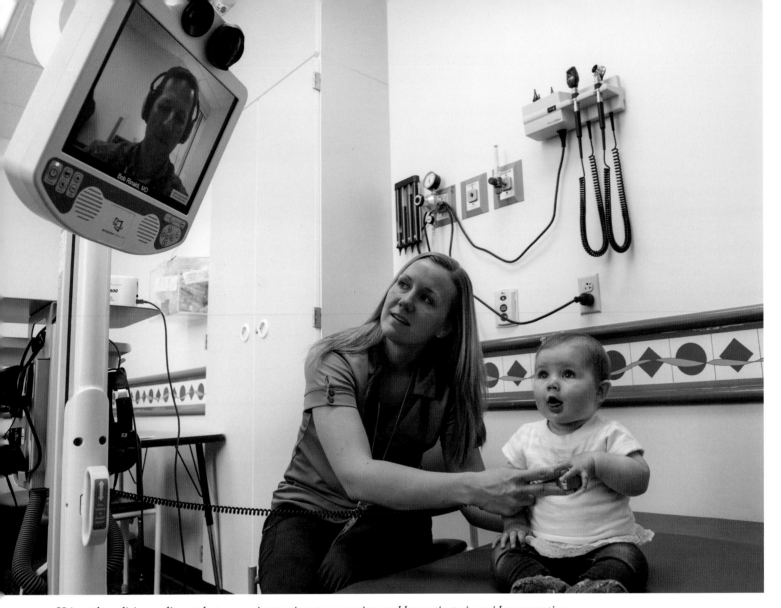

*Using telemedicine, a distant doctor gave instructions to a caregiver and her patient via a video connection.*

and context.

"Enchanted worlds still exist because the child within us never fades," the campaign materials proclaimed. "Fairy tales are more than true – not because they tell us dragons exist, but because they tell us that dragons can be beaten."

Children's Mercy was known for slaying dragons. Its success in taking care of children, in growing to become nationally recognized as one of the best, in expanding services where it could care for almost any pediatric condition, fueled the campaign.

By June 30, 2013, nearly $140 million had been raised. More than 21,000 donors made some 37,000 contributions, large and small. The hospital began a more active campaign to engage business. More than one company held a golf tournament to raise funds. (The Tom Watson event ended,

after 25 years, in 2004.) Hospital employees were engaged in new ways.

Money from Healthier Ever After supported construction of the new Elizabeth Ann Hall Patient Tower, the conversion of the urgent care center at Children's Mercy South into the Tom Watson Emergency Room and the opening of Children's Mercy East and the Clinics on Broadway. It also supported more research, five more endowed chairs and the hospital foundation.

Major new sources of philanthropy were also nurtured. The Hands and Heart Auxiliary, which had been raising money for the hospital since 1986, upped its game in 2005 by establishing a black-tie gala, Red Hot Night. By 2017, it was raising more than $2 million annually and was the single largest gathering of Children's Mercy supporters each year.

FOR ALL CHILDREN EVERYWHERE

*Behind a crew of mostly helpful shovelers, Adele and Don Hall, second from right and right, ceremonially broke ground for a new tower in 2010. Joining them were (back row from left), Page Reed, Sarah and Jon Baum and CEO Randall L. O'Donnell.*

In 2010, nationally known celebrities with ties to Kansas City launched a poker tournament and auction known as Big Slick. They later added softball and dropped poker for bowling. Big Slick quickly became the hottest ticket in town, with dozens of celebrities coming to Kansas City for the weekend to shine a light on Children's Mercy. The event, which engaged a new generation of generous Kansas Citians, also raised more than $1 million a year for the Children's Mercy Cancer Center.

Mary Hunkeler, who served on the hospital Central Governing Board and on hospital auxiliaries for decades, said the passion of people who supported children and Children's Mercy made it successful.

"It's not a hard sell," she said. "It's the right thing to do and you just do it. You always find time for the things you want to do. Some of the busiest people I know always found time for Children's Mercy.

"It's not about you. It's about helping those parents who have it 24/7, to give them a chance. It's about helping those children, giving them hope. And you know, the more that you give, the more that you have to give. It becomes an endless stream."

It's a stream that leads to a future of better health for children, their families and, ultimately, the community that cares for them.

*Following pages: The Elizabeth Ann Hall Tower, under construction in 2010. The colorful Gary Dickinson Family Bridge of Hope would connect it to Truman Medical Center.*

# A GIFT TO THE FUTURE

*"Others shall sing the song,*
*Others shall right the wrong.*
*Finish what I begin,*
*And all I fail of win"*

— From "My Triumph" by John Greenleaf Whittier,
engraved on the bench at Katharine Richardson and Alice Graham's gravesite

The task of caring for children never ends. Ask any parent. Your children are always your children. Your babies are always your babies.

When they set out to care for the poor, sick children of Kansas City 120 years ago, sisters Alice Berry Graham and Katharine Berry Richardson knew there was no end to the children and families who needed help. The leaders of Children's Mercy know the same holds true today.

All around "the hospital of the little people," progress and growth continue. The challenges are daunting. Sick children arrive nearly non-stop – more than 500,000 times a year, nearly one every single minute. Some have mysterious conditions that only a few years ago would have gone undiagnosed and untreated. Some have conditions that remain mysterious. Still, scientists come into the laboratories every day, and doctors and nurses visit the bedsides around the

*Facing page: Suma P. Goudar, MD, a pediatric heart specialist, examined a patient in 2015 while a parent looked on.*

clock, bringing hope and answers.

The leaders of Children's Mercy – whether the two strong women who in 1897 defied the odds to begin a charity hospital, or the doctors, nurses and others who in 2017 cared for all children and their families – have never shied away from a challenge.

Well into its second century of service, Children's Mercy finds itself continuing to take bold steps.

## "We are the experts"

As the 2010s unfolded, Children's Mercy found itself facing challenges as never before. When Alice and Katharine began their quest, they did so in part because no one else was doing what they did. Even today, Children's Mercy remains the only hospital in the region with a mission of caring solely for children, regardless of their ability to pay.

In the 1950s and 1960s, support grew in Kansas City for a single regional children's medical center. Children's Mercy was the choice. Other hospitals supported the idea and by the

*Celebrity hosts of the Big Slick benefit gathered with Children's Mercy patients and the Kansas City Royals' mascot, Slugerrr, at the pitcher's mound at Kauffman Stadium in June 2016. Hosts, from left: Jason Sudeikis, Rob Riggle, Eric Stonestreet, David Koechner and Paul Rudd.*

1980s several shuttered their pediatric services.

But by the 2010s, others in Kansas City, including for-profit companies, began to expand and market their care for kids. In 2016, CEO O'Donnell told employees Children's Mercy would not be deterred and reminded them of their legacy.

"No one is better at delivering excellent care than Children's Mercy," he wrote in a letter to employees. "We are the experts. No other health care system in our region can match what we provide.

"Perhaps most important, our non-profit doors are open to every child within our community – regardless of the family's ability to pay. As one of our co-founders, Katharine Berry Richardson, once said, 'I have not served children unless I have served them all.' Our community depends on us and we have delivered for 119 years."

## Raising the profile

Hospital leaders were determined to ensure a bright future. Consumer research showed that Children's Mercy had a near-universal positive reputation, yet most respondents struggled with articulating *why* it was a valuable and essential community asset. Given the hospital's new buildings, programs, equipment and staff, many in Kansas City had forgotten that Children's Mercy was a non-profit charity. Leaders decided to do something about that.

Among other things, they stepped up efforts to tell the unique Children's Mercy story: the story of its 700-plus-member pediatric medical staff; the story of thousands of patients and families who receive healing and hope; the story of amazing treatments and outcomes; and the promise of answers through expanded research.

To help tell those stories, the hospital in 2012 launched Discover Children's Mercy. The program invites a select group of people behind the scenes. The visitors – elected officials, business leaders, current or potential donors – ask questions, listen and learn. During their "mini-internship," visitors put on surgical gowns to observe open-heart surgery up close. They may spend time in the Neonatal Intensive Care Nursery, where some babies weigh less than two pounds. Others look at the pharmacy, lab or emergency transport operations. At the end of the program, the universal reaction is one of amazement.

"Discover Children's Mercy was beyond my expectations and well worth an entire day," said former Chiefs quarterback Trent Green. "In fact, I left wanting more."

Lynn Jenkins, a U.S. Representative from Kansas, said, "They are doing extraordinary work for the Kansas City area and region."

In 2014, the hospital gave even more people a look behind the scenes through a video documentary series shown on local and regional TV stations. "Inside Pediatrics" told stories of the patients, families and staff that make every day extraordinary at Children's Mercy.

The series took television viewers inside the clinics and operating rooms where pediatric specialists have one mission: bringing hope to every child. Narrated by actor Paul Rudd, co-founder of the Big Slick celebrity fundraiser for the hospital, "Inside Pediatrics" gave viewers an unprecedented look behind the walls.

In its two seasons, the series received impressive ratings and won two regional Emmys for outstanding programming. The series was just one example of the expanded effort on behalf of the hospital to provide the "why."

Boosting national reputation and raising the academic profile were both goals of a strategic plan updated in 2016. More emphasis was put on reaching out to national pediatric specialists throughout the United States with news and information. The hospital's website was revamped, expanded and supported by a dedicated team of programmers, database administrators and editors. As video production grew more commonplace with the advent of YouTube and cameras on mobile telephones, the hospital increased use of it to provide education and information to children, parents and referring partners. Telling stories through the traditional news media

*At work in the Center for Pediatric Genomic Medicine. Above: Sarah E. Soden, MD, left, and Carol J. Saunders, PhD. Below: A laboratory technician.*

as well as Facebook and Twitter also were expanded.

## Breakthroughs

Marketing could be successful only because Children's Mercy had stories to tell and news to report. Both kept coming. Medical advancements keep pushing the limits of the possible.

In 2011, Children's Mercy launched the Center for Pediatric Genomic Medicine. Among the first of its kind with a pediatric focus, the center serves patients directly and operates as a laboratory for genomic research. Hundreds of children affected by undiagnosed genetic diseases are referred to Children's Mercy each year. The center helps those families end the frustration of a diagnostic odyssey. In some cases the center discovers novel genetic causes of childhood diseases. In 2012, the Center introduced a test that analyzes the entire human genome in barely more than two days.

"Fifty hours. That's how long it now takes to decode and interpret a newborn baby's genome – an undertaking that used to take weeks or even months," *TIME* magazine reported in its "Top 10 Medical Breakthroughs of 2012." The test was named number seven on the list.

"And those two days," the report continued, "can mean the difference between life and death for a critically ill infant."

Three years later, in 2015, Children's Mercy scientists had reduced the time to a remarkable 26 hours.

The genome center works closely with many hospital programs, like cancer research, to develop personalized care based on individual genetics.

The hospital's Ward Family Heart Center also is embracing new technology to improve care and enhance quality of life through its innovative Cardiac High Acuity Monitoring Program, or CHAMP. The program relies on a computer application, or app, designed for patients with a specific heart condition. Patients can live in their homes, sometimes hundreds of miles from their cardiologist, while their conditions are monitored.

Parents use a tablet computer to enter the child's data into the app, which instantly analyzes the information and transmits it to the care team. Cameras allow video consultations with specialists. The program not only improves care and saves lives, but also reduces cost.

Nationally, 5 to 20 percent of babies with the rare single-ventricle heart disease, for which CHAMP was designed, will not survive the time between the first and second surgery necessary to correct the condition. A child with a single-ventricle defect is born with a heart that has only one ventricle – instead of two in a healthy heart – that is strong enough to pump effectively. In the first two years of using the CHAMP app, beginning in 2014, none of its 62 single-ventricle patients died. The American Nurse Credentialing Center awarded Children's Mercy its 2016 Magnet Prize to further develop CHAMP.

By summer 2016, CHAMP was being used for patients at Children's Mercy and also a children's hospital in Seattle, with plans to spread it to as many as 40 more.

Education of medical professionals, including nurses, doctors and allied health professionals, also remains critical to the hospital's mission. Just as the founders established a nursing school before Children' s Mercy had its own building, the training of doctors was, and is, vital to the future. Established as the training hospital for the University

*Winston Wahlgren had three heart surgeries in his first three years, the first in 2014 when he was only six days old. From his home home in Buhler in central Kansas, Children's Mercy monitored his health daily by way of the CHAMP software.*

of Missouri – Kansas City and the University of Kansas School of Medicine, Children's Mercy continues to expand opportunities for doctors through fellowship training in dozens of specialties. In 2016, Children's Mercy reported 465 medical students underwent training, along with 99 doctors in fellowship programs and 100 residents who play a crucial role in the care of patients. More than 1,400 students from dozens of nursing schools receive training at Children's Mercy.

## Research in the real world

Medical research has been a part of the Children's Mercy DNA since the beginning. Katharine Berry Richardson, one of the founding sisters, worked tirelessly to establish a research program at Children's Mercy. While she made some progress, she was not entirely satisfied.

In the 1920s, she wrote, "Never in the world did Mercy

want anything so much as it wants the Laboratory. Never in all its undertakings was there so great a possibility of good to be accomplished."

Yet the research program went unrealized and just months before her death in 1933, she wrote:

"Our work, yours and mine, is to hold Mercy Hospital to its very best while we live, to keep fully up with all that's decent – to somehow, some way, get a Research Laboratory for children's diseases – to work as though we are going to stay forever and to realize that what is best will live on in the hearts of others."

Fast forward about nine decades, and you can see much good. Children's Mercy scientists have been involved in a wide variety of successful research – into infectious diseases, clinical pharmacology, surgical techniques, diabetes and kidney disease.

Children's Mercy is one of the country's leading centers of neonatal research, particularly into chronic lung disease. William Truog, MD, Director of the Center for Infant Pulmonary Disorders, said he was particularly excited about the multidisciplinary approach – through cardiology, pulmonology, genetics and pharmacology – taken by Children's Mercy to find answers to help some of the 30,000 premature infants born each year in the United States.

Cancer research is unparalleled. Children's Mercy is the pediatric partner for the University of Kansas' National Cancer Institute consortium, which provides the most advanced cancer care and access to cutting-edge clinical trials. In addition, as a member of the international Children's Oncology Group, Children's Mercy participates in hundreds of research initiatives that have made a significant difference in the lives of children.

One example is in the treatment of neuroblastoma. Children's Mercy patients were part of national clinical trials that provided new methods of

treatment. In the late 1980s, only 10 percent survived the illness. By 2016, those surviving four years or more had risen past 50 percent.

"We are seeing tremendous advances," said Alan S. Gamis, MD, chief of Oncology at Children's Mercy. "Scientists at centers like Children's Mercy are moving from the test tube to the bedside."

In 2015, Children's Mercy took a giant step to boost its research program with the formation of the Children's Research Institute. The institute builds on the research initiatives laid out by the Research Vision in 1999. That effort increased funding for existing research and launched several research programs, including Clinical Pharmacology. The new institute serves as a bridge for all research at the hospital, helping researchers move their work more efficiently and effectively to patients. It will help ensure that genomics and clinical pharmacology are incorporated across the board to promote truly individualized, precise health care.

Tom Curran, PhD, became chief scientific officer and the first executive director of the Children's Research Institute in February 2016. Dr. Curran had been at Children's Hospital

*Oncology Section Chief Alan S. Gamis, MD, showed results to a patient named Pepito in 2015.*

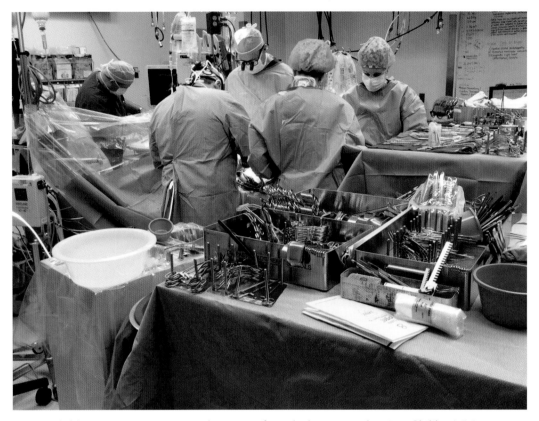

*Surrounded by equipment, surgeons and nurses performed a heart transplant in a Children's Mercy operating room.*

and uncollaborative," said David Westbrook, Children's Mercy senior vice president for strategy and innovation. His comments echoed those of hospital founder Katharine Richardson in the 1920s.

Westbrook said the large number of patients at Children's Mercy as well as efforts to share more information with other centers would benefit all patients. Medical advances in the future, he predicted, will depend on "big data."

"Doctors are very wise," he said. "But up to this point, the data they have been relying on has been mostly in their heads and the heads of a few close colleagues. We need volume. We need to tap into the data, into the minds of more doctors. We need information about all kinds of treatments and outcomes, not just our own."

Data warehouses and the internet cloud will make that possible. One goal for the Research Institute is to increase federal grants to Children's Mercy, which received $6.5 million from the National Institutes for Health in 2015. One way to do that is to attract researchers who bring established programs. And one way to do *that* is to increase the number of research-focused endowed chairs. Endowed chairs are faculty positions supported by a permanent source of funding.

As 2016 came to a close, Kansas City area philanthropists endowed four new such chairs, bringing the total at Children's Mercy to 20 endowed chairs.

The hospital received a grant from the Hall Family Foundation in 2016 to begin drawing plans for a new research building on the Adele Hall Campus. Dr. Curran said the building, projected to be nine stories tall with a total of 42,000 square feet, will be an outstanding recruiting tool and the "envy of the world" when it is completed.

of Philadelphia, where he served as deputy scientific director and director of basic scientific research in the Center for Childhood Cancer Research.

"Science and medicine should not be viewed as distinct entities," he said, "but rather as close partners, working in concert, to improve the health and well-being of all children."

The Children's Research Institute focuses on four main areas: pediatric genomic medicine, clinical pharmacology, health services and outcomes, and health care delivery.

Before establishing the Research Institute, Children's Mercy assembled a panel of national experts to consider the hospital's existing research capabilities. The group saw opportunity in the hospital's unique culture, its financial strength and its community support. Collectively, the group said, those assets set the stage for "extraordinary potential."

Part of the advantage is that Children's Mercy research is more collaborative than programs within larger academic medical centers and universities.

"Academic research tends to become very parochial

*Lights, color, action! The vivid front door to Children's Mercy. Not far away, a festive arch welcomes patients, families and visiotrs to the hospital.*

Research laboratories are not the only place where medical and health care advances happen. In 2015, on the day before Valentine's Day, Children's Mercy performed its first pediatric heart transplant. The recipient was 15-year-old Hanna Mountz of Kansas City, Missouri. She began her senior year of high school in fall of the next year.

Also in 2015, the Brendan Tripp Elam Transplant Center opened, gathering the collective strengths of the liver, kidney and heart transplant teams. The center's work is supported through a philanthropic gift from the family of Brendan, who in December 2012 received a liver transplant when he was 10 years old.

## Ideas from every corner

Part of the hospital strategic plan is an emphasis on innovation. Concrete evidence of that initiative is the Center for Pediatric Innovation, which opened in October 2015. The center is a gathering place for employees to brainstorm ideas.

"The Center for Pediatric Innovation carries on our

founders' forward-thinking beliefs by promoting a culture that empowers the masses to innovate, regardless of rank or status," said Dawn Wolff, senior director of strategy and initiative development.

The center is dedicated to new ways of thinking. In July 2016, the center hosted an Employee Innovation Bash to highlight two dozen new ideas from employees. Among ideas voted "best" by employees were ones to develop special padding on cribs for children with seizures, to "reinvent" arm bands and to provide new transportation wagons for children

*In March 2016, representatives of various business and government agencies gathered for a Children's Health Summit to discuss the biggest health problems facing children in Kansas City.*

in the hospital.

"Ideas come from every corner of the hospital – from physicians and nurses to human resources and security," said Krista Nelson, director of innovation development. "It's a great example of how empowered we all should feel to generate and advance creative solutions that will benefit the hospital and the kids and families we serve."

## Casting the net far and wide

Clearly, Children's Mercy could not fulfill its mission by itself. The adage that "it takes a village to raise a child" was nowhere more apparent than in the success of Children's Mercy.

First, the village itself has expanded. Growth that began in the early 2000s by ringing Kansas City with new clinic and urgent care locations continues beyond the metropolitan areas

to such places at Joplin and St. Joseph, Missouri, and Wichita, Kansas. Jo Stueve, a chief operating officer, said in 2016 that Children's Mercy was considering further expansion, both inside the metropolitan areas and in the region. Expanded services in conjunction with Olathe Medical Center were announced in late 2016, along with specialty clinics in Junction City, Kansas.

The hospital continued to expand its efforts in other countries through educational exchange programs in Mexico, Panama and China. The use of computer technology for remote monitoring of patients, telemedicine to eliminate travel time and inconvenience, and home care for a wider variety of patients helped move care outside the hospital. In 2014, for the first time, income from outpatient services exceeded that of inpatient revenue, signaling the growth of hospital care beyond the walls.

Children's Mercy was enhancing its International Services program to provide a single point of coordination for scheduling, lodging, treating and billing international patients and their families. In recent years, Children's Mercy received requests for care from patients from more than 36 countries.

In 2013 and again in 2016, Children's Mercy conducted a Community Health Needs Assessment. The survey, required by the federal government to justify the hospital's non-profit status, included focus groups, individual interviews and the compilation of considerable data. The goal was to determine for the Kansas City metropolitan area the overall health of children, their health needs, how to address shortcomings and a direction for the $175 million a year in "community benefit" that Children's Mercy provides.

*Spectators cheered on the players of Sporting Kansas City on opening night 2016 at the soccer stadium in Kansas City, Kansas. The complex had recently been renamed Children's Mercy Park.*

Through that work, it became abundantly clear that the challenges facing children and their health were not solely the responsibility of Children's Mercy or any other single provider. Instead, the health and well-being of children and their families is the responsibility of the entire community – the "village."

In March 2016, Children's Mercy brought together more than 150 individuals from a variety of agencies, governments and businesses for a Children's Health Summit. The group reviewed the findings of the health needs assessment and defined priorities. Months later, when the survey was published, Children's Mercy outlined the most pressing problems it needed to address in the next three years: access to health services, infant mortality and mental/behavioral health.

To make that happen, partners were needed. In 2016, Children's Mercy found a big one in an unlikely place: a soccer field.

Children's Mercy signed a 10-year deal with Sporting Kansas City, a Major Soccer League team. The most visible feature of the agreement was naming rights for the stadium,

Children's Mercy Park. But a more compelling part of the partnership was the new state-of-the-art Children's Mercy Sports Medicine and Rehabilitation Center, which broke ground in mid-2016 as part of the U.S. Soccer Federation's new, $62 million national training center in western Wyandotte County.

The National Training and Coaching Development

Center will be one of a kind and will serve as the home base for both Sporting KC and U.S. Soccer coaches and referees. The complex was expected to be completed in early 2018.

The partnership with Sporting had these goals: improved access to pediatric-trained sports medicine, strengthening the community, protection of young athletes and education of parents and coaches.

Stueve said expansion of the Children's Mercy sports medicine and rehabilitation program at the national training center would help children in all sports, not just soccer.

In addition, the partnership helped raise nearly $300,000 for the hospital in its first year, including a $100,000 commitment from Sporting's Victory Project, which raises money for kids with cancer and their families. The money helped establish a new playroom at the hospital for siblings of sick children.

The Sporting Kansas City project is just one Children's Mercy partnership. Working with the Kohl's Cares program,

## Finding his passion

To be able to play the blues, you first have to understand the blues. It's the mantra of every blues artist – finding creative inspiration through pain and perseverance. For 17-year-old C.J. Walker, a dramatic shoulder injury and years of therapy taught him plenty about both.

As he was being born, C.J.'s shoulder got stuck on his mother's pelvis. When the delivery doctor pulled him through the birth canal, the force tore every major nerve in his tiny left shoulder. The traumatic delivery was considered necessary for the safety of C.J. and his mother, but it caused severe damage to his arm.

C.J. was just one week old when his parents brought him to Children's Mercy Kansas City. Twice a week he visited the hospital to spend time in the therapy pool, practice using scissors, pull apart Legos, and do other therapeutic exercises disguised as everyday child's play. Occupational therapists Andrea Melanson and Connie Chesser oversaw his care.

Progress was slow and painstaking. C.J. underwent five surgeries in the next several years to graft nerves, transfer muscles, and rearrange the bone structure of his arm. Therapy remained regular as he approached his teenage years. Although he would never regain full function of his arm, that didn't keep him idle. Eventually, he was able to handle routine tasks, play sports and drive a car.

His determination fed directly into C.J.'s passion for playing guitar – and specifically, playing the blues.

In the summer of his freshman year at Center High School, C.J. decided to make his longstanding desire to play the guitar a reality. But with only one fully functional hand, he would have to get creative.

He turned the guitar upside down and figured out how to play, fingering the strings with his right hand. A part of the

*C.J. Walker plays the blues.*

guitar called a whammy bar assisted his left hand with the strumming motion.

Within two years, C.J. began to find his own voice as a player. His confidence and ability quickly rose, and eventually he was able to take part in regular open jam sessions at a venue in the 18th and Vine blues and jazz district.

*All smiles on a sunny day: Nicholas A. Clark, MD, with a grinning patient.*

an outgrowth of the Kohl's department-store group, Children's Mercy developed a program that targeted third- and fourth-graders with fun, interactive activities centered on relaxation, self-esteem and healthy eating. Nutrition and weight were part of the Children's Mercy-led Weighing In Coalition, which brought together dozens of metropolitan area agencies focused on improving the overall health of the community through education, nutrition and exercise. Children's Mercy also

offered education and other resources for school nurses and youth coaches. Even more partnerships and collaboration were expected to grow from the Children's Health Summit.

## Generosity in money and time

One of the threads that has run through Children's Mercy since 1897 is support from a generous community.

Inadequate support from government-backed programs

such as Medicaid continued to pressure the hospital budget. In fiscal year 2016, nearly 50 percent of all patients had Medicaid insurance, which nationwide paid only about 75 percent of the full cost of care. Competition for certain profitable parts of the business also affected the budget.

Thanks to a concerted effort by the Department of Philanthropy – and its focus on making a personal connection to children, doctors and programs – Children's Mercy in fiscal year 2016 raised more than $45 million in philanthropic donations and pledges, a record.

A significant part of that went to the I Love Children's Mercy Fund, an unrestricted resource directed toward caring for all children regardless of their need or their ability to pay. That modern-day flexibility harkened back to what Katharine Richardson called "free gifts" – free from conditions so the hospital could do what was best.

Another part of the past became a part of the future in 2016 with the launching of the Small Change/Big Difference campaign. Recalling the early days of the hospital when children like those in the Mercy Hospital Club put on shows and donated the proceeds to Children's Mercy, the new campaign encouraged children to fill up a Children's Mercy-branded piggy bank. In the early 1900s, young donors filled tiny socks with dimes as their admission to tea; more than a century later, children and families were reminded that every little bit helped the non-profit hospital.

"In times past, school children saved pennies and nickels in special banks," said Jenea Oliver, vice president of philanthropy, "and to this day, families strolling the Country Club Plaza toss coins for Children's Mercy into fountains and into the Wild Boar sculpture as they rub his big, bronze snout for luck.

"Children's Mercy has a history of generous community support that began when the hospital founders wrote the list of needs on a chalkboard in front of the hospital. Neighbors and businesses donated everything from blankets to apples, making a big difference in advancing the hospital's mission. Today, the Children's Mercy mission and the need for community support remain the same."

Support for the hospital also comes from hundreds of volunteers who pledge thousands of hours in support of the hospital. Volunteers staff the information desks, walk patients

*Susan Abdel-Rahman, PhD, tried out the Mercy Tape, which helps caregivers determine a child's weight when scales are not available. The World Health Organization is helping promote use of the Children's Mercy invention in developing countries*

and their families to appointments throughout the maze of the medical center and complete a variety of jobs from the cash register in the gift shop to the rocking chairs in the intensive care nursery. Professional athletes, musicians and a wide variety of celebrities donate time to brighten the days of patients, helping kids feel like kids.

## Among employees, dedication

A generous community makes possible the hard work and dedication of the employees.

*Facing page: Mother and child worked on a crafts project.*

## "Right where we needed to be"

Easter is a miraculous day for Christians, yet the news that Casie and Dave Katzer received one Easter about their baby Hudson wasn't what other parents might consider divine.

Now, though, the Katzers look back and believe something truly miraculous happened that day.

After his birth in 2011, baby Hudson showed constant colicky behavior and a low-grade fever. The Katzers' pediatrician wasn't troubled by that. But after several months of worry and then obvious signs that their 9-month-old's mobility was regressing, they ignored their doctor's reassurances. That April night of Easter 2012, the Katzers drove the hour from their home in Osawatomie, Kansas, to the Children's Mercy South Emergency Department in Overland Park.

Tests justified the parents' concerns. Hudson was soon rushed to the main hospital in downtown Kansas City, Missouri. There, a late-night MRI revealed a cancerous tumor, neuroblastoma, wrapped around the baby's spine.

Pediatric neurosurgeon John A. Clough, MD, spent hours that night examining Hudson's MRI. He wanted to remove the tumor and decompress the spine, allowing Hudson possibly to move his lower extremities. But his main goal was basic: to save Hudson's life. After hours of study and conferring with a colleague, the other doctor talked to Casie and Dave.

"We're not sure that he'll ever move his legs again," he told the couple. Medical staff had done tests, and the baby

*Quite the cowhand: Hudson Katzer, standing tall.*

had shown no feeling below the middle of his back. "If he is able to move his legs again, it will be a miracle."

The next morning, only hours after the surgery, a resident doctor stopped in to check on Hudson's progress. She ran her finger up the bottom of his foot and was shocked at the result: Hudson curled his toes.

"We all just started crying," Casie said.

The surgery proved remarkable, but it was able to remove only 20 percent of the cancerous tumor. Chemotherapy would attack the rest. Again, Hudson's health showed dramatic improvements. Within nine days, he started moving his feet. Soon, he could raise one of them. Eventually, he could raise both. After four rounds of chemo, the tumor had shrunk by 90 percent. More aggressive chemo followed.

Hudson's young age was one reason for his successful recovery, but Casie thinks the staff at Children's Mercy was just as critical to Hudson's turnaround.

She also believes a divine hand led her family to the hospital.

"I tell everybody, 'We've been blessed with the best'," she said. "I believe all of this was orchestrated – that the right people have fallen in our path. We were right where we needed to be.

"It's been a divine experience, as bad as it got. It couldn't have gone any better."

---

"Everyone is focusing on the needs of the patient," said Joe Galeazzi, the vice president of medical administration. "We continue to invest in them, to encourage them to find what they do best and we really focus on how that translates to the patient."

In 2016, the American Nurse Credentialing Center, in awarding Magnet designation to Children's Mercy for the fourth time, called it an unparalleled example of excellence.

"None of this would be possible without this incredible nursing staff," said Dr. Charles Roberts, the executive medical

director. "I think that's another thing that makes Children's Mercy unique. The nurses have had a voice.

"The care that the nurses at this hospital provide every day, every time has just been a marvel. If you ask the kids what they remember, they're not going to remember the doctors; they are going to remember those nurses."

Dr. O'Donnell, whose mother was a nurse, extended that praise beyond the nursing staff.

"I love to come to work every day and I love the people I work with and am literally fascinated by them and inspired

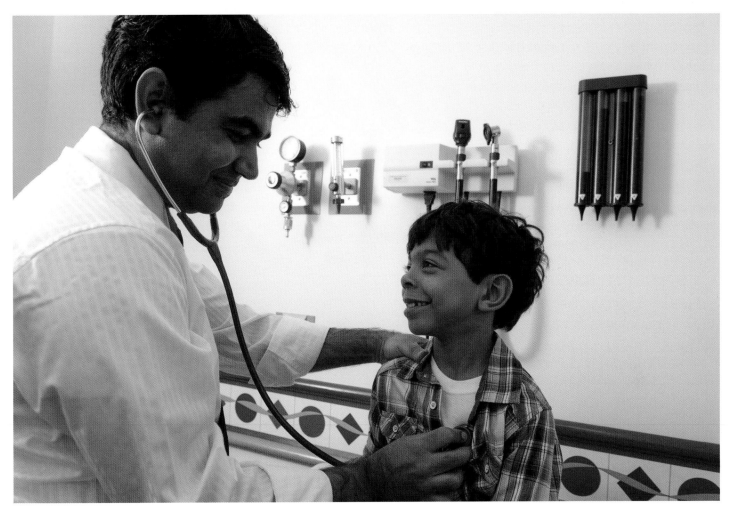

*Pediatric geneticist Shivarajan M. Amudhavalli examined a patient.*

by them and I'm in awe of them. I don't say it lightly that the people who work at Children's Mercy are my heroes. They do just incredible things and they care for people in incredible ways."

## Patients first

Throughout the past century-plus, the focus has remained on the children in everything about Children's Mercy. Children's Mercy leadership, along with employees from bedside to shuttle bus, insist on it.

"Kids are in the driver's seat," says Stacey Koenig, the senior director of Patient and Family Experience. "If we allow the children to help us, to direct us, to lead us … we can't go wrong with that."

Koenig was echoing the founders, who knew children were not simply small adults, but needed special and total commitment. Katharine Richardson was more than one of the best facial-reconstruction surgeons of her time. She also emphasized the importance of sympathy and understanding, tending to her patients' emotional needs as well as physical ailments. She encouraged hospital designs integrating light and fresh air, filled the wards with toys and recruited comedians and circus clowns visiting Kansas City to perform for the children.

Those same things are alive today.

The family focus is everywhere. Some employees' entire focus is on the "patient experience" and every employee's job is tied to patient care. The Child Life program is nationally recognized as one of the best, and more and more evidence shows that making the hospital stay easier and more comfortable improves outcomes and satisfaction.

Interview after interview and news report after news

report recount the stories of remarkable children and their families. From doctors to nurses to volunteers, it's the stories of children, the faces of children, children's laughter and children's tears that are etched in their hearts and their minds.

Dr. Roberts told of children he grew close to, children who inspired him, and children who made him laugh when there was so much pain. And then there were the families.

"Oh yes, I remember," he said, recalling the grandmother of one of the children he had cared for. "She came to see me a few weeks after he died to make sure *I* was doing OK.

"I still get emotional thinking about that. *They* care for *us*. That is a testament to the kind of people we take care of."

"It really is patient first, family first," said Galeazzi. "We do a pretty good job of literally every decision being, 'How does this advance the needs of the patient?'

"Katharine Berry Richardson taught us: Take the time.

*Randall L. O'Donnell*

Do what's necessary. Patient-focused. Family-focused. We did that before it was cool. We did that long before it was cool."

And by all accounts, Children's Mercy will continue to do that.

"As we look back and remember the Berry sisters, we marvel at the infinite ripple they created with that first act of mercy," said the CEO, Dr. O'Donnell. "More than 120 years later, that one Mercy bed has grown to more than 350, and the story of one healed child has transformed a community and provided hope and healing to literally millions of children and their families.

"Today, the speed of progress and innovation at Children's Mercy continues to accelerate even faster, bringing advancements in clinical care, education and research. While we can all be proud of the history we've written, I'm even more excited about the future we are poised to create together."

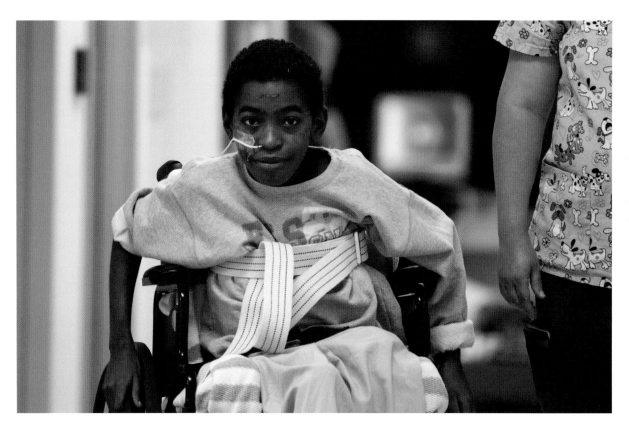

*Rolling on his own, a Children's Mercy patient wheels along the hospital hallways.*

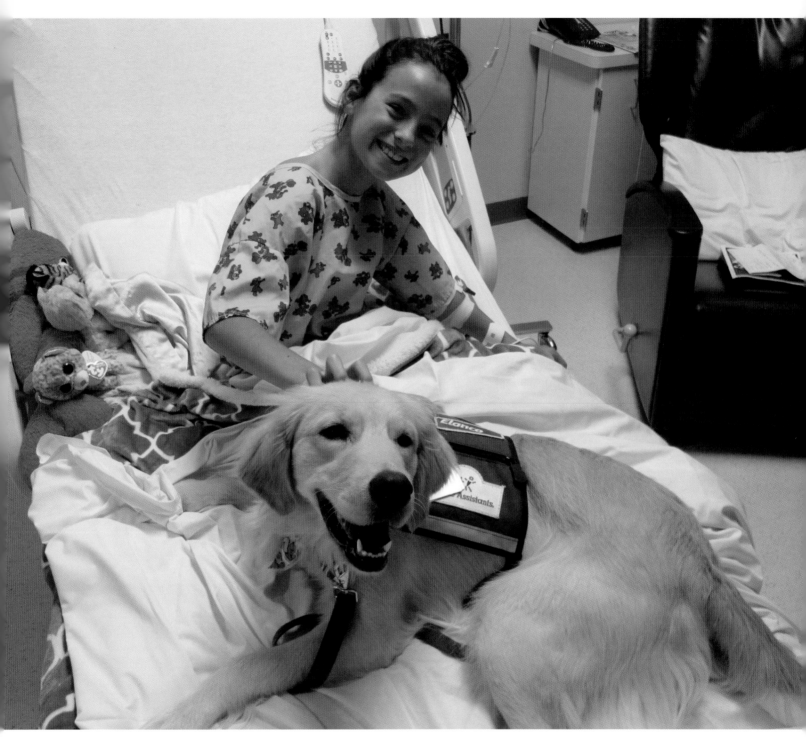

*A canine therapy animal, Hope, brought a smile to the face of a Children's Mercy patient.*

*Following pages: Children's Mercy has come a long way from a single bed in 1897. The sprawling Adele Hall campus on Hospital Hill looked like this in 2016.*

*Decked out in cowboy togs for the annual Doctors' Day celebration in 2005 were, from left, Drs. V. Fred Burry, Lloyd Olson and Charles Roberts.*

# Acknowledgments

Y ou learn quickly, as the author of a book like this, that you cannot do it yourself.

First, an apology. At the beginning of this project, I swore I would not be one of those writers who became obsessed and neglected other parts of life. Depending on your definition of obsession and neglect, I have failed. I apologize to those who suffered inadvertently from my addictive personality. But it did make for a better book.

It is important to give credit and thanks to the many, many people who made this book the superb publication that it is.

Roger Swanson, Beatrice Johns and Drs. Herb Wenner and Sydney Pakula wrote previous histories that served as an invaluable foundation. The family of Dr. Wenner provided additional information.

Stuart Hinds and Teresa Gipson of the Miller Nichols Library at the University of Missouri-Kansas City accepted our archival collection and organized it so that I and future researchers will be able to make good use of it.

Lena Dagley, who as secretary to founding sister Katharine Berry Richardson and later to the Central Governing Board of the hospital into the 1950s, kept a detailed memoir that provided personal insight into and details of the life of Dr. Richardson.

Carol Belt, a Children's Mercy nurse, took on the role of voluntary archivist in the 1990s when everyone else around the hospital was too busy on other matters. She saved many documents and artifacts. I spent many hours with Carol, long before this book was envisioned, and she fanned a flame of inspiration inside me to tell the story. Dr. Gary Pettett, a neonatologist, took up Carol's work after she died and continued it until he retired in the mid-2000s. Dr. Pettett was generous with his time and personal files.

Drs. Jane Knapp and Bobby Schremmer, both emergency medicine specialists, have researched various aspects of Children's Mercy history to preserve them and share them, particularly with colleagues through the Pediatric Academic Societies.

Bruce Matthews, former hospital photographer, and Steve Byers, former fundraising director, gave early support to this project and pointed me in the right direction for sources and other help.

Carey Bickford, the mom of a Children's Mercy patient, serves on the Archives Committee and researched and wrote the sidebar on former hospital administrator Elizabeth Martin because she thought it would be fun. Likewise, Ina Maliqis, a communications intern, volunteered to write the sidebar about former Board chair Leah Nourse and tracked down two of her grandchildren, Jim Nourse and Leah Harrison, who willingly shared family photos and information.

Publisher Doug Weaver committed to this project and helped me find editor Monroe Dodd. Monroe is one of the two finest editors I have been privileged to work with in my 40-year writing career. Jean Dodd, designer, helped bring the words to life. Proofreaders Sherry Osburn and Doug Weaver saved the day by catching more than one overlooked typo or grammatical misstep.

Thanks for inspiration, ideas and many other forms of help also go to: all members of the Children's Mercy Archive committee who went on this adventure with me; Jean Svadlenak, museum consultant, who uncovered some new material and relentlessly pushed for details; Randall L. O'Donnell, PhD, hospital CEO, who gave me a chance and welcomed me back; my parents, who encouraged me to march to the beat of a different drummer; my brothers and sisters (especially Mariann for spiritual direction), children and grandchildren, all who are among my best teachers; my other "family," past and present, in communications and marketing at Children's Mercy who made their own brand of history; the dozens of people who sat for interviews, took phone calls and answered emails in my pursuit of stories big and small; John and Kim Ratliff, Kim and Nate Harbur and other families for sharing their stories here and in private; pack rats; countless doctors and nurses and other staff over the years; the many, many children who have crossed my path; all of you – too many to name – who inspired me spiritually and intellectually; my higher power; and, finally and most of all, my wife, Carla Young McCormally, for kindness, love and always having more faith in me than I have in myself.

*– Thomas McCormally*

## Chairs of the Board

Alice Berry Graham .........1901-11
Mrs. Edwin Fowler ...........1911-21
Mrs. W.C. Bowman ......... 1922-37
Mrs. Frank Servatius ...... 1937-38
Mrs. Leah Nourse .......... 1938-56
Mrs. Garrett A. Walsh ..... 1957-60
Mrs. C.E. Weaver ........... 1961-64
Herman R. Sutherland ... 1965-70

Joseph B. Gregg .............1971-72
Abraham Margolin ...........1973-74
John A. Kroh ...................1975-76
William P. Harsh Sr. .........1977-78
Marion Kreamer ............. 1981-82
Adele Hall ...................... 1983-85
Shawsie Branton ............. 1985-87
Harry McCray Jr. ............. 1988-89

Mary Jane Barnes ........... 1990-93
Don Chisholm .................. 1993-94
Judy Hunt ...................... 1995-96
David Oliver.....................1997-98
Bob Long.......................1999-2000
Margi Pence.................... 2001-02
Maurice Watson ..........2003-2006
Mary Hunkeler................ 2006-08

Ed Connolly Jr. ................. 2008-10
Page Reed ...................... 2010–12
Jack Ovel........................ 2012–14
Charles Schellhorn......... 2014–16
Debbie Sosland-Edelman ...2016–

## Medical Directors

The following had various titles and some different responsibilities, but all served as administrative leaders of the medical staff at the time.

Katharine Berry Richardson......
...........................1897-1933
Lawrence Hart........... 1953-58
Herb Miller.................. 1959-62
Ned Smull ................... 1963-78
Dick Dreher................ 1978-86
Marvin Kolb ............... 1992-94
Thomas Holder (interim)............
.................................... 1994-96
Fred Burry ..............1997-2010
Charles C. Roberts ..........2010-

## Administrators/CEOs

Despite having various titles and different responsibilities, all served as administrative leaders of hospital operations at the time.

Alice Graham .................................................1897-1911
Katharine Richardson ..................................... 1911-33
Janette Flanagan............................................ 1933-36
Elizabeth Martin ............................................. 1936-55
Mary Hanna..................................................... 1955-57
Melvin Dunn ........................................................1958
John Stockwell ................................................ 1958-62
Ned Smull (director)/Eric Jones (administrator) .............. 1963-78
Dick Dreher (director)/Larry Harness (administrator) ..... 1978-82
Dick Dreher/John O'Shaughnessy (administrator).......... 1982-87
Larry McAndrews (CEO) .....................................1987–92
Randall L. O'Donnell (CEO).....................................1993-present

## Children's Mercy locations in metropolitan Kansas City, 2017

- Adele Hall Campus, 2401 Gillham Road, Kansas City, Missouri

- Children's Mercy Hospital – Kansas, 5808 W. 110th St., Overland Park, Kansas

- Children's Mercy College Boulevard Clinics, 5520 College Blvd., Overland Park, Kansas

- Children's Mercy Blue Valley, 6750 W. 135th St.., Overland Park, Kansas

- Children's Mercy West, 4313 State Ave., Kansas City, Kansas

- Children's Mercy Northland, 501 NW Barry Road, Kansas City, Missouri

- Children's Mercy East, 20300 East Valley View Parkway, Independence, Missouri

- Children's Mercy Clinics on Broadway, 3101 Broadway Blvd., Kansas City, Missouri

- Children's Mercy Pediatric Eye Care, 4820 College Blvd., Leawood, Kansas.

## Fast Facts: Fiscal Year 2016 (July 1, 2015 – June 30, 2016)

**Admissions**.................................................. 14,538

**Patient Days**
Average Length of Stay ..................................... 6.1
Medical/Surgical................................................ 5.1
Intensive Care Nursery ................................... 27.1
Pediatric Intensive Care Unit............................6.9
CM Kansas Patient Care Unit......................... 2.5
Fetal Health Center .......................................... 2.5
Average Daily Census................................... 263.1
Licensed Beds Available ..................................354

**Outpatient Visits**
Specialty Clinics .......................................127,903
CM Kansas Specialty Center ......................49,023
CM Northland Specialty Clinics.................. 22,797
CM East Specialty Clinics ............................ 9,403
College Boulevard Clinics .......................... 16,081
CM Blue Valley.............................................. 2,892
Primary Care Clinics.................................... 77,899
Other ............................................................46,288
Total Outpatient Visits............................. 352,286

**Uncompensated care** (2015) ..... $119,734,985

**Emergency/Urgent Care Visits**
CM Emergency Room................................. 66,814
CM Kansas Emergency Room....................42,409
CM Blue Valley Urgent Care...................... 21,906
CM Northland Urgent Care ........................ 31,424
CM East Urgent Care.................................. 28,947
Total Emergency/Urgent Care Visits .....................
...........................................................191,500

**Surgical Procedures**
Inpatient...................................................... 4,230
Outpatient................................................. 15,888
Total Surgical Procedures........................ 20,118

**Transports** ................................................. 5,586

Home Care Visits ........................................ 3,704
Full-time Employees ....................................7,910
Volunteers ......................................................945
Medical Staff .................................................. 768

## Children's Mercy Golf Classic

Hosted by Tom Watson

Guests:

1980 - Jack Nicklaus
1981 - Nicklaus, Lee Trevino
1982 - Trevino, Johnny Miller
1983 - Nicklaus, Bob Gilder, Bob Murphy
1984 - Peter Jacobsen, Arnold Palmer, D.A. Weibring
1985 - Jacobsen, Greg Norman, Lanny Wadkins

1986 - Byron Nelson, Joanne Carner, Fuzzy Zoeller
1987 - Sam Snead, Chi Chi Rodriguez, Norman
1988 - Raymond Floyd, Payne Stewart, Andy Bean
1989 - Nicklaus, Trevino, Curtis Strange
1990 - Tim Kite, Palmer, Rodriguez
1991 - Paul Azinger, Fred Couples, Trevino
1992 - Seve Ballesteros, Couples, Jose Maria Olazabal
1993 - Ben Crenshaw, John Daly, Kite
1994 - Phil Mickelson, Norman, Wadkins

1995 - Corey Pavin, Nick Price, Craig Stadler
1996 - Laura Davies, Jacobsen, Michelle McGann
1997 - Davis Love III, Mickelson, Steve Stricker
1998 - Ernie Els, Annika Sorenstam, Karrie Webb
1999 - Steve Elkington, Vijay Singh, Trevino
2000 - Nancy Lopez, Nicklaus, Juli Inkster
2001 - Tom Lehman, Gary McCord, Hal Sutton
2002 - Nicklaus, Palmer, Gary Player, Trevino
2003 - Daly, Bruce Lietzke, Price
2004 - Jacobsen, Kenny Perry, Love III

## Big Slick Celebrity Weekend

Beginning in 2010, the Big Slick Celebrity Weekend has provided generous fundraising support each summer along with laughter and hope to the kids at Children's Mercy.

The event started as a celebrity poker tournament and party hosted by Kansas City natives and comedy actors Rob Riggle, Paul Rudd and Jason Sudeikis. In 2014, Kansas City area natives David Koechner and Eric Stonestreet joined as official Big Slick co-hosts and the weekend evolved to feature a celebrity softball game at Kauffman Stadium, a celebrity bowling tournament at Pinstripes in the Prairiefire shopping center, a party and live auction at The Midland Theater, and hanging out with the patients at Children's Mercy. Each year Rob, Paul, Jason, David and Eric have invited their celebrity friends to Kansas City. They have hosted more than 75 celebrities since 2010.

In six years, Big Slick has donated more than $3.25 million to support cancer programs and children and families at Children's Mercy. Guests who have attended Big Slick from 2010 through 2016:

Dianna Agron
Rory Albanese
Tom Arnold
Scott Aukerman
Matt Besler
Michael Ian Blac
George Brett
Owen Burke
Hilarie Burton
Bobby Cannavale
Sarah Chalke

Josh Charles
Dustin Colquitt
David Cook
Andy Daly
Chris Daughtry
Rich Eisen
Will Ferrell
Al Fitzmorris
Neil Flynn
Will Forte
Jon Glaser

Jamie Gold
Ian Gomez
Selena Gomez
Judy Greer
Jon Hamm
Chris Henchy
Seth Herzog
John Hodgman
Josh Hopkins
Rob Huebel
Jake Johnson

Travis Kelce
Richard Kind
Angela Kinsey
Johnny Knoxville
Nick Kroll
Samm Levine
Adam McKay
Jason Mantzoukas
Ken Marino
James Marsden
Curt Menefee

Jeffrey Dean
Morgan Mitch
Morris
Seth Morris
Dermot Mulroney
John Oliver
Haley Joel Osment
Kevin Pollak
Missi Pyle
Kevin Rahm
Dallas Roberts

Bret Saberhagen
Andrea Savage
Horatio Sanze
Paul Scheer
Adam Scott
J.K. Simmons
Robert Smigel
Martin Starr
Aisha Tyler
Jake Tapper
Joe Lo Truglio

Wilmer Valderrama
Nia Vardalos
James Van Der Beek
Matt Walsch
Damon Wayans Jr.
George Wendt
Olivia Wilde
Weird Al Yankovic
David Zayas

## Illustrations

Portions of the hospital's collection of images are archived in the Children's Mercy Collection at the Dr. Kenneth J. LaBudde Department of Special Collections, University of Missouri-Kansas City. They appear on the following pages: 8 (top right and bottom right), 31, 36, 44-45, 47, 52, 58, 62, 65 (top), 67 (top right), 69 (top right), 70, 72, 73, 79 (top), 80, 83, 87 (bottom), 88, 89, 115, 116 (top), 118, 121, 123 (top left and top right, bottom right), 124, 128, 131, 132, 134, 135 (bottom), 141, 142, 143, 144, 145, 147, 148, 150, 153, 154, 157, 159 (top left).

Other sources and the pages on which their images appear:

Census of the United States, 1860. 10 (bottom).

Drexel University College of Medicine Archives & Special Collections 13. (middle center and right).

Kyle Rivas, Getty Images, 192.

La Crosse Public Library Archives, Courtesy of (La Crosse, Wisconsin). 14 (inset, center).

Library of Congress. 10 (top and center, right), 14 (bottom), 16 (top).

Library, University of Mount Union, Alliance, Ohio. 11, 12, 13 (top center and right).

Missouri Valley Special Collections, Kansas City Public Library, Kansas City, Missouri. 19.

The State Historical Society of Missouri. Native Sons of Kansas City Photograph Collection, K0528, f.018, . 18.

The State Historical Society of Missouri. George A. Fuller Company Photograph Collection, 1911-ca. 1922, (K0080). 59.

Truman Medical Center, 109.

University of Missouri, Courtesy of, MU Libraries. 21.

## Children's hospitals nationwide

Source: Children's Hospital Association

| Year Founded | Hospital Name | City | State |
|---|---|---|---|
| 1834 | MUSC Children's Hospital | Charleston | SC |
| 1855 | The Children's Hospital of Philadelphia | Philadelphia | PA |
| 1869 | Children's Hospital Boston | Boston | MA |
| 1869 | CHRISTAS Santa Rosa Health Care | Santa Rosa | TX |
| 1870 | Children's National Medical Center | Washington | DC |
| 1875 | St. Christopher's Hospital for Children | Philadelphia | PA |
| 1875 | The Hospital for Sick Children - Toronto | Toronto | Can |
| 1879 | St. Louis Children's Hospital | St. Louis | MO |
| 1883 | Children's Hospital of Cincinnati | Cincinnati | OH |
| 1883 | The Hospital for Sick Children | Washington | DC |
| 1886 | Children's Hospital of Michigan | Detroit | MI |
| 1887 | Children's Hospital of New York - | New York | NY |
| 1890 | Children's Hospital Medical Center of Akron | Akron | OH |
| 1890 | Children's Hospital of Pittsburgh | Pittsburgh | PA |
| 1891 | Children's Specialized Hospital | Mountainside | NJ |
| 1892 | Kosair Children's Hospital | Louisville | KY |
| 1892 | Children's Hospital - Columbus | Columbus | OH |
| 1892 | The Women & Children's Hospital of Buffalo | Buffalo | NY |
| 1894 | Children's Hospital of Wisconsin | Milwaukee | WI |
| 1896 | UMDNJ - University Hospital | Newark | NJ |
| 1896 | LaRabida Children's Hospital | Chicago | IL |
| 1897 | Gillette Children's Specialty Hospital | St. Paul | MN |
| **1897** | **Children's Mercy Hospital** | **Kansas City** | **MO** |
| 1898 | Connecticut Children's Medical Center | Hartford | CT |
| 1901 | Children's Hospital Los Angeles | Los Angeles | CA |
| 1906 | Johns Hopkins Children's Center | Baltimore | MD |
| 1907 | Children's Hospital & Regional Medical | Seattle | WA |
| 1908 | The Children's Hospital - Denver | Denver | CO |
| 1909 | Kapiolani Medical Center for Women and Children | Honolulu | HI |
| 1910 | Children's Medical College of Georgia | Augusta | GA |
| 1912 | Arkansas Children's Hospital | Little Rock | AR |
| 1912 | Children's Hospital Oakland | Oakland | CA |
| 1912 | The Children's Hospital of Alabama | Birmingham | AL |
| 1913 | Children's Medical Center of Dallas | Dallas | TX |
| 1915 | *Scottish Rite Children's Hospital | Atlanta | GA |
| 1918 | Cook Children's Health Care System | Fort Worth | TX |
| 1920 | Children's Hospital - Richmond | Richmond | VA |
| 1920 | The Detroit Institute for Children | Detroit | MI |
| 1922 | Shriners Hospitals | Tampa | FL |
| 1922 | Mt. Washington Pediatric Hospital | Baltimore | MD |
| 1922 | Primary Children's Medical Center | Salt Lake City | UT |
| 1924 | Children's Hospitals and Clinics - St. Paul | St. Paul | MN |
| 1924 | James Whitcomb Riley Hospital for Children | Indianapolis | IN |
| 1926 | Dorenbecher Children's Hospital | Portland | OR |
| 1926 | All Children's Hospital, Inc. | St. Petersburg | FL |
| 1928 | Children's & Women's Health Centre of Vancouver | Vancouver | BC |
| 1928 | *Egelston Children's | Atlanta | GA |
| 1931 | University Medical Center of Southern Nevada | Las Vegas | NV |
| 1937 | Kennedy Krieger Institute | Baltimore | MD |
| 1937 | Carrie Tingley Hospital | Albuquerque | NM |
| 1944 | Blank Children's Hospital | Des Moines | IA |
| 1948 | U. of Maryland Childen's Hospital | Baltimore | MD |
| 1948 | Children's Hospital | Omaha | NE |
| 1949 | Children's Hospital of Central California | Madera | CA |
| 1950 | Miami Children's Hospital | Miami | FL |
| 1952 | LeBonneur Children's Medical Center | Memphis | TN |
| 1953 | Driscoll Children's Hospital | Corpus Christi | TX |
| 1954 | Children's Hospital and Health Center | San Diego | CA |
| 1954 | Texas Children's Hospital | Houston | TX |
| 1955 | Children's Hospital-New Orleans | New Orleans | LA |
| 1955 | Wolfson Children's Hospital | Jacksonville | FL |
| 1956 | Cardinal Glennon Children's Hospital | St. Louis | MO |
| 1961 | Children's Hospital of the King's Daughters | Norfolk | VA |
| 1962 | St. Jude Children's Research Hospital | Memphis | TN |
| 1964 | Children's Hospital of Orange County | Orange | CA |
| 1967 | The Children's Medical Center of Dayton | Dayton | OH |
| 1969 | C.S. Mott Children's Hospital | Ann Arbor | MI |
| 1970 | Miller Children's Hospital | Long Beach | CA |
| 1972 | Tod Children's Hospital | Youngstown | OH |
| 1973 | Children's Hospitals and Clinics | Minneapolis | MN |
| 1983 | Children's Hospital of Palmetto Health | Columbus | SC |
| 1983 | Phoenix Children's Hospital | Phoenix | AZ |
| 1986 | Brenner Children's Hospital | Winston-Salem | NC |
| 1987 | St. Vincent Pediatric Rehabilitation | Indianapolis | IN |
| 1990 | Children's Hospital of Illinois at OSF | Peoria | IL |
| 1991 | Lucile Packard Children's Hospital | Palo Alto | CA |
| 1992 | Joe DiMaggio Children's Hospital | Hollywood | FL |
| 1992 | George and Marie Backus Children's | Savannah | GA |
| 1993 | Yale-New Haven Children's Hospital | New Haven | CT |
| 1993 | Toledo Children's Hospital | Toledo | OH |
| 1993 | Loma Linda University Children's | Loma Linda | CA |
| 1994 | The Children's Hospital of Southwest | Ft. Myers | FL |
| 1995 | Fletcher Allen Health Care | Burlington | VT |
| 1995 | Mattel Children's Hospital at UCLA | Los Angeles | CA |
| 1996 | UF Health Shands Children's Hospital | Gainesville | FL |
| 1997 | University of Kentucky Children's | Lexington | KY |
| 1998 | Mercy Children's Hospital | Toledo | OH |
| 1998 | Children's Healthcare of Atlanta | Atlanta | GA |
| 2000 | The Children's Hospital at Hackensack | Hackensack | NJ |

* Merged to become Children's Healthcare of Atlanta, 1998

# Source notes

This is not an academic textbook or even a thesis or dissertation. This is a storybook. That is one reason you will not find footnotes throughout the text. Another reason, made after considerable thought, is that the story had to keep moving without distractions.

There were, of course, innumerable sources critical to the writing and authenticity of this book. In the cases where sources conflicted, we relied on primary research where possible and sometimes chose the information that "felt" right. We did our best to be accurate.

Throughout the text, you will find many sources named and much information attributed, some through direct quotes from personal interviews, news articles or books, and others through paraphrasing. Here are details about sources.

## General Information

Before *For All Children Everywhere*, two books were published about the history of Children's Mercy. Both provided valuable guidance.

The first, *A History of the Children's Mercy Hospital* by Roger Swanson, appeared in 1961. Swanson, a former newspaper reporter, worked for the hospital at the time; the same is true of the author of this book. Swanson had access to many primary sources – current and former hospital employees – from the earliest days of Children's Mercy. Printing and other costs were paid by the hospital, as was the case with this book.

A second book, *Women of Vision*, by Beatrice Johns, was published in 2004. That book contained much information from Johns' personal experience with the hospital as a patient in the 1920s, but covered little after 1933. Information from that book was used here with permission from the publisher, ImagineInk Publishing Co. of Wentzville, Missouri.

A third account, "The History of The Children's Mercy Hospital," was written but never published. Two Children's Mercy doctors, Herbert A. Wenner and Sydney F. Pakula, dated their final manuscript October 1, 1984. They relied heavily on documents in the Children's Mercy Archive, as well as Swanson's book and a memoir by Lena Dagley. Drs. Wenner and Pakula provided a rich history particularly of the development of the medical staff and medical specialties beginning in the 1960s.

Lena Dagley – who served Children's Mercy for about 50 years first as personal secretary to Katharine Richardson and then as a secretary to the Board – wrote a memoir that contained stories of her time with Katharine and the workings of Children's Mercy. A complete copy of the unpublished work has not survived, but many pieces of it have, typewritten in blue ink. It is cited throughout the first half of this book.

The Children's Mercy Collection is housed in the LaBudde Special Collections at UMKC Miller Nichols Library. Children's Mercy retains ownership of the collection, but it is available through the library for researchers. It contains a vast assortment of documents related to the founding, floundering and, finally, flourishing of Children's Mercy. Information contained in the collection – including personal letters of the founding sisters,

newsletters dating to the early 20th Century and a 100-year-old-plus collection of minutes from board meetings – was crucial to telling this story. Many source materials – mostly copies, not originals – for this book are currently in possession of the author. Originals will be turned over to the Collection at UMKC after publication. Where newspaper articles are credited, copies of them are included in those materials.

The Internet proved to be a valuable source of information. Websites containing genealogical, news and medical information were consulted for background or historical perspective. Care was taken to use information from credible sources.

The book *Kansas City: An American Story*, published by Kansas City Star Books in 1999, provided Kansas City historical context. Scores of newspaper clippings – both in hard copy and online – provided important data.

Beginning in 2015, Children's Mercy embarked on a formal program of collecting oral histories of former and current employees, volunteers, patients and their families and others. Those histories offer first-hand recollection of the time from the 1950s to the present. Many were used in this book and are mentioned throughout the text. The author and editor acknowledge the potential deficiencies in sources' recollections, intentional or not. The collection of oral histories was continuing at the time of publication and written transcripts and videos of those interviews were scheduled to become part of the Children's Mercy Collection at UMKC.

## Chapter 1

The story of the first child treated by Alice Berry Graham has many versions and there seems to be no official documentation. Probably the founding sisters were not aware of the impact of their single act of mercy and did not write it down. It seems certain, based on numerous sources, both published (in Swanson, Johns, *Messenger* newsletters and newspaper accounts) and unpublished (Wenner/Pakula) that a little girl was taken in on a June day in 1897. Details are sketchy, though we have selected the most oft-repeated here.

Dr. Gary Pettett, former Children's Mercy neonatologist, did a lot of the historical research on the Berry family. He used information from Kentucky tax records (1849-1860), the *Brooklyn (KY) Daily Eagle* (November 6, 1881), and listings of the 1861-1865 Index to Enrolled Militia for Bourbon County from the Kentucky Historical Library to provide details of the early days of our story. Dr. Pettett also received some information in the early 2000s from the family of Clara Berry, sister of the Children's Mercy founders. Attempts to reach survivors in 2015 and 2016 were unsuccessful.

Information about Stephen Berry's personality comes, in part, from an obituary published in the *Warren County (PA) Ledger*, June 12, 1891. Quotations attributed to him are found in the unpublished memoir of Lena Dagley, now in the Children's Mercy Collection at UMKC. The same quotations are repeated in several other places, some of them primary sources with direct contact with Katharine and Alice, but most probably repeating what had been written previously.

Details of the sisters' college education comes from the universities themselves. Mt. Union College in Alliance, Ohio, provided records of degrees and copies of graduation programs, as did the institution that absorbed Women's Medical College of Pennsylvania, Drexel University. Philadelphia Dental College, now a part of Drexel University, also provided information. Details about the Medical College itself came from "Vignette of Medical History" from the *Maryland Medical Journal*, July 1994. *History of Women's Medical College of Philadelphia, Pennsylvania, 1859-1950* also was used here.

The Chippewa Valley Museum in La Crosse, Wisconsin, provided information from city directories about Katharine's time in La Crosse, as well as information about her husband, James Richardson and his family. The La Crosse County Historical Society and La Cross Public Library also helped in this endeavor. The La Crosse newspaper of August 10, 1893, told the story of their wedding and honeymoon.

Children's Mercy doctors Jane Knapp and Robert Schremmer prepared information about the orphan trains for a poster display at the 2014 meeting of the Pediatric Academic Societies. Other historical perspective was gained from internet research and *Kansas City: An American Story*.

The story of the early days of the sisters' lives in Kansas City was culled from city directories, previously published histories, internal Children's Mercy newsletters and the spring 2000 edition of the Jackson County Historical Society Journal.

Information about the first buildings that housed children for Alice and Katharine was taken primarily from previously published histories and the Dagley memoir. Newspaper articles from the time helped confirm locations and dates.

In November 1912, Alice wrote the story of the little girls from Kingsley, Kansas, in the *Messenger*. There has been some confusion over the years about whether or not the little girl mentioned in that story, Stella Samuels, was in fact, the very first patient. Because there is no date given for the gift from Kingsley and the girls obviously knew about the work of Alice and Katharine before they sent "everything nice" the bed needed, it seems apparent that, although Alice may have called this the beginning of Mercy Hospital, the actual work had begun earlier when a little girl was picked up in the stockyards and taken to the hospital near 15th Street and Cleveland Avenue. Even before that, Katharine had taken at least a few children from their homes to her own to care for them temporarily, according to "Little Known Medical History" by Dr. Charles C. Dennie, who worked at Children's Mercy beginning in 1911, published in the *Greater Kansas City Medical Bulletin* in December 1969.

Copies of official incorporation papers and other corporate documents came from the hospital's archive. The Children's Mercy Collection at UMKC also contains original documents detailing information about establishing the nursing school. *Messengers* from the time also provide information.

Newspaper articles, including one from the *Kansas City Star*, January 4, 1903, announcing the settlement, tell the story of the lawsuit involving the Hospital for Women and Children. It is also recounted in published histories.

*Women of Vision*, Page 15, and Wenner's and Pakula's account, Page 17, tell the story of the hospital location at 414 Highland Avenue. A *Kansas City Star* article on November 25, 1903, established that the new location was opened in fall 1903. *A Brief History of Philanthropy in Kansas City*, published in 1980, also recounts the story of the first Mercy Hospital and much of the other history. A biographical sketch of Katharine Richardson from the spring 1982 edition of *Women and Health* tells the story of the founding and also of the progressive era that supported the founding of a children's hospital.

## Chapter 2

The Lena Dagley memoir and Swanson's book, Pages 7-10, recounted the early days of the Highland Avenue property. Dagley also provided many of the quotes from Katharine; other quotes were taken from Katharine's writings.

Patient ledgers show hometowns to demonstrate the reach of Children's Mercy.

Copies of the *Messenger* newsletter, attributed here, are available in the Children's Mercy Collection at UMKC.

The story of Sybil Silkwood was told in an oral history by Davoren Tempel, former vice president of philanthropy, and is part of hospital lore. Tempel's source was Silkwood's family. The Mary Shaw story was from an oral history she recorded in 2015.

The "junior list" was included in a letter from Katharine Richardson to John Eylar, September 21, 1916. Eylar was a member of the George Washington Club and provided vegetables and other items to the hospital.

The Passing was documented in Johns' *Women of Vision* and Swanson's *A History of the Children's Mercy Hospital,* and in her memoir Dagley related stories of the many clubs that helped Children's Mercy. A photo with a caption describing The Passing was taken by E. Blanche Reineke, as were many other early Children's Mercy photos. The Maywood Club published an annual report for many years; those are available in the Children's Mercy Collection at UMKC. *Messengers* also tell the stories of the club's support.

Historical perspective on the Progressive Era and the development of the federal Children's Bureau was provided primarily from the website of the National Center for Education in Maternal and Child Health at Georgetown University.

Swanson, Johns and Wenner and Pakula all tell similar stories about the growth at Highland Avenue. There is some discrepancy about the total number of beds after remodeling the home and building the addition; the most likely number was chosen.

Information about the female physicians at the Hospital for Women and Children comes from a history of the Jackson County, Missouri, medical society and from internet genealogical research into their names. The online Kansas City Medical Index – Lancet provided background on the doctors, the hospital and the Women's Medical College.

Dr. Schauffler left an unpublished memoir that provided much information about his work for Children's Mercy and relationship with Katharine. It is in the Children's Mercy Collection at UMKC.

Wenner and Pakula (Pages 58-65) provided valuable

information about the early and not-so-early medical staff.

R.R. Brewster's role in the Board of Trustees and Kansas City's business community is well documented in Dagley's memoir and in *Kansas City Star* and *Times* newspaper articles, including one published July 29, 1952, that included an interview with Brewster. It was written by Roger Swanson when he was a newspaper reporter.

Details of early fund-raising activities are documented in the *Messenger* newsletter, which Alice wrote until her death in 1913, and Katharine continued for the next 20 years. Newspaper articles from the time, including the *Kansas City Star*, April 21, 1910, also demonstrated the efforts.

A *Kansas City Star* article January 3, 1911, told the story of Alice's illness and her move to California. Accounts after her death told the story of the work until her final days.

The story of Jacob Loose offering money to Katharine in exchange for renaming the hospital was recounted in Dr. Dennie's history in the medical bulletin referenced above. He was on the staff of Children's Mercy at the time so likely heard of the offer first hand. Bea Johns tells a similar story in her book.

The William Rockhill Nelson story was recounted in *Women of Vision*.

The extensive details of the fund drive were included in the Dagley memoir. Some of the details were also verified by newspaper reports of the meetings of the fund-raising committee. The *Messenger* also included some information on this topic.

Names of the patients who helped with the cornerstone were found on a document inside the cornerstone when it was opened in 1997.

## Chapter 3

Lena Dagley's memoir paints vivid stories about the early days and Children's Mercy patient ledgers provide details of patient conditions in the early 1900s.

Dennie's history for the medical bulletin recounted health concerns and early pediatrics.

The *Messengers* and scrapbooks kept by hospital staff, including Katharine, include details of these stories. An especially helpful scrapbook included newspaper clippings and personal correspondence related to the work at Wheatley-Provident Hospital.

C.L. Hobart was the editor of the *Holden Progress* newspaper in Holden, Missouri.

Dane Sommer's oral history was recorded in 2015.

Drs. Knapp and Schremmer produced another historical poster for Pediatric Academic Societies on the "Model Ward" at Wheatley-Provident.

The Niles Home for Children includes information about its benefactor's work for Children's Mercy on its website.

The book *Hospital Hill: An Illustrated Account of Public Healthcare Institutions in Kansas City, Missouri* by James L. Soward contains considerable history about health care, including care for African-Americans, in Kansas City. The documentary, "From Separate to Equal: The Creation of Truman Medical Center," by public television station KCPT in Kansas City also provided background.

Personal correspondence from Katharine to "Miss Wood" at the Laboratory, February 5, 1932, demonstrates her belief in the importance of research and the care for animals. Elsewhere in the *Messengers* from the 1910s to her death, devotion to research is also documented.

Previously published histories and a handbook from the nursing school dated 1927 describe Nurses' Hall and the nursing school requirements and programs. The story of the quilts at Nurses' Hall was included in *The Kansas City Star* in 1928 and in *Needlecraft* magazine circa 1926.

Lena Dagley wrote about Katharine's personal struggles with loneliness and lack of friendships. Her loneliness, along with family background provided presumably by Katharine, were included in an article in the *Kansas City Star*, "She Spells Success the Old-Fashioned Way," published August 3, 1924. It was well documented through the *Messengers* and other hospital publications that sometimes Katharine took children into her home, children who needed long-term care but not hospitalization. The spring 1935 *Journal of the University of Kansas City* reported on her personal life and interests.

The story of her adopted son is an interesting one, completely overlooked in previous histories. Paul Lowell appears in the 1930 census as an "adopted son" and he is mentioned in a *Kansas City Star* article as accompanying Katharine to Ohio to receive her honorary doctorate. He is not included in the 1920 census with Katharine. What is reported in this chapter is the extent of our current knowledge of Lowell – limited despite numerous attempts at research sources – and the exact nature of his relationship with Katharine.

*The Kansas City Star* reported on Katharine's death. Hospital records provide a sense of the aftermath. Information about some of the women who helped carry the torch of Children's Mercy after Katharine was found in hospital records and through internet research. Information in the sidebar about Mrs. Jack Nourse was provided by her grandchildren.

Board minutes paint a picture of tight financial times for the hospital. Wenner and Pakula's text provides some details, as do hospital annual reports from the era.

Joseph Marcel Vanderpopuliere's autobiography tells his story.

The text of Dr. Schlauffler's speech is in the Children's Mercy Archive at UMKC.

## Chapter 4

This chapter, which covers 1947 to 1970, is the first that benefits from oral histories conducted by the author with doctors, nurses and others associated with Children's Mercy at the time of these events.

Oral histories by Drs. Fred Burry and Keith Ashcraft were conducted by the author in 2015. An oral history with Dr. Holder was conducted upon his retirement from Children's Mercy in 1996. Eric Jones and Dr. Wayne Hart gave videotaped interviews sometime after 1970, although the dates are unknown.

*Kansas City: An American Story* and the website of the U.S. Census Bureau were consulted for details on demographic changes of the Baby Boom.

Hospital Board of Directors and Board of Trustees minutes were used extensively to chronicle events of the 1950s and '60s. Annual reports were also more regularly published (and preserved) from this era. All are in the Children's Mercy Collection at UMKC. These documents provide considerable detail of hospital finances and dealings with outside agencies and organizations.

The histories by Wenner and Pakula and Swanson were also used to fill in gaps of the story.

*The Kansas School of Medicine: Eyewitness Reflections on Its Formative Years*, published in 1996, helped provide some perspective and details (pages 183-195 and 242-248) on the workings between Children's Mercy and the University of Kansas.

John Stockwell's papers are part of the University of Massachusetts Medical School Archives.

Miscellaneous newspaper clippings of news articles and letters to the editor involving Children's Mercy and its partners were used to complement the official Children's Mercy documents.

A special report from hospital attorneys about legal issues involved in moving Children's Mercy to Kansas is part of the Children's Mercy Collection at UMKC.

Herman Sutherland's remarks were part of an oral history he provided to Children's Mercy in 1996.

The book *Hospital Hill,* used by permissino of the Truman Medical Center Foundation, provided background and detail on the development of what was at one time called Health Hill.

Copies of the agreements with General Hospital, the University of Missouri and others are in the Children's Mercy Collection at UMKC.

Biographies of the medical staff are included with portraits of esteemed staff members displayed near the Medical Staff Office at Children's Mercy Hospital. Additional information was obtained in annual reports, newspaper articles and other papers in the Children's Mercy Collection at UMKC.

Information about donors and volunteers is contained in annual reports, newspaper clippings and the Swanson and Wenner and Pakula histories.

Fund-raising campaign materials are included in the Children's Mercy Collection at UMKC, as is a report on the Children's and Youth Program.

Oral histories with former nurses Fannie Ludwig and Marjorie Trinkl provided information about working conditions on Independence Avenue.

**Chapter 5**

Reaching back less than 50 years has more than one advantage: The collection of hospital records is better preserved, more people are alive who lived through the times and many of them are accessible for oral histories.

*Kansas City: An American Story* provides context for the metropolitan area. Historical context for the country in the 1960s and '70s is from internet research and a general knowledge of the times by the author, who although not affiliated with Children's Mercy in those years, lived through this period.

The move to Hospital Hill was well-planned and, because of delays in construction, well-rehearsed, so there was plenty of time to put plans in motion. Documents describing the planning and moving are included in the Children's Mercy Collection at UMKC.

Several oral histories covered this crucial time. The histories were videorecorded. Transcripts were provided by the videographers, as well as raw and edited video files. They are a part of the author's Children's Mercy files and eventually will be transferred to the Children's Mercy Collection at UMKC. Interviews with the following individuals contributed to this chapter: Drs. Keith Ashcraft (Surgery), Fred Burry (Hospital Administration), Lloyd Olson (Department of Pediatrics), Robert T. Hall (Neonatology), Mike Sheehan (Neonatology), Jane Knapp (Emergency Medicine), Dick Dreher (Hospital Administration), Karen Cox (Hospital Administration); nurses Fannie Ludwig, Betty Boyd and Pam Dennis; Joe Galeazzi (Medical Administration); Larry McAndrews (hospital CEO); Mary Jane Barnes (Board of Directors and volunteers); Davoren Tempel (Philanthropy); and Jo Stueve (Hospital Administration).

*A Proven Experiment: Looking Back at the UMKC School of Medicine*, edited by Jerald A. Burton and Patricia G. Burton, published in 2014, provided details on the early days of the medical school and how Children's Mercy and its staff were involved.

The Wenner and Pakula history (Pages 68-120) provides great detail of the development of the medical staff and the medical departments during the 1970s. Hospital annual reports – although a complete set was not available at the time of the writing of this book – provided details about new programming. The reports also provided numbers for patient visits and other activity. The Wenner/Pakula manuscript and the annual reports are part of the Children's Mercy Collection at UMKC.

An extensive collection of Children's Mercy Golf Classic programs, memorabilia, posters, newsletters and more provide details about the value of this "friend-raising" event over 25 years, 1980 to 2004. The collection is in the Children's Mercy Collection at UMKC.

Minutes of the Central Governing Board and the Board of Trustees paint the picture of space needs and financial status, including regular "borrowing" from the endowment for operating costs.

Scrapbooks were created to preserve the story of the Kelce Foundation and a feature story in the American Medical Association newsletter of December 1975 provided outside verification of the special features of the Kelce addition. The *Kansas City Star* regularly reported on the financial condition of Children's Mercy.

News reports from *The Kansas City Star* about elusive bachelor George Sombart provide some detail of his life and the gifts he made to Children's Mercy. The notebook to support fund-raising to cover costs of building and equipping the addition over and above the Sombart gift provides details of the building's initial use.

Roles and Missions Committee minutes are included in the Children's Mercy Collection at UMKC, as are the fund-raising materials related to the Continuing the Commitment campaign.

The debate over General Hospital demolition was the subject

of news articles from *The Kansas City Times* (October 25, 1985; November 22, 1989) and *Star* (November 26, 1989, editorial) and the *Kansas City Business Journal* (November 1, 1991), which were used to reconstruct the events of the time. In addition, several internal hospital memos (September 19, 1986) and oral histories with those involved in the fight were consulted.

A letter dated April 28, 1987, describes a study by one of the hospital's law firms, Lathrop Koontz and Norquist, and consultation with the office of William Webster, Missouri attorney general, determined that it would be permissible for Children's Mercy to operate a hospital and clinics in Kansas, as long as it was not moving its hospital out of the state of Missouri. This allowed for the opening of clinics in 1987. When the hospital discussed moving next to KU Medical Center in the 1950s, it would have been leaving Missouri entirely and that would not have been allowed under its articles of incorporation.

## Chapter 6

A history of the last quarter-century can be based on bountiful information from a variety of sources. Such a difference from the research from 100 or more years ago!

Of particular note in this chapter is that the author started to work in the Community Relations (now Marketing and Communications) department in 1994 and witnessed firsthand the transformation of Children's Mercy. He wrote many of the press releases and other documents referred to in his chapter. In addition, there is a plethora of electronic records (notes, internal and external newsletters, and planning documents) that have been saved both by the author and a variety of other employees inside and outside of the public relations office. Official hospital board and committee records are also preserved and were consulted. Reports in the news media – adding third-party objectivity to the information presented here – are also extensive in the files of Children's Mercy, both on paper and in video.

Oral histories conducted by the author in 2015 and 2016 helped greatly. Current and former hospital employees and volunteers were consulted. Those who contributed to this chapter include: CEOs Larry McAndrews and Randall L. O'Donnell; Executive Medical Directors Marvin O. Kolb, V. Fred Burry and Charles W. Roberts; Chief of Staff Leland McGinness; Chief of Pediatrics Lloyd Olson; Executive Vice Presidents Karen Cox and Jo Stueve; Vice President Joe Galeazzi; Senior Director Stacey Koenig; Director Dane Sommer, and Chairman of the Board Mary Jane Barnes. These oral histories, video and transcripts, are currently in possession of the author (along with other materials that were instrumental to the writing of this book) but are destined to become part of the Children's Mercy Collection at UMKC.

Hospital financial and other records from this time are mostly intact and although many are still privately held were made available for this publication. The same was true of fund-raising materials and records. These items will find their way to the Children's Mercy Collection at UMKC at the appropriate time when their sensitive nature subsides.

Press releases included in the Children's Mercy Collection and news reports from the time detail the growth in both patient volume and buildings in this expansive period. Hospital newsletters and records that are still part of files of hospital employees were consulted for information throughout this chapter. Internal memos and personal experience of the author contributed to the information describing the Cultural Transformation sidebar, the airlift from New Orleans during the Hurricane Katrina aftermath, and the Healthier Ever After fund-raising campaign.

## Chapter 7

This was, perhaps, the most difficult chapter to write, not because of a lack of sources, but because it can be difficult to differentiate between current events and historical ones when you and everyone else are living through them. We did the best that we could.

Most of the information for this chapter came from press releases, internal hospital documents including employee newsletters, and personal experience of the author and current employees. Much of the information was on the hospital website, www.childrensmercy.org, as of December 2016. Most of the documents will become a part of the Children's Mercy Collection at UMKC at the time when they become "history" and not "current."

Background on the Discover Children's Mercy program and the Inside Pediatric documentary series comes primarily from the author's personal experience and files covering the planning and execution of those two significant outreach events. Documents pertaining to these are in the files of the Government Relations and Marketing and Communications departments.

Katharine Richardson's writings in both a report to the Central Governing Board (1933) and in the *Messenger* (1931) are recalled here as pertinent to the continuing pursuit of research at Children's Mercy.

Aside from the oral histories that contributed to this chapter (O'Donnell, Koenig, Roberts and Galeazzi, detailed in the source notes for Chapter 6) there were some less-detailed interviews conducted with current employees for this chapter. That includes the quotes from David Westbrook, Senior Vice President; Jenea Oliver, Vice President, and Dawn Wolff, Senior Director. Other quotes came from press releases or employee newsletter articles on the Intranet, known as The Scope.

The hospital's 2015 and 2016 annual reports included information about new programs (including fund-raising), and the Cancer Care Annual Report in 2016 included data on progress in the fight against cancer. All of these reports are part of the Children's Mercy Collection at UMKC. The Community Health Needs Assessment is required by the federal government and is posted on the hospital's website. The assessment will become a part of the archive at UMKC.

# Index